SECONDARY TEACHERS GUIDE TO FREE CURRICULUM MATERIALS

*

Edited by
Kathleen Suttles Nehmer

*

Educational Consultant
Michael Belongie, B. S.
Curriculum Manager, Randolph Public Schools

*

122nd ANNUAL EDITION
2013-2014

EDUCATORS PROGRESS SERVICE, INC.
214 Center Street
Randolph, Wisconsin 53956

Published by

Educators Progress Service, Inc.

Randolph, Wisconsin 53956

Formerly EDUCATORS INDEX OF FREE MATERIALS

Library of Congress Catalog Card Number 44-32700

Printed and Bound in the United States of America

International Standard Book Number 978-0-87708-550-8

TABLE OF CONTENTS

FROM THE PUBLISHER'S DESK

Obviously, you know what's in the news today. The state of the economy, environmental disasters, school violence, racism and ethnic cleansing, deadly weather, and other disturbing items have been in the news in just the last few months. Naturally, textbooks which have to go through the adoption process (as well as a lengthy production process), simply cannot publish information to help teachers be informed on these topics in a timely fashion. Teaching guides, flyers, booklets, posters, and other teaching materials can be produced rapidly to meet this demand–and fortunately a great number of these materials are being offered to educators FREE OF CHARGE. Timeliness is just one of the reasons the SECONDARY TEACHERS GUIDE is published on an annual basis.

This edition tells you where to find these teaching aids, free of charge. **ALL of these materials are brand new to this edition–rarely has there been such a large quantity of new titles available**. As you might imagine, the process of revising the annual editions of the EDUCATORS GUIDES is a time consuming process (there are now seventeen titles in the series). In our efforts to find new materials every year, we write thousands of letters to companies inquiring about materials they are willing to offer free to educators and others. Each and every year these letters are written. **If no response is received, no materials from that source are included**. All addresses are verified as well. Your requests for FREE educational aids WILL BE ANSWERED. (Another one of the reasons for an annual publication).

It's a lot of work but it is very rewarding. It really is a pleasure to be able to point educators to teaching aids that not only **save tight budgets** but **add to the educational environment**. We like to find materials that "help teachers teach," not only to make their jobs easier but to help students learn more. Any comments you may have regarding this GUIDE are welcomed–we like to learn from you, too.

Kathy

Kathy Nehmer

P. S. **Be sure to use only the 2013-2014 GUIDE for the current school year**, as hundreds of titles available last year are no longer available!

HOW TO USE THE SECONDARY TEACHERS GUIDE TO FREE CURRICULUM MATERIALS

The 2013-2014 Secondary Teachers Guide provides busy (and cash-strapped) educators with information about over 1,144 free books, teacher's guides, web sites, lesson plans, charts, posters, maps, articles and more to help save money and enrich the classroom. Finding the materials you desire, and requesting them, is easy.

The **BODY** of the GUIDE (white pages) gives you full information on each of the 1,144 titles, **ALL of which are new in this edition**. These 1,144 new titles dramatically illustrate one reason that it is so important to use only the most current edition of the GUIDE.

The **TITLE INDEX** (blue pages) is an alphabetical listing of all items appearing in the body of the GUIDE, with page references. This enables readers to locate any item whose title is known. The TITLE INDEX guides you directly to any specific item in the GUIDE, where you can read the description of the material and find all ordering information.

In the **SUBJECT INDEX** (yellow pages) all materials relating to topics of a more specific nature than the general subject headings in the body of the GUIDE are categorized. These "yellow pages" work like the familiar "yellow pages" of a telephone directory.

The **SOURCE INDEX** (green pages) provides an alphabetical list of the names of the 733 generous organizations from which materials can be obtained. Also included in each entry are page numbers which indicate where the materials from that particular source appear in the body of the GUIDE. Use of this feature facilitates the ordering, with one letter, of more than one selection if a source offers several.

ANALYSIS OF SECONDARY TEACHERS GUIDE TO FREE CURRICULUM MATERIALS–2013

	TOTAL ITEMS
Agriculture and Animal Care	19
Career Education	63
Computer Education	53
Economics and Consumer Education	69
Fine Arts	59
Government	43
Guidance	38
Health	
Alcohol, Tobacco, and Other Drugs	24
Diseases	67
Mental Health	13
Safety and First Aid	16
Home Economics	
Food and Nutrition	63
Home Management and Child Care	17
Language Arts	72
Mathematics	39
Physical Fitness	16
Science	
Aerospace Education	25
Biology	19
Environmental Education	25
General Science	81
Nature Study	45
Social Studies	
Famous People	33
Geography–US	25
Geography–World	37
History	36
Maps	28
Special Education	25
Teacher Reference	94
TOTALS	**1,144**

YOUR LETTERS OF REQUEST

When requesting materials, please make your letter of request clear. Identify yourself and your organization. Be sure to use any identifying numbers provided and **observe any restrictions** on distribution as indicated in the GUIDE.

Do not be alarmed if everything you request does not come. The list of materials changes; materials go out of date and are replaced by new items. We cannot tell at the time of printing how long each item will last. Sponsors are asked to assure us, with reasonable certainty, that their materials will be available for approximately one year. It is to meet this need that the GUIDE is revised annually.

There are 733 sources of free materials listed in the **2013-2014 SECONDARY TEACHERS GUIDE TO FREE CURRICULUM MATERIALS.** Please make certain that the request you are making is to the proper company.

In writing for materials, the following form is suggested. The listing used as an example is selected from page 5.

REGIONAL SCHOOL #7
Central Avenue
Winstead, Connecticut 06098

July 7, 2013

Society of Wood Science and Technology
P. O. Box 6155
Monona, WI 53716-6155

Dear Sponsor:

We would like to receive one copy of the following item as listed in the 2011 edition of SECONDARY TEACHERS GUIDE TO FREE CURRICULUM MATERIALS:

Career Opportunities in Applied Science and Engineering

Thank you for your cooperation in assisting us to enrich the curriculum of our school.

Sincerely,

Gina Sabel
High School Science

HOW TO COOPERATE WITH THE SPONSORS

Subscribers to EPS services have frequently asked us for guidelines to follow in requesting sponsored materials. The following 14 questions are quoted from an address given by Thomas J. Sinclair, Ph.D., formerly Manager of Educational and Group Relations for the Association of American Railroads, at a convention of the National Science Teachers Association.

1. Poor handwriting, which you strive to correct in your pupils, often makes coupons and other requests useless. Is your handwriting distinct on requests?

2. Neither industry nor the U. S. Postal Service is omniscient. Do you include complete and accurate details of your address, including zip number?

3. Postcards, small social stationery, or slips of paper present filing problems and can easily be lost. Do you use standard sized stationery?

4. Remember that in big companies thousands of pieces of mail go in and out every day. Do you allow sufficient time for handling your request.

5. Most students advise businesses that they are <u>studing</u> a topic. Do you check your spelling?

6. If you were on the receiving end, you'd have a different view of mass classroom letter-writing projects to the same business organization. Do you make certain that only one request goes to a particular source from your classroom?

7. Instructions on a coupon, in a guide, or on an order form are there for a purpose. Do you read and follow these instructions?

8. Some organizations have dozens–sometimes hundreds–of different teaching aids. Specific needs should be outlined. Do you say "Send me everything you've got" or its equivalent?

9. Source lists and guides get out of date. Do you check to see if the list you are consulting is a recent one?

10. Sometimes aids are in limited supply or available only to teachers in single copies. Do you keep requests reasonable and show some respect for the costs of materials?

11. Sample copies are for examination, with the privilege of ordering quantities subsequently. Do you order classroom quantities blind–without first examining an item for suitability for your purpose?

12. Companies keep records and files. They frequently like to know precisely where their materials are going. Are you careful to mention your school connection?

13. Do you make a real effort to make certain the organization you are writing to is the correct one, and that it could reasonably have the material you are seeking?

14. Duplications and unnecessary correspondence only slow good service to the teaching profession. Do you consult your associates to see whether needed materials have already been supplied to your school?

These questions provide specific suggestions that should, in the long run, make for happier sponsors and better service to educators.

EVALUATION OF INDUSTRY-SPONSORED EDUCATIONAL MATERIALS

The business community has long recognized its obligation to support the agencies of the community that contribute to its security and well-being. In partial fulfillment of this obligation, industry trade associations and non-profit organizations have been producing supplementary materials for use in our nation's schools for some time. Properly planned, sponsored educational resources serve a valuable role and are particularly effective in giving information to students in an area where the sponsoring organization has achieved a high degree of specialization. When properly designed, sponsored materials can be used to motivate students and direct their energies into productive channels of growth.

Educational systems can respond more effectively to changes in technology, job structure, income, population, and manpower requirements with close support and involvement of industry. Both sectors have a common goal of strengthening the institutional programs at all levels in our schools. Operationally, this requires a strong industry-education alliance, particularly at the local level in preparing people for a productive role in the marketplace.

The National Association for Industry-Education Cooperation (NAIEC) was established in 1964 as a logical development out of the Business Industry Section of the National Science Teachers Association. Its purposes were (and still are) to bring about a better understanding between Education and the Business community and to mobilize the resources of education and industry to improve the relevance and quality of educational programs at all levels.

NAIEC members represent a variety of private and public organizations. Major trade associations, corporations, schools, and school districts are members. School superintendents, college presidents, curriculum and other education coordinators, business executives, industry-education coordinators, deans, department chairpersons, career education and job placement specialists, and faculty participate in the Association's programs.

The membership works together to identify problems of mutual interest, formulate plans and procedures, develop acceptable business-sponsored instructional materials, and communicate the advantages of industry-education cooperation.

The NAIEC membership has determined that the set of guiding principles (see below) for the preparation of materials for distribution to schools established by a study financed by American Iron and Steel Institute and carried out by the George Peabody Teachers College are valid and has found that materials embracing these criteria have usually found acceptance and use in the nation's schools and classrooms.

1. Work with a representative group of teachers and administrators to ensure meeting a curricular need.

2. Provide factual material desired by the schools. Include only that information which is significant to the study of particular problems or topics of concern to the teacher and student.

3. Exclude all advertising. A credit line naming the sponsor is enough; indeed schools need to know the publisher and the date of the material.

4. Materials must be written to the particular age level, reading level, interests, and maturity of the group for whom they are intended.

5. Keep the materials free of persuasion; avoid special pleading of the interests of any one point of view or group.

6. Make the materials available to educators only upon request.

In 1976 members of the NAIEC developed "A Guide for Evaluating Industry-Sponsored Educational Materials" which embodies the above listed criteria from the educator's viewpoint. This guide is an effort by the National Association for Industry-Education Cooperation (NAIEC) to present teachers with an instrument for evaluating sponsored education resources. These supplemental materials may take the form of teacher guides, filmstrips, games actually designed for the classroom, or pamphlets, reprinted articles, annual reports which may provide valuable background information but are not developed specifically for the teacher's use. (It is suggested that the Guide is more effective with the items actually designed for the classroom.)

If, after completing your evaluation of those items designed for the classroom, you have no further use for the instrument, the sponsoring organization providing the item would appreciate your evaluation with any comments you might have for guidance in the development of future materials. Hopefully this will foster closer industry-education cooperation.

A GUIDE FOR EVALUATING INDUSTRY-SPONSORED EDUCATIONAL MATERIALS

Title of material ______________________ Date produced, if available __________

Sponsor (name of organization)______________________________

Type of material: Audio ________ Audiovisual ________ Printed ________ Other ________

Type of instruction suitable for this material: Individual __________ Group __________

This evaluation is based on usage in ______________________ (grade level)

Evaluator ______________________________ Date __________

Subject area/School ______________________________

Address ______________________________

____

INSTRUCTIONS FOR USE:

Use the following scale by evaluating the material as it relates to your situation. Each of the descriptive statements is followed by a scale of (1), (2), (3), (4), (5). Indicate your assessment of the material by circling the appropriate number in the scale:

(1) Definitely yes
(2) Yes
(3) No
(4) Definitely no
(5) Material cannot be evaluated on this concept

OBJECTIVES	SCALE
Identified outcomes may be obtained through use of the material.	1 2 3 4 5
The materials are representative of the curriculum involved; that is, they help further the objectives of the curriculum.	1 2 3 4 5
ABILITY RANGE	
The materials provide for the range of abilities and aptitudes of all pupils.	1 2 3 4 5
CONTENT	
The material is contemporary.	1 2 3 4 5
The material is controversial.	1 2 3 4 5
The material presents alternative views.	1 2 3 4 5
The material does not present a bias for a product, organization, or social cause.	1 2 3 4 5
The material does present a bias for a product, organization, or social cause.	1 2 3 4 5
If such a bias exists, it does not invalidate the material for my purposes.	1 2 3 4 5
The nature and scope of the material content is adequate to meet curriculum objectives.	1 2 3 4 5
The material is supplementary to the curriculum.	1 2 3 4 5
The material offers opportunity for integration of the subject within the existing curriculum.	1 2 3 4 5
The material correlates with a specific discipline area.	1 2 3 4 5
The material introduces experiences that would not otherwise be available in the classroom.	1 2 3 4 5
The material suggests other resources, supplementary and/or instructional.	1 2 3 4 5

UTILIZATION CHARACTERISTICS	SCALE
The anticipated time utilization is commensurate with anticipated value of outcome.	1 2 3 4 5
The material demands special conditions for use.	1 2 3 4 5
The material is appropriate for student's reading level.	1 2 3 4 5
The material is appropriate for student's interest level.	1 2 3 4 5
The material is attractive to students.	1 2 3 4 5
The material provides motivation for students.	1 2 3 4 5
PRESENTATION OF MATERIALS	
Provisions are made for evaluating the material as it is used within the educational program.	1 2 3 4 5
Instructional procedures are outlined.	1 2 3 4 5
The style of the presentation is likely to lead students toward accomplishing basic goals.	1 2 3 4 5
Sample student activities and questions are included.	1 2 3 4 5
The instructions to teachers are clearly stated.	1 2 3 4 5
The intended use is easily understood.	1 2 3 4 5
The production quality of the materials is acceptable.	1 2 3 4 5
EVALUATION	
The material provides for feedback to the user.	1 2 3 4 5
The material provides for self-evaluation.	1 2 3 4 5

Appaloosa Youth Judging Guide
Learn how to judge horses of ANY breed.
Availability: Classroom quantities to schools, libraries, and homeschoolers world-wide.
Suggested Grade: 4-12
Order Number: order by title
Format: Booklet; 44 pages

Source: Appaloosa Horse Club, The
Attn: Marketing Department
2720 West Pullman Road
Moscow, ID 83843
Phone: 1-208-882-5578, ext. 229
Fax: 1-208-882-8150
World Wide Web URL: http://www.appaloosa.com
Email Address: promotions@appaloosa.com

Cancer in Animals
Answers commonly asked questions about cancer in animals.
Availability: Single copies to schools, libraries, and homeschoolers in the United States and Canada.
Suggested Grade: 6-Adult
Languages: English; Spanish
Order Number: order by title
Format: Brochure
Special Notes: May also be downloaded from the web site.

Source: American Veterinary Medical Association
Attn: Order Dept.
1931 North Meacham Road, Suite 100
Schaumburg, IL 60173-4360
Phone: 1-847-285-6655
Fax: 1-847-925-1329
World Wide Web URL: http://www.avma.org
Email Address: productorders@avma.org

Canine Distemper
Understand the risk to puppies and adult dogs for contracting this serious disease and current prevention and treatment.
Availability: Single copies to schools, libraries, and homeschoolers in the United States and Canada.
Suggested Grade: 6-Adult
Languages: English; Spanish
Order Number: order by title
Format: Brochure
Special Notes: May also be downloaded from the web site.

Source: American Veterinary Medical Association
Attn: Order Dept.
1931 North Meacham Road, Suite 100
Schaumburg, IL 60173-4360
Phone: 1-847-285-6655
Fax: 1-847-925-1329
World Wide Web URL: http://www.avma.org
Email Address: productorders@avma.org

Canine Parvovirus
Explains this deadly disease-what it does, where it comes from, how it is detected, how it is treated, and how it can be prevented.
Availability: Single copies to schools, libraries, and homeschoolers in the United States and Canada.
Suggested Grade: 6-12
Order Number: order by title
Format: Brochure
Special Notes: May also be downloaded from the web site.

Source: American Veterinary Medical Association
Attn: Order Dept.
1931 North Meacham Road, Suite 100
Schaumburg, IL 60173-4360
Phone: 1-847-285-6655
Fax: 1-847-925-1329
World Wide Web URL: http://www.avma.org
Email Address: productorders@avma.org

Choosing a Veterinarian
Helpful tips on when and how to find a veterinarian for your pet.
Availability: Single copies to schools, libraries, and homeschoolers in the United States and Canada.
Suggested Grade: 6-Adult
Languages: English; Spanish
Order Number: order by title
Format: Brochure
Special Notes: May also be downloaded from the web site.

Source: American Veterinary Medical Association
Attn: Order Dept.
1931 North Meacham Road, Suite 100
Schaumburg, IL 60173-4360
Phone: 1-847-285-6655
Fax: 1-847-925-1329
World Wide Web URL: http://www.avma.org
Email Address: productorders@avma.org

Classroom Poster
Illustrates how veterinarians protect animals, people, and the environment.
Availability: Single copies to schools, libraries, and homeschoolers in the United States and Canada.
Suggested Grade: All ages
Order Number: order by title
Format: Double-sided poster

Source: American Veterinary Medical Association
Attn: Order Dept.
1931 North Meacham Road, Suite 100
Schaumburg, IL 60173-4360
Phone: 1-847-285-6655
Fax: 1-847-925-1329
World Wide Web URL: http://www.avma.org
Email Address: productorders@avma.org

CyberPet
All sorts of articles and information about dogs and cats.

Availability: All requesters
Suggested Grade: 4-12
Order Number: not applicable
Format: Online Articles

Source: CyberPet
World Wide Web URL: http://www.cyberpet.com/

Fish Farming

Upon completion of this task and the assigned activities, you will have gained enough knowledge to explain the world of water farming to others who have limited contact with this exciting field of agriculture.

Availability: All requesters
Suggested Grade: 8-12
Order Number: not applicable
Format: WebQuest

Source: Ramona Andrus
World Wide Web URL:
http://www.mofb.org/WebQuest.aspx/FishFarming.aspx

Grains of Truth

Explains North Dakota agriculture, hard red spring wheat, and durum facts.

Availability: Single copies to schools, libraries, and homeschoolers in the United States.
Suggested Grade: 7-12
Order Number: order by title
Format: Brochure

Source: North Dakota Wheat Commission
2401 46th Avenue SE, Suite 104
Mandan, ND 58554-4829
Phone: 1-701-328-5111
Fax: 1-701-663-5787
World Wide Web URL: http://www.ndwheat.com
Email Address: ndwheat@ndwheat.com

How to Links

Here are links to several "how to" articles about caring for cattle.

Availability: All requesters
Suggested Grade: 9-Adult
Order Number: not applicable
Format: Web Site

Source: ALOT Angus Association
World Wide Web URL: http://www.alotangus.org/ht.html

Internal Parasites in Cats and Dogs

Learn about the transmission, treatment and prevention of roundworms, hookworms, and other common intestinal parasites in dogs and cats.

Availability: Single copies to schools, libraries, and homeschoolers in the United States and Canada.
Suggested Grade: 6-Adult
Order Number: order by title
Format: Brochure
Special Notes: May also be downloaded from the web site.

Source: American Veterinary Medical Association
Attn: Order Dept.
1931 North Meacham Road, Suite 100
Schaumburg, IL 60173-4360
Phone: 1-847-285-6655
Fax: 1-847-925-1329
World Wide Web URL: http://www.avma.org
Email Address: productorders@avma.org

Online Ag Periodicals, Magazines and Newsletters

Lots of reading for those interested in this topic.

Availability: All requesters
Suggested Grade: 9-Adult
Order Number: not applicable
Format: Web Site

Source: ALOT Angus Association
World Wide Web URL: http://www.alotangus.org/opm.html

Pet Euthanasia...How Do I Know It's Time?

When to humanely terminate a pet's life is explored in this brochure, along with the grieving process and resources for help in managing the loss.

Availability: Single copies to schools, libraries, and homeschoolers in the United States and Canada.
Suggested Grade: 6-12
Order Number: order by title
Format: Brochure
Special Notes: May also be downloaded from the web site.

Source: American Veterinary Medical Association
Attn: Order Dept.
1931 North Meacham Road, Suite 100
Schaumburg, IL 60173-4360
Phone: 1-847-285-6655
Fax: 1-847-925-1329
World Wide Web URL: http://www.avma.org
Email Address: productorders@avma.org

Selecting a Cat

Learn how to select the best breed and age of cat for your lifestyle.

Availability: Single copies to schools, libraries, and homeschoolers in the United States and Canada.
Suggested Grade: 6-Adult
Order Number: order by title
Format: Brochure
Special Notes: May also be downloaded from the web site.

Source: American Veterinary Medical Association
Attn: Order Dept.
1931 North Meacham Road, Suite 100
Schaumburg, IL 60173-4360
Phone: 1-847-285-6655
Fax: 1-847-925-1329
World Wide Web URL: http://www.avma.org
Email Address: productorders@avma.org

Selecting a Dog

Learn how to select the best breed and age of dog for your lifestyle.

Availability: Single copies to schools, libraries, and homeschoolers in the United States and Canada.
Suggested Grade: 6-Adult
Order Number: order by title
Format: Brochure
Special Notes: May also be downloaded from the web site.

Source: American Veterinary Medical Association
Attn: Order Dept.
1931 North Meacham Road, Suite 100
Schaumburg, IL 60173-4360
Phone: 1-847-285-6655
Fax: 1-847-925-1329
World Wide Web URL: http://www.avma.org
Email Address: productorders@avma.org

Today's American Miniature Horse: The Horse for Everyone!

Tells about the characteristics of this horse.

Availability: Classroom quantities to schools, libraries, and homeschoolers world-wide.
Suggested Grade: 4-12
Order Number: order by title
Production Date: 2007
Format: Booklet

Source: American Miniature Horse Association
Attn: Alison Elrod, Marketing Manager
5601 South Interstate 35W
Alvarado, TX 76009
Phone: 1-817-783-5600
Fax: 1-817-783-6403
World Wide Web URL: http://www.amha.org
Email Address: information@amha.org

Traveling With Your Pet

Local or long distance travel, whether by car or by plane, this brochure tells what you need to do to ensure safety on the road or in the air for your dog or cat.

Availability: Single copies to schools, libraries, and homeschoolers in the United States and Canada.
Suggested Grade: 6-Adult
Languages: English; Spanish
Order Number: order by title
Format: Brochure
Special Notes: May also be downloaded from the web site.

Source: American Veterinary Medical Association
Attn: Order Dept.
1931 North Meacham Road, Suite 100
Schaumburg, IL 60173-4360
Phone: 1-847-285-6655
Fax: 1-847-925-1329
World Wide Web URL: http://www.avma.org
Email Address: productorders@avma.org

Unique Health Conditions of Animals

Explains different diseases found in pets.

Availability: All requesters
Suggested Grade: All ages
Order Number: not applicable
Format: Web Site
Special Notes: This URL will lead you to a subject page. Then click on the appropriate subject heading.

Source: ThinkQuest
World Wide Web URL:
http://www.thinkquest.org/pls/html/think.library

Wisconsin Ag in the Classroom Website

Learn about Wisconsin agriculture, download lesson plans and activities, and much more.

Availability: All requesters
Suggested Grade: 4-12
Order Number: not applicable
Format: Web Site

Source: Wisconsin Farm Bureau Federation
Phone: 1-608-828-5719
World Wide Web URL: http://www.wisagclassroom.org
Email Address: darneson.fbcenter@wfbf.com

Actuarial Science: A Career Choice Worth Exploring
Tells about a career in this field.
Availability: Classroom quantities to schools, libraries, and homeschoolers in the United States and Canada.
Suggested Grade: 6-Adult
Order Number: order by title
Format: Brochure
Special Notes: Order via web site.

Source: Casualty Actuarial Society
1100 North Glebe Road, Suite 600
Arlington, VA 22201
Phone: 1-703-276-3100
Fax: 1-703-276-3108
World Wide Web URL:
http://www.beanactuary.org/counselors/speakit/order.cfm
Email Address: office@casact.org

Actuary Career Classroom Poster
Encourages students to consider a career in this field.
Availability: Classroom quantities to schools, libraries, and homeschoolers in the United States and Canada.
Suggested Grade: 6-Adult
Order Number: order by title
Format: Poster
Special Notes: Order via web site.

Source: Casualty Actuarial Society
1100 North Glebe Road, Suite 600
Arlington, VA 22201
Phone: 1-703-276-3100
Fax: 1-703-276-3108
World Wide Web URL:
http://www.beanactuary.org/counselors/speakit/order.cfm
Email Address: office@casact.org

American Psychological Association Web Site
Covers topics such as health care, parenting, depression, and career planning.
Availability: All requesters
Suggested Grade: 9-Adult
Order Number: not applicable
Format: Web Site

Source: American Psychological Association
World Wide Web URL: http://www.apa.org/

Apprenticeships: Career Training, Credentials--and a Paycheck in Your Pocket
Apprenticeships are available in more than 850 occupations. Learn how they work and how to choose the best program for you.
Availability: All requesters
Suggested Grade: 9-Adult
Order Number: not applicable
Production Date: 2002
Format: Downloadable Booklet; 20 pages
Special Notes: Use the on-site search engine to easily find this title. You may request a printed copy mailed to you for a fee.

Source: Federal Citizen Information Center
World Wide Web URL: http://www.pueblo.gsa.gov/

Career Development of Older Adults
Describes how information from research and theory can be used to address the career development needs of late midlife adults.
Availability: All requesters
Suggested Grade: Adult
Order Number: not applicable
Production Date: 2003
Format: Online Article

Source: Susan Imel
World Wide Web URL:
http://www.ericdigests.org/2005-1/older.htm

Career Development and Gender, Race, and Class
Investigates broader perspectives on career development that are being built on emerging research focused on gender, race, ethnicity, and social class.
Availability: All requesters
Suggested Grade: Teacher Reference
Order Number: not applicable
Production Date: 1998
Format: Online Article

Source: Sandra Kerka
World Wide Web URL:
http://www.ericdigests.org/1999-2/career.htm

Career Development for African American and Latina Females
Discusses ways for schools and other institutions to provide this type of education.
Availability: All requesters
Suggested Grade: Teacher Reference
Order Number: not applicable
Production Date: 1997
Format: Online Article

Source: Jeanne Weiler
World Wide Web URL:
http://www.ericdigests.org/1998-1/career.htm

Career Development for Meaningful Life Work
Career development theory and practices that foster the development of meaningful work are reviewed.
Availability: All requesters
Suggested Grade: Teacher Reference
Order Number: not applicable
Production Date: 2002
Format: Online Article

Source: Susan Imel
World Wide Web URL:
http://www.ericdigests.org/2003-2/career.html

Career Education for Teen Parents
Examines the demographic, life course, and employment characteristics of teenaged parents and explores their psychosocial, life management, and job-related needs.

Availability: All requesters
Suggested Grade: 7-Adult
Order Number: not applicable
Format: Online Article

Source: Bettina Lankard Brown
World Wide Web URL:
http://www.ericdigests.org/1995-2/teen.htm

Career Games
Features several workshops and games that facilitate the PIE career development method practiced by this European career specialist.
Availability: All requesters
Suggested Grade: 9-Adult
Order Number: not applicable
Format: Web Site

Source: Daniel Porot
World Wide Web URL: http://www.careergames.com/

Career in the Sewn Products Industry, A
Tells about careers in designing, making, and selling clothing.
Availability: All requesters
Suggested Grade: 5-12
Order Number: not applicable
Format: Web Site

Source: American Apparel & Footwear Association
World Wide Web URL: http://www.careerthreads.com/

Career Opportunities in Applied Science and Engineering
Describes careers in wood science and technology as well as qualifications needed for these jobs.
Availability: Single copies to schools, libraries, and homeschoolers world-wide.
Suggested Grade: 5-12
Order Number: order by title
Format: Pamphlet

Source: Society of Wood Science and Technology
P. O. Box 6155
Monona, WI 53716-6155
Phone: 1-608-577-1342
Fax: 1-608-467-8979
World Wide Web URL: http://www.swst.org
Email Address: vicki@swst.org

Career Planning for High School Students
A pre-college career planning site that is presented as a starting point to help students generate some tentative ideas for college majors and future career plans.
Availability: All requesters
Suggested Grade: 9-12
Order Number: not applicable
Format: Web Site

Source: Rutgers University, Career Services
World Wide Web URL:
http://careerservices.rutgers.edu/PCCPmain.shtml

Career Profiles
Here are a number of essays that describe a wide variety of careers for which a background in the mathematical sciences is useful.
Availability: All requesters
Suggested Grade: 6-Adult
Order Number: not applicable
Format: Online Articles
Special Notes: Hasn't been updated in a while, but the information is still relevant.

Source: Mathematical Association of America
World Wide Web URL:
http://www.maa.org/careers/index.html

Careers in Ecology--High School Version
Addresses what ecologists do, kinds of jobs, job outlook, and how to gain experience.
Availability: All requesters
Suggested Grade: 9-12
Order Number: not applicable
Format: Online Fact Sheet

Source: Ecological Society of America, The
World Wide Web URL:
http://www.esa.org/education_diversity/webDocs/highschool.php

Careers in Ecology--Undergraduate Version
Geared to undergrads, this brochure addresses what ecologists do, kinds of jobs, job outlook, and how to gain experience.
Availability: All requesters
Suggested Grade: 11-Adult
Order Number: not applicable
Format: Online Fact Sheet

Source: Ecological Society of America, The
World Wide Web URL:
http://www.esa.org/education_diversity/webDocs/undergraduate.php

Careers in Nursing
Here is information about the many different specialties available within the field of nursing.
Availability: All requesters
Suggested Grade: 6-12
Order Number: not applicable
Format: Web Site

Source: Nursing Spectrum
World Wide Web URL:
http://www.nurse.com/students/careersinnursing.html

Careers in Population
Discusses why one should study population, why the discipline matters, where specialists work, and how to be trained for a career in population.
Availability: Limit of 50 copies to schools, libraries, and homeschoolers in the United States and Canada.
Suggested Grade: 6-12

Order Number: order by title
Format: Booklet

Source: Population Association of America
8630 Fenton Street, Suite 722
Silver Spring, MD 20910
Phone: 1-301-565-6710
Fax: 1-301-565-7850
World Wide Web URL: http://www.popassoc.org
Email Address: adminasst@popassoc.org

Careers in Psychology

Answers questions about what working in psychology is like and what educational requirements are needed.

Availability: All requesters
Suggested Grade: 7-12
Order Number: not applicable
Format: Downloadable Brochure

Source: American Psychological Association
World Wide Web URL:
http://www.apa.org/careers/resources/guides/careers.aspx

Careers in Sociology

Answers the often-asked question, "What can I do with a degree in sociology?"

Availability: All requesters
Suggested Grade: 9-Adult
Order Number: not applicable
Format: Downloadable Book
Special Notes: Print copies may be purchased for $6.00 each.

Source: W. Richard Stephens, Jr.
World Wide Web URL:
http://www.abacon.com/socsite/careers.html

Careers in the Geosciences

Details the many opportunities for a career as a geoscientist, ranging from atmospheric scientist to volcanologist.

Availability: Limit of 10 copies to schools, libraries, and homeschoolers world-wide.
Suggested Grade: K-12
Order Number: order by title
Format: Brochure

Source: American Association of Petroleum Geologists
Communications Department
P. O. Box 979
Tulsa, OK 74101
Phone: 1-918-584-2555
Fax: 1-918-560-2636
World Wide Web URL: http://www.aapg.org
Email Address: postmaster@aapg.org

Career Toolkit

A career quiz, career calculator, career profiles and lots more!

Availability: All requesters
Suggested Grade: 4-12
Order Number: not applicable
Format: Web Site

Source: Manufacturing Institute
World Wide Web URL:
http://www.dreamit-doit.com/content/toolkit/toolkit.aspx

CareerZone

A free career exploration and planning system.

Availability: All requesters
Suggested Grade: 6-12
Order Number: not applicable
Format: Web Site

Source: New York State Department of Labor
World Wide Web URL:
http://www.nycareerzone.org/index.jsp

College Preparation Checklist

Provides information about what students from pre-high school through their senior year can do to prepare for college.

Availability: Single copies to schools, libraries, and homeschoolers in the United States.
Suggested Grade: 7-12
Language: Spanish
Order Number: EN0920H
Production Date: 2009
Format: Brochure
Special Notes: May also be downloaded from the web site.

Source: ED Pubs
P. O. Box 1398
Jessup, MD 20794-1398
Phone: 1-877-4-ED-PUBS
Fax: 1-301-470-1244
World Wide Web URL:
http://www.edpubs.org/webstore/Content/search.asp

Cover-Letters.com

Here are a number of letters, for a number of different situations, useful for those seeking a job.

Availability: All requesters
Suggested Grade: 11-Adult
Order Number: not applicable
Format: Web Site

Source: Careerlab.com
World Wide Web URL: http://www.cover-letters.com/

Discover

Describes what the people working in the fields of agricultural, biological, and food systems engineering do and how they do it.

Availability: Limit of 1 copy to professional staff of schools, libraries, and homeschoolers in the United States and Canada. Make request on official stationery.
Suggested Grade: 5-12
Order Number: order by title
Format: Magazine

Source: ASABE
2950 Niles Road
St. Joseph, MI 49085-9659

Phone: 1-269-429-0300
Fax: 1-269-429-3852

Discover Biological and Agricultural Engineering
Discusses what biological and agricultural engineers do and why you might want to become one.
Availability: Limit of 10 copies to professional staff of schools, libraries, and homeschoolers in the United States and Canada. Make request on official stationery.
Suggested Grade: 5-12
Order Number: order by title
Format: Brochure
Source: ASABE
2950 Niles Road
St. Joseph, MI 49085-9659
Phone: 1-269-429-0300
Fax: 1-269-429-3852

Engineering: K12 Center
Seeks to identify and gather in one place the most effective engineering education resources available.
Availability: All requesters
Suggested Grade: 9-12
Order Number: not applicable
Format: Web Site
Source: American Society for Engineering Education
World Wide Web URL: http://egfi-k12.org/

Exciting Career Opportunities in AI
Highlights some of the positions available in the Artificial Insemination field and explains why each is vital.
Availability: Reasonable classroom quantities to schools, libraries and homeschoolers in the United States and Canada.
Suggested Grade: 7-12
Order Number: order by title
Format: Brochure
Special Notes: May also be downloaded from the web site.
Source: National Association of Animal Breeders, Inc.
P. O. Box 1033
Columbia, MO 65205-1033
Phone: 1-573-445-4406
Fax: 1-573-446-2279
World Wide Web URL: http://www.naab-css.org/education
Email Address: naab-css@naab-css.org.

Explore: Careers in Agricultural Technology and Systems Management
Discusses career opportunities and answers questions for students interested in pursuing a career in agricultural technology or systems management.
Availability: One copy to professional staff of schools, libraries, and homeschoolers in the United States and Canada. Make request on official stationery.
Suggested Grade: 9-12
Order Number: order by title
Format: Magazine
Source: ASABE
2950 Niles Road
St. Joseph, MI 49085-9659
Phone: 1-269-429-0300
Fax: 1-269-429-3852

Exploring Careers in Technology
A WebQuest about computers, life skills, and math.
Availability: All requesters
Suggested Grade: 9-12
Order Number: not applicable
Format: WebQuest
Source: Angie Marquart
World Wide Web URL:
http://www.clearfork.k12.oh.us/sites/webquest/marquarta/webquest.html

Exploring Occupations: Getting You Started on Your Career Path!
Lots of links to descriptions of various occupations.
Availability: All requesters
Suggested Grade: 6-12
Order Number: not applicable
Format: Web Site
Source: University of Manitoba Counseling Service
World Wide Web URL:
http://www.umanitoba.ca/counselling/careers.html

Finance and Accounting Career Guide
Presents information about a number of careers in these fields.
Availability: All requesters
Suggested Grade: 6-12
Order Number: not applicable
Format: Online Article
Source: Saludos Hispanos
World Wide Web URL:
http://www.saludos.com/cguide/bguide.html

Frequently Asked Questions About Music Therapy
Explains what music therapy is and how it is utilized.
Availability: All requesters
Suggested Grade: 6-Adult
Order Number: not applicable
Format: Online Article
Source: American Music Therapy Association
8455 Colesville Road, Suite 1000
Silver Spring, MD 20910
Phone: 1-301-589-3300
Fax: 1-301-589-5175
World Wide Web URL:
http://www.musictherapy.org/faqs.html
Email Address: info@musictherapy.org

Fun Works, The...For Careers You Never Knew Existed
An interactive site to help students in grades 6-9 explore careers.

Availability: All requesters
Suggested Grade: 6-9
Order Number: not applicable
Format: Web Site

Source: National Science Foundation
World Wide Web URL: http://www.thefunworks.org/

Get a Job!

Learn about different jobs.

Availability: All requesters
Suggested Grade: 11-12
Order Number: not applicable
Format: WebQuest

Source: Catrina Eddington
World Wide Web URL:
http://www.yorkville.k12.il.us/webquests/webqeddington3/webqseddington3.htm

Global Positioning System Primer

An introduction to the Global Positioning System with clear explanations of basic concepts and terms.

Availability: Limit of 30 copies to schools, libraries, and homeschoolers world-wide. Please do not allow each individual student to write.
Suggested Grade: 4-12
Order Number: order by title
Format: Brochure
Special Notes: May also be downloaded from the web site.

Source: Aerospace Corporation, The
World Wide Web URL: http://www.aero.org
Email Address: corpcom@aero.org

Gold Collar Workers

Explains what "gold collar workers" are and reviews their characteristics.

Availability: All requesters
Suggested Grade: Teacher Reference
Order Number: not applicable
Format: Online Article

Source: Michael E. Wonacott
World Wide Web URL:
http://www.ericdigests.org/2003-2/gold.html

Guide to Zoological Park Careers

A guide to the many careers available within the field of zoology from animal training to veterinarian.

Availability: All requesters
Suggested Grade: 6-Adult
Order Number: not applicable
Format: Downloadable Booklet

Source: Sea World/Busch Gardens
World Wide Web URL:
http://www.seaworld.org/infobooks/ZooCareers/home.html

Handouts and Information Guides

Here are a number of articles covering a range of preK-12 educational, career planning, and decision-making topics and issues.

Availability: All requesters
Suggested Grade: All ages
Order Number: not applicable
Format: Web Site

Source: State of Queensland, The
World Wide Web URL:
http://education.qld.gov.au/students/service/career/handouts.html

High Earning Workers Who Don't Have a Bachelor's Degree

Identifies 50 jobs that require less than a bachelor's degree.

Availability: All requesters
Suggested Grade: 6-Adult
Order Number: not applicable
Production Date: 1999
Format: Online Article; 9 pages
Special Notes: Use the on-site search engine to easily find this title. You may request a printed copy mailed to you for a fee.

Source: Federal Citizen Information Center
World Wide Web URL: http://www.pueblo.gsa.gov/

How to Get a Job in the Federal Government

Here's a step-by-step plan to find and apply for federal jobs, with detailed information on finding openings, understanding vacancy announcements, developing your resume, and more.

Availability: All requesters
Suggested Grade: 9-Adult
Order Number: not applicable
Production Date: 2004
Format: Downloadable Booklet; 24 pages
Special Notes: Use the on-site search engine to easily find this title. You may request a printed copy mailed to you for a fee.

Source: Federal Citizen Information Center
World Wide Web URL: http://www.pueblo.gsa.gov/

Job Genie

Provides descriptions for 12,741 different jobs. (Available on CD for $99--website is absolutely free.)

Availability: All requesters
Suggested Grade: 6-Adult
Order Number: not applicable
Format: Web Site
Special Notes: Available to purchase on CD for $99.

Source: Stephen Fournier
World Wide Web URL: http://www.stepfour.com/jobs/

Leadership Development in Career and Technical Education

Reviews the literature on leadership development in CTE and in other areas to describe how leadership development in CTE is evolving to prepare leaders for the future.

Availability: All requesters
Suggested Grade: Teacher Reference
Order Number: not applicable

Production Date: 2001
Format: Online Article

Source: Michael E. Wonacott
World Wide Web URL:
http://findarticles.com/p/articles/mi_pric/is_200100/ai_71679807

LifeWorks

An interactive career web site on which users can browse for information on more than 100 medical science and health careers.

Availability: All requesters
Suggested Grade: 6-12
Order Number: not applicable
Format: Web Site

Source: National Institutes of Health, Office of Science Education
World Wide Web URL:
http://science.education.nih.gov/LifeWorks.nsf/feature/indexhtm

Me, Myself, and My Future Job

This unit will start young people thinking of jobs they might find satisfying and what they can do now to start getting the proper skills and education.

Availability: All requesters
Suggested Grade: 5-10
Order Number: not applicable
Format: Online Lesson Plan

Source: Jeanne Guthrie
World Wide Web URL:
http://www.eduref.org/Virtual/Lessons/Vocational_Education/Careers/CAE0200.html

Military Careers

Provides information about each of the 4,100 careers available in the armed services.

Availability: All requesters
Suggested Grade: 6-Adult
Order Number: not applicable
Format: Web Site

Source: Today's Military
World Wide Web URL:
http://www.todaysmilitary.com/careers

New Universe to Explore, A: Careers in Astronomy

Explains the various careers available in the field of astronomy and how to prepare for them.

Availability:
Suggested Grade: 6-12
Order Number:
Format: Downloadable brochure

Source: American Astronomical Society, The
World Wide Web URL:
http://www.aas.org/education/publications/careerbrochure.html

One-Stop Career Centers

Provides background on the one-stop employment and training system, describes the experiences of early one-stop career centers, and raises issues related to the continued development of the one-stop system.

Availability: All requesters
Suggested Grade: 9-Adult
Order Number: not applicable
Production Date: 1999
Format: Online Article

Source: Susan Imel
World Wide Web URL:
http://www.ericdigests.org/2000-2/one.htm

Part-Time Work and Other Flexible Options

Examines flexible work options, including the characteristics of workers who select them, the organizations that offer them, and the influence they have on worker satisfaction, performance, productivity, and career progression.

Availability: All requesters
Suggested Grade: 6-12
Order Number: not applicable
Production Date: 1998
Format: Online Article

Source: Bettina Lankard Brown
World Wide Web URL:
http://www.ericdigests.org/1998-3/work.html

Pathology A Career in Medicine

Tells about the career duties and opportunities for a pathologist.

Availability: Limit of 2 copies to schools, libraries, and homeschoolers world-wide. Bulk copies are available; contact source for shipping and handling charges.
Suggested Grade: 6-12
Order Number: order by title
Format: Booklet; 12 pages
Special Notes: Email requests preferred.

Source: Intersociety Council for Pathology Information
9650 Rockville Pike, Suite E133
Bethesda, MD 20814-3993
Phone: 1-301-634-7130
Fax: 1-301-634-7990
World Wide Web URL: http://www.pathologytraining.org
Email Address: dstivers@asip.org

Personal Interests and Career Traits

Students will develop an awareness of their personal interests and relate them to career traits and match these to various jobs.

Availability: All requesters
Suggested Grade: 10-12
Order Number: not applicable
Format: Online Lesson Plan

Source: Harold Adams
World Wide Web URL:
http://youth.net/cec/cecmisc/cecmisc.72.txt

Resumes, Applications, and Cover Letters
Provides sample resumes and cover letters so that you may create your own.
Availability: All requesters
Suggested Grade: 6-Adult
Order Number: not applicable
Production Date: 1999
Format: Online Article; 15 pages
Special Notes: Use the on-site search engine to easily find this title. You may request a printed copy mailed to you for a fee.
Source: Federal Citizen Information Center
World Wide Web URL: http://www.pueblo.gsa.gov/

Role of the African-American Teacher, The: Why It's Essential in the School System
Examines the role of teachers, and particularly the contributions African-American teachers can make.
Availability: All requesters
Suggested Grade: 6-12
Order Number: not applicable
Format: Online Article
Source: Dr. Gilbert Brown
World Wide Web URL:
http://www.black-collegian.com/career/career-reports/teacher2000-1st.shtml

Self-Efficacy Beliefs and Career Development
Discusses ways in which self-efficacy beliefs are influenced by various internal, external, and interactive factors and reflected in career-related outcome expectations and performance.
Availability: All requesters
Suggested Grade: Teacher Reference
Order Number: not applicable
Production Date: 1999
Format: Online Article
Source: Bettina Lankard Brown
World Wide Web URL:
http://www.ericdigests.org/1999-4/self.htm

So You Want to Be a Doctor? Career Opportunities Grow in Health and Biomedicine
Discusses, in detail, the many careers available as a doctor.
Availability: All requesters
Suggested Grade: 6-12
Order Number: not applicable
Format: Online Article
Source: Roderick K. King, M.D.
World Wide Web URL:
http://www.black-collegian.com/career/career-reports/biomedicine2000-2nd.shtml

Students with Disabilities in Career and Technical Education
Career and technical education can provide significant benefits to students with disabilities. This digest provides more information.
Availability: All requesters
Suggested Grade: Teacher Reference
Order Number: not applicable
Production Date: 2001
Format: Online Article
Source: Michael E. Wonacott
World Wide Web URL:
http://www.ericdigests.org/2002-3/career.htm

Technology in the Work Force
In this WebQuest, you will answer the question "which skills are required in the 21st Century work force, and how do I prepare myself to function successfully?"
Availability: All requesters
Suggested Grade: 9-12
Order Number: not applicable
Format: WebQuest
Source: Carolyn O. Burleson
World Wide Web URL:
http://drb.lifestreamcenter.net/Lessons/techwork/index.htm

Veterinarians
Explains the diversity of career opportunities available in veterinary medicine.
Availability: Single copies to schools, libraries, and homeschoolers in the United States and Canada.
Suggested Grade: 6-Adult
Order Number: order by title
Format: Brochure
Special Notes: May also be downloaded from the web site.
Source: American Veterinary Medical Association
Attn: Order Dept.
1931 North Meacham Road, Suite 100
Schaumburg, IL 60173-4360
Phone: 1-847-285-6655
Fax: 1-847-925-1329
World Wide Web URL: http://www.avma.org
Email Address: productorders@avma.org

Veterinary Technicians
Describes the educational requirements and career opportunities in the field of veterinary technology.
Availability: Single copies to schools, libraries, and homeschoolers in the United States and Canada.
Suggested Grade: 6-Adult
Order Number: order by title
Format: Brochure
Special Notes: May also be downloaded from the web site.

Source: American Veterinary Medical Association
Attn: Order Dept.
1931 North Meacham Road, Suite 100
Schaumburg, IL 60173-4360
Phone: 1-847-285-6655
Fax: 1-847-925-1329
World Wide Web URL: http://www.avma.org
Email Address: productorders@avma.org

What Do Earth and Space Scientists Do?

Answers this question.

Availability: All requesters
Suggested Grade: 6-12
Order Number: not applicable
Format: Downloadable Brochure

Source: American Geophysical Union
World Wide Web URL:
http://www.agu.org/about/our_science/

What Is a Paralegal?

Explains the duties of a "legal assistant."

Availability: All requesters
Suggested Grade: 6-12
Order Number: not applicable
Format: Online Article

Source: National Federation of Paralegal Associations, Inc.
World Wide Web URL: http://www.paralegals.org/displaycommon.cfm?an=1&subarticlenbr=110

Women in Oceanography

This site focuses on women who have dedicated their professional lives to academic research in the field of oceanography.

Availability: All requesters
Suggested Grade: 6-Adult
Order Number: not applicable
Format: Web Site

Source: Scripps Institution of Oceanography
World Wide Web URL:
http://web.archive.org/web/20010802232238/http://www.siommg.ucsd.edu/wio/

Ainsworth Computer Seminar
Students will learn more about all aspects of computers with this self-paced program.
Availability: All requesters
Suggested Grade: All ages
Order Number: not applicable
Format: Downloadable FULL PROGRAM
Source: Dick Ainsworth
World Wide Web URL:
http://www.qwerty.com/startacs.htm

Analytical Eye Typing Tutor
Learn how to type.
Availability: All requesters
Suggested Grade: All ages
Platform: Windows
Order Number: not applicable
Format: Downloadable FULL PROGRAM
Source: Analytical Eye Technologies
World Wide Web URL: http://www.aetech.co.uk/ttutor/

Back to School
A beginner's course in the Internet and its various tools targeted toward librarians and other information professionals.
Availability: All requesters
Suggested Grade: 9-Adult
Order Number: not applicable
Format: Online Tutorials
Source: Ellen Chamberlain
World Wide Web URL: http://www.sc.edu/bck2skol/

Basic Network Design
Design a basic computer network for your high school.
Availability: All requesters
Suggested Grade: 9-12
Order Number: not applicable
Format: WebQuest
Source: Doug Plunkett
World Wide Web URL:
http://www.yorkville.k12.il.us/webquests/webqplunkett/webqsplunkett.html

Becoming Webwise
Learn at your own pace about the Internet.
Availability: All requesters
Suggested Grade: All ages
Order Number: not applicable
Format: Online Course
Source: BBC Learning
World Wide Web URL:
http://www.bbc.co.uk/webwise/learn/

Beginner's Web Glossary, A
Definitions that help to clear up some of the confusing terminology that surrounds the World Wide Web.
Availability: All requesters
Suggested Grade: 6-Adult
Order Number: not applicable
Format: Online Glossary
Source: Tabor Griffin Communications
World Wide Web URL:
http://www.cwru.edu/help/webglossary.html

bNetS@vvy
Designed to give adults tools to connect with kids and help them stay safer online.
Availability: All requesters
Suggested Grade: Adults
Order Number: not applicable
Format: Online newsletter; bimonthly
Source: National Education Association Health Information Network
World Wide Web URL: http://bnetsavvy.org/wp/

CGI Resource Index, The
A lists of numerous links to resources on programming in CGI.
Availability: All requesters
Suggested Grade: 6-Adult
Order Number: not applicable
Format: Web Site
Source: Matt's Script Archive, Inc.
World Wide Web URL: http://cgi.resourceindex.com/

Circuit
Learn all about the parts of your computer.
Availability: All requesters
Suggested Grade: 5-12
Order Number: not applicable
Format: Web Site
Special Notes: This URL will lead you to a subject page. Then click on the appropriate subject heading.
Source: ThinkQuest
World Wide Web URL:
http://www.thinkquest.org/pls/html/think.library

Classroom Learning 2.0
A site for teachers to learn more about the Internet.
Availability: All requesters
Suggested Grade: Teacher Reference
Order Number: not applicable
Format: Online Tutorial
Source: California School Library Association
World Wide Web URL:
http://classroomlearning2.blogspot.com/

Comprehensive Resource for Publishing on the Worldwide Web
A publishing guide for the World Wide Web.
Availability: All requesters
Suggested Grade: 6-Adult
Order Number: not applicable
Format: Online Guide
Source: WebCom
World Wide Web URL: http://www.webcom.com/html/

Computer and Internet Use by Children and Adolescents in 2001: Statistical Analysis Report
Describes computer and Internet use by children and teens ages five to seventeen.
Availability: All requesters
Suggested Grade: Teacher Reference
Order Number: not applicable
Production Date: 2004
Format: Downloadable Booklet
Source: ED Pubs
World Wide Web URL: http://www.edpubs.org

Computer Circus
Learn keyboarding, Internet navigation, e-mail usage, and HTML. Learn how to write a web page.
Availability: All requesters
Suggested Grade: 4-12
Order Number: not applicable
Format: Web Site
Special Notes: This URL will lead you to a subject page. Then click on the appropriate subject heading.
Source: ThinkQuest
World Wide Web URL:
http://www.thinkquest.org/pls/html/think.library

Computer User High-Tech Dictionary
Search for definitions to more than 7,000 high-tech terms.
Availability: All requesters
Suggested Grade: 6-12
Order Number: not applicable
Format: Online Glossary
Source: Computer User.com
World Wide Web URL:
http://www.computeruser.com/resources/dictionary/

Computers Only Do What They Are Told
This activity demonstrates how computers are literal machines--they only do as instructed!
Availability: All requesters
Suggested Grade: 7-12
Order Number: not applicable
Format: Online Lesson Plan
Source: Daniel Swomley
World Wide Web URL:
http://youth.net/cec/cecmisc/cecmisc.38.txt

Copyright and Technology Law
Q WebQuest designed to help students learn the proper use of technology in regards to copyright.
Availability: All requesters
Suggested Grade: 9-12
Order Number: not applicable
Format: WebQuest
Source: Stephen Eichhammer
World Wide Web URL:
http://www.yorkville.k12.il.us/webquests/webqeichhammer/webqseichhammer1.htm

Creating a Blog: A Workshop for Teens
A complete curriculum for downloading that will teach teens how to create and maintain their own blogs.
Availability: All requesters
Suggested Grade: 7-Adult
Order Number: not applicable
Format: Downloadable Curriculum
Special Notes: This is a PDF file which will open automatically on your computer.
Source: Children's Partnership, The
World Wide Web URL:
http://www.childrenspartnership.org/AM/Template.cfm?Section=Home&Template=/CM/ContentDisplay.cfm&ContentFileID=1017

CyberU Internet Basics
A one-semester, student-centered high school course that "introduces the Internet, what it is, and how to use its major applications."
Availability: All requesters
Suggested Grade: 9-12
Order Number: not applicable
Format: Web Site
Source: A. Wolinsky
World Wide Web URL: http://oii.org/cyberu/

Ethics in Computing
A collection of articles and essays that discuss topics related to the ethics of computer use.
Availability: All requesters
Suggested Grade: 9-Adult
Order Number: not applicable
Format: Web Site
Source: Dr. Edward F. Gehringer
World Wide Web URL: http://ethics.csc.ncsu.edu/

EZ Instructions
Information and instructions, with computer novices in mind, for some of the most popular computer programs.
Availability: All requesters
Suggested Grade: 9-Adult
Order Number: not applicable
Format: Web Site
Source: EZ Instructions.com
World Wide Web URL: http://www.ezinstructions.com/

Finding Information Tutorial
Provides a list of tools and techniques you can use to find what you want on the Internet: a sort of over-your-shoulder guide to suggest places and searches to try next to find the information you want.
Availability: All requesters
Suggested Grade: 6-12
Order Number: not applicable
Format: Online Tutorial
Source: Laura Mengel
World Wide Web URL:
http://www-ed.fnal.gov/linc/spring96/find/find_tutorial.html

Find Lost Files and Folders

A "techtorial" that will help you to learn how to find files you saved on your hard drive.

Availability: All requesters
Suggested Grade: 6-Adult
Order Number: not applicable
Format: Online Article

Source: Lorrie Jackson
World Wide Web URL:
http://www.educationworld.com/a_tech/techtorial/techtorial050.shtml

Front Page 2000 Tutorial

Learn how to use this program to easily create web sites.

Availability: All requesters
Suggested Grade: 4-Adult
Order Number: not applicable
Format: Online Tutorial

Source: Act360 Media Ltd.
World Wide Web URL: http://www.actden.com/

FTP Editor

Create description files for directories served by the Windows NT FTP server.

Availability: All requesters
Suggested Grade: Adult
Platform: Windows
Order Number: not applicable
Format: Downloadable FULL PROGRAM

Source: Maximized Software, Inc.
World Wide Web URL:
http://www.maximized.com/freeware/

Getting Started with PowerPoint

Explains what this computer program does and provides opportunities to help students learn how to use it.

Availability: All requesters
Suggested Grade: 4-Adult
Order Number: not applicable
Format: Online Lesson Plan

Source: Judy Salmon
World Wide Web URL:
http://teachertech.rice.edu/Participants/jsalmon/lessons/powerpoint/index.html

Getting Started with Java

A lesson on beginning programming in the Java language.

Availability: All requesters
Suggested Grade: 9-Adult
Order Number: not applicable
Format: Online Lesson Plan

Source: Sherika Dumes
World Wide Web URL:
http://teachertech.rice.edu/Participants/sdumes/Lesson/index.html

History of Computers, ThinkQuest 1998

The first electronic digital computer was called ENIAC, built in 1945. Trace the history and learn fun facts.

Availability: All requesters
Suggested Grade: 4-12
Order Number: not applicable
Format: Web Site
Special Notes: This URL will lead you to a subject page. Then click on the appropriate subject heading.

Source: ThinkQuest
World Wide Web URL:
http://www.thinkquest.org/pls/html/think.library

How the Internet Came to Be

Details the history of this medium of communication.

Availability: All requesters
Suggested Grade: 4-12
Order Number: not applicable
Format: Online Article

Source: Vinton Cerf
World Wide Web URL:
http://www.netvalley.com/archives/mirrors/cerf-how-inet.txt

How to Learn to Use Any Software Application You Want

Highlights the qualities of each learning modality commonly used to learn new software applications.

Availability: All requesters
Suggested Grade: Teacher Reference
Order Number: not applicable
Format: Online Article

Source: TeAch-nology.com
World Wide Web URL: http://www.teach-nology.com/tutorials/learn_software/

HTML Goodies

This site hosts seven primers for learning about HTML in addition to over 100 different tutorials.

Availability: All requesters
Suggested Grade: 6-Adult
Order Number: not applicable
Format: Web Site

Source: Joe Burns
World Wide Web URL: http://www.htmlgoodies.com/

HTML Imager Version 1.2a

Produces web pages showing all GIF and/or JPG pictures from the directory you select.

Availability: All requesters
Suggested Grade: 6-Adult
Platform: Windows
Order Number: not applicable
Format: Downloadable FULL PROGRAM

Source: Eric G. V. Fookes
World Wide Web URL:
http://www.fookes.com/software/html-img.htm

Java Tutorials, The

This online version of a book by the same name, will help you work your way through the object-oriented programming language.

Availability: All requesters
Suggested Grade: 9-Adult
Order Number: not applicable
Format: Online Tutorial

Source: Sun Microsystems, Inc.
World Wide Web URL:
http://java.sun.com/docs/books/tutorial/

Kid's Typing Skills

Learn beginning keyboarding.

Availability: All requesters
Suggested Grade: All ages
Platform: Windows
Order Number: not applicable
Format: Downloadable FULL PROGRAM

Source: KIDware
World Wide Web URL:
http://www.kidwaresoftware.com/kidtype.htm

Learning About Tasks That Computers Can Perform

Written for the novice.

Availability: All requesters
Suggested Grade: Teacher Reference
Order Number: not applicable
Production Date: 1995
Format: Online Article

Source: Patricia Brosnan
World Wide Web URL:
http://www.ericdigests.org/1996-1/tasks.htm

Lissa Explains It All

A very helpful primer about Web page construction put together by a 12-year-old girl.

Availability: All requesters
Suggested Grade: 6-Adult
Order Number: not applicable
Format: Web Site

Source: Lissa
World Wide Web URL: http://www.lissaexplains.com/

Making the Connection: How to Go Online

Explains how to get online and choose the best Internet service provider.

Availability: All requesters
Suggested Grade: 4-Adult
Order Number: not applicable
Format: Online Article; 9 pages
Special Notes: Use the on-site search engine to easily find this title. You may request a printed copy mailed to you for a fee.

Source: Federal Citizen Information Center
World Wide Web URL: http://www.pueblo.gsa.gov/

On-Line Practice Modules

A collection of tutorials written to help teachers, staff, and students to use some of the more common computer programs.

Availability: All requesters
Suggested Grade: 9-Adult
Order Number: not applicable
Format: Online Tutorials

Source: Susan Brooks and Bill Byles
World Wide Web URL:
http://www.internet4classrooms.com/on-line.htm

Online Security and Safety Tips

Outlines three important steps you can take to protect your computer and your personal information.

Availability: All requesters
Suggested Grade: 6-Adult
Order Number: not applicable
Production Date: 2004
Format: Online Article; 5 pages
Special Notes: Use the on-site search engine to easily find this title. You may request a printed copy mailed to you for a fee.

Source: Federal Citizen Information Center
World Wide Web URL: http://www.pueblo.gsa.gov/

Outlook Express Tutorial

A tutorial for this popular email program.

Availability: All requesters
Suggested Grade: 4-Adult
Order Number: not applicable
Format: Online Tutorial

Source: Act360 Media Ltd.
World Wide Web URL: http://www.actden.com/

Philip and Alex's Guide to Web Publishing

A complete book that tells how to set up a really great website.

Availability: All requesters
Suggested Grade: 6-Adult
Order Number: not applicable
Format: Online Book

Source: Philip Greenspun
World Wide Web URL:
http://www.philip.greenspun.com/panda/

Power Point 98 Tutorial

A tutorial that will help you use this program and your computer for great presentations.

Availability: All requesters
Suggested Grade: 4-Adult
Order Number: not applicable
Format: Online Tutorial

Source: Act360 Media Ltd.
World Wide Web URL: http://www.actden.com/

Primer on Digital Literacy, A

Discusses the concept of "digital literacy"--directed at the field of education.

Availability: All requesters
Suggested Grade: Teacher Reference
Order Number: not applicable

Format: Online Primer

Source: Paul Gilster
World Wide Web URL:
http://horizon.unc.edu/projects/resources/digital_literacy.asp

Rainwater Press Publishing Glossary
Features more than 1,000 terms related to the digital publishing, graphic arts, and printing industries.
Availability: All requesters
Suggested Grade: 6-Adult
Order Number: not applicable
Format: Online Dictionary

Source: Rainwater Press
World Wide Web URL:
http://www.rainwater.com/glossary.html

Script Source
A series of commands you write, so a browser can display special features on your web site.
Availability: All requesters
Suggested Grade: 6-12
Order Number: not applicable
Format: Web Site
Special Notes: This URL will lead you to a subject page. Then click on the appropriate subject heading.

Source: ThinkQuest
World Wide Web URL:
http://www.thinkquest.org/pls/html/think.library

Secret Art of HTML Programming and Web Design, The
Beginner, intermediate, and advanced lessons teach HTML, Images, Text, Entities, Graphics, and Javascript.
Availability: All requesters
Suggested Grade: 6-12
Order Number: not applicable
Format: Web Site
Special Notes: This URL will lead you to a subject page. Then click on the appropriate subject heading.

Source: ThinkQuest
World Wide Web URL:
http://www.thinkquest.org/pls/html/think.library

SkillsDEN
Sheds new light on information technology.
Availability: All requesters
Suggested Grade: 4-Adult
Order Number: not applicable
Format: Online Course

Source: Act360 Media Ltd.
World Wide Web URL: http://www.actden.com/

Social Networking Sites: Safety Tips for Tweens and Teens
Urges parents and kids to talk about the risks involved in using social networking sites and offers tips for using them safely.
Availability: Limit of 49 copies to schools, libraries, and homeschoolers world-wide.
Suggested Grade: 6-12
Order Number: order by title
Format: Booklet

Source: Federal Trade Commission
Consumer Response Center
600 Pennsylvania, N. W., Room H-130
Washington, DC 20580
World Wide Web URL:
http://www.ftc.gov/bcp/consumer.shtm

Spinning the Web: A Hands-On Introduction to Building Mosaic and WWW Documents
A lesson on web site language and web site building.
Availability: All requesters
Suggested Grade: 9-Adult
Order Number: not applicable
Format: Downloadable Booklet
Special Notes: This is a PDF file which will open automatically on your computer.

Source: James Powell
World Wide Web URL:
http://scholar.lib.vt.edu/reports/html-int.pdf

Teach Me HTML
Learn how to create web basics--in only 1 hour.
Availability: All requesters
Suggested Grade: 6-Adult
Order Number: not applicable
Format: Downloadable FULL PROGRAM

Source: Pinsoft Software
World Wide Web URL:
http://www.pinsoft.com.au/teachhtml.htm

Web Pages for Absolute Beginners
Here is information on how to make your own web pages using HTML code, using Windows 95 and Microsoft Internet Explorer.
Availability: All requesters
Suggested Grade: 6-Adult
Platform: Windows
Order Number: not applicable
Format: Online Tutorial
Special Notes: This is a PDF file which will open automatically on your computer.

Source: Ruth Livingstone
World Wide Web URL:
http://www.nuceng.ca/teach/web4beginners.pdf

Web-Wizard's Spellbook
Step-by-step tutorial to web page design with lots of links and tutorials.
Availability: All requesters
Suggested Grade: 6-12
Order Number: not applicable
Format: Web Site
Special Notes: This URL will lead you to a subject page. Then click on the appropriate subject heading.

Source: ThinkQuest
World Wide Web URL:
http://www.thinkquest.org/pls/html/think.library

Writing HTML

Created to help teachers create learning resources that access information on the Internet, this is a well done tutorial to help you learn.

Availability: All requesters
Suggested Grade: Teacher Reference
Languages: English; Spanish
Order Number: not applicable
Format: Online Tutorial

Source: Maricopa Center for Learning and Instruction
World Wide Web URL:
http://www.mcli.dist.maricopa.edu/tut/

You've Got Spam: How to "Can" Unwanted E-Mail

Find out how marketers get your email address, how to reduce the amount of spam you receive, and more.

Availability: All requesters
Suggested Grade: 6-Adult
Order Number: not applicable
Format: Online Article
Special Notes: Use the on-site search engine to easily find this title. You may request a printed copy mailed to you for a fee.

Source: Federal Citizen Information Center
World Wide Web URL: http://www.pueblo.gsa.gov/

Accounting Terminology Guide
An educational tool for journalists who report on and interpret financial information.
Availability: All requesters
Suggested Grade: Adult
Order Number: not applicable
Format: Online Dictionary
Source: New York State Society of CPAs
World Wide Web URL:
http://www.nysscpa.org/prof_library/guide.htm

Advertising and Marketing on the Internet: The Rules of the Road
Useful not only if you plan to advertise, but reading this article can help you understand what others are doing.
Availability: Limit of 49 copies to schools, libraries, and homeschoolers world-wide.
Suggested Grade: 6-Adult
Order Number: order by title
Format: Brochure
Special Notes: May also be downloaded from the Web site. Quantities in excess of 50 are available from Federal Trade Commission, Distribution Office, 600 Pennsylvania Avenue, NW, Washington, D. C. 20580-0001 or fax to: 1-703-739-0991.
Source: Federal Trade Commission
Consumer Response Center
600 Pennsylvania, N. W., Room H-130
Washington, DC 20580
World Wide Web URL:
http://www.ftc.gov/bcp/consumer.shtm

Advertising: Be Careful What You Buy!
Depicts different types of ads to show how to shop and avoid buying something you might not really want.
Availability: All requesters
Suggested Grade: 6-12
Order Number: not applicable
Format: Web Site
Special Notes: This URL will lead you to a subject page. Then click on the appropriate subject heading.
Source: ThinkQuest
World Wide Web URL:
http://www.thinkquest.org/pls/html/think.library

Aerospace Industry, The: Its History and How It Affects the U. S. Economy
Discuses the history of flying and the impact of the aerospace industry on the economy of the United States--one of the most powerful industries in the United States.
Availability: All requesters
Suggested Grade: 7-12
Order Number: not applicable
Format: Online Lesson Plan
Source: Carol L. Cook
World Wide Web URL: http://www.yale.edu/ynhti/curriculum/units/1990/7/90.07.06.x.html

American Currency Exhibit
Filled with periodic music and historical trivia that traces the evolution of American paper money from the American Revolution to present day.
Availability: Single copies to schools, libraries, and homeschoolers in the United States.
Suggested Grade: 4-12
Order Number: not applicable
Format: Web Site
Source: Federal Reserve Bank of San Francisco
World Wide Web URL:
http://www.frbsf.org/currency/index.html

Auditing Dictionary of Terms
Definitions to a number of terms, all of which have appeared on CPA exams.
Availability: All requesters
Suggested Grade: 9-Adult
Order Number: not applicable
Format: Online Dictionary
Source: Accounting Institute Seminars
World Wide Web URL: http://www.ais-cpa.com/glosa.html

Avoiding Credit & Charge Card Fraud
Details scams so that you can avoid them.
Availability: Limit of 49 copies to schools, libraries, and homeschoolers world-wide.
Suggested Grade: 10-Adult
Order Number: order by title
Format: Brochure
Special Notes: May also be downloaded from the Web site. Quantities in excess of 50 are available from Federal Trade Commission, Distribution Office, 600 Pennsylvania Avenue, NW, Washington, D. C. 20580-0001 or fax to: 1-703-739-0991.
Source: Federal Trade Commission
Consumer Response Center
600 Pennsylvania, N. W., Room H-130
Washington, DC 20580
World Wide Web URL:
http://www.ftc.gov/bcp/consumer.shtm

Becoming a Consumer Activist
Students will learn to identify and apply the steps used in the decision making process, to analyze consumer options, and send an effective letter of complaint.
Availability: All requesters
Suggested Grade: 6-12
Order Number: not applicable
Format: Online Lesson Plan
Source: Skip Adams
World Wide Web URL:
http://www.col-ed.org/cur/misc/misc89.txt

Billed for Merchandise You Never Received?
Explains your rights and steps to take to correct the problem.

Availability: Limit of 49 copies to schools, libraries, and homeschoolers world-wide.
Suggested Grade: 10-Adult
Order Number: order by title
Format: Brochure
Special Notes: May also be downloaded from the Web site. Quantities in excess of 50 are available from Federal Trade Commission, Distribution Office, 600 Pennsylvania Avenue, NW, Washington, D. C. 20580-0001 or fax to: 1-703-739-0991.

Source: Federal Trade Commission
Consumer Response Center
600 Pennsylvania, N. W., Room H-130
Washington, DC 20580
World Wide Web URL:
http://www.ftc.gov/bcp/consumer.shtm

Building a Better Credit Report

Explains how to build a good record of credit.

Availability: Limit of 49 copies to schools, libraries, and homeschoolers world-wide.
Suggested Grade: 10-Adult
Order Number: order by title
Format: Brochure
Special Notes: May also be downloaded from the Web site. Quantities in excess of 50 are available from Federal Trade Commission, Distribution Office, 600 Pennsylvania Avenue, NW, Washington, D. C. 20580-0001 or fax to: 1-703-739-0991.

Source: Federal Trade Commission
Consumer Response Center
600 Pennsylvania, N. W., Room H-130
Washington, DC 20580
World Wide Web URL:
http://www.ftc.gov/bcp/consumer.shtm

Buying, Giving, and Using Gift Cards

What to look for when buying and using gift cards, especially the terms and conditions of their use.

Availability: Limit of 49 copies to schools, libraries, and homeschoolers world-wide.
Suggested Grade: 6-Adult
Order Number: order by title
Format: Brochure
Special Notes: May also be downloaded from the Web site. Quantities in excess of 50 are available from Federal Trade Commission, Distribution Office, 600 Pennsylvania Avenue, NW, Washington, D. C. 20580-0001 or fax to: 1-703-739-0991.

Source: Federal Trade Commission
Consumer Response Center
600 Pennsylvania, N. W., Room H-130
Washington, DC 20580
World Wide Web URL:
http://www.ftc.gov/bcp/consumer.shtm

Collapse of Corporate Giants, The

Written to help students understand how industry giants brought about their own collapse.

Availability: All requesters
Suggested Grade: 9-12
Order Number: not applicable
Format: WebQuest

Source: Charlotte Higler
World Wide Web URL:
http://www.econedlink.org/lessons/index.cfm?lesson=EM391

Consumer Financial Emergency Survival Kit, The

Provides consumers with basic helpful guidance and resources on a broad range of consumer financial topics.

Availability: Limit of one copy to schools, libraries, and homeschoolers in the United States and Canada. Make request on a postcard.
Suggested Grade: 9-Adult
Order Number: order by the title
Format: Booklet
Special Notes: May also be downloaded from the web site.

Source: Federal Reserve Bank of Boston
World Wide Web URL:
http://www.bos.frb.org/consumer/survival-guide/index.htm

Consumer's Guide to E-Payments, A

Describes online payment technologies and how to make you transactions as secure as possible.

Availability: Limit of 49 copies to schools, libraries, and homeschoolers world-wide.
Suggested Grade: 10-Adult
Order Number: order by title
Format: Brochure
Special Notes: May also be downloaded from the Web site. Quantities in excess of 50 are available from Federal Trade Commission, Distribution Office, 600 Pennsylvania Avenue, NW, Washington, D. C. 20580-0001 or fax to: 1-703-739-0991.

Source: Federal Trade Commission
Consumer Response Center
600 Pennsylvania, N. W., Room H-130
Washington, DC 20580
World Wide Web URL:
http://www.ftc.gov/bcp/consumer.shtm

Cosigning a Loan

Explains the consequences of co-signing a loan.

Availability: Limit of 49 copies to schools, libraries, and homeschoolers world-wide.
Suggested Grade: 4-12
Order Number: order by title
Format: Brochure

Source: Federal Trade Commission
Consumer Response Center
600 Pennsylvania, N. W., Room H-130
Washington, DC 20580
World Wide Web URL:
http://www.ftc.gov/bcp/consumer.shtm

Credit and Your Consumer Rights
Explains credit laws that protect your right to obtain, use, and maintain credit. Offers practical tips to help you solve credit problems.
Availability: Limit of 49 copies to schools, libraries, and homeschoolers world-wide.
Suggested Grade: 9-Adult
Order Number: order by title
Format: Brochure
Special Notes: May also be downloaded from the Web site. Quantities in excess of 50 are available from Federal Trade Commission, Distribution Office, 600 Pennsylvania Avenue, NW, Washington, D. C. 20580-0001 or fax to: 1-703-739-0991.

Source: Federal Trade Commission
Consumer Response Center
600 Pennsylvania, N. W., Room H-130
Washington, DC 20580
World Wide Web URL:
http://www.ftc.gov/bcp/consumer.shtm

Credit Card Usage and Debt Among College and University Students
Discusses this very important issue.
Availability: All requesters
Suggested Grade: Teacher Reference
Order Number: not applicable
Production Date: 2003
Format: Online Article

Source: Tamara Holub
World Wide Web URL:
http://www.ericdigests.org/2003-2/credit.html

Cybershopping: Protecting Yourself When Buying Online
Tips to follow when shopping in cyberspace.
Availability: Limit of 49 copies to schools, libraries, and homeschoolers world-wide.
Suggested Grade: 6-Adult
Order Number: order by title
Format: Brochure
Special Notes: May also be downloaded from the Web site. Quantities in excess of 50 are available from Federal Trade Commission, Distribution Office, 600 Pennsylvania Avenue, NW, Washington, D. C. 20580-0001 or fax to: 1-703-739-0991.

Source: Federal Trade Commission
Consumer Response Center
600 Pennsylvania, N. W., Room H-130
Washington, DC 20580
World Wide Web URL:
http://www.ftc.gov/bcp/consumer.shtm

Dot Cons
Explains a number of opportunities con artists are using to scam you via the Internet.
Availability: Limit of 49 copies to schools, libraries, and homeschoolers world-wide.
Suggested Grade: 6-Adult
Order Number: order by title
Format: Brochure
Special Notes: May also be downloaded from the Web site. Quantities in excess of 50 are available from Federal Trade Commission, Distribution Office, 600 Pennsylvania Avenue, NW, Washington, D. C. 20580-0001 or fax to: 1-703-739-0991.

Source: Federal Trade Commission
Consumer Response Center
600 Pennsylvania, N. W., Room H-130
Washington, DC 20580
World Wide Web URL:
http://www.ftc.gov/bcp/consumer.shtm

Easy Economics: The Asian Crisis
Uses news and articles to discuss what the Asian economic crisis is, and how to prevent it happening again.
Availability: All requesters
Suggested Grade: 9-12
Order Number: not applicable
Format: Web Site
Special Notes: This URL will lead you to a subject page. Then click on the appropriate subject heading.

Source: ThinkQuest
World Wide Web URL:
http://www.thinkquest.org/pls/html/think.library

eBiz4Teens
Essential vocabulary, main concepts, and resources related to eBusiness and entrepreneurship.
Availability: All requesters
Suggested Grade: 6-12
Order Number: not applicable
Format: Web Site
Special Notes: This URL will lead you to a subject page. Then click on the appropriate subject heading.

Source: ThinkQuest
World Wide Web URL:
http://www.thinkquest.org/pls/html/think.library

ECONnections
An assortment of lesson plans and WebQuests for all ages about economics.
Availability: All requesters
Suggested Grade: 4-12
Order Number: not applicable
Format: Online Lesson Plans and WebQuests

Source: National Council on Economic Education
World Wide Web URL: http://www.e-connections.org/

Economic History of European Empires
Focuses on the major European Empires to provide a clear history in the field of economics.
Availability: All requesters
Suggested Grade: 6-12

Order Number: not applicable
Format: Web Site
Special Notes: This URL will lead you to a subject page. Then click on the appropriate subject heading.

Source: ThinkQuest
World Wide Web URL:
http://www.thinkquest.org/pls/html/think.library

Economics
Provides reference and slide show libraries to a business game simulator.
Availability: All requesters
Suggested Grade: 6-12
Order Number: not applicable
Format: Web Site
Special Notes: This URL will lead you to a subject page. Then click on the appropriate subject heading.

Source: ThinkQuest
World Wide Web URL:
http://www.thinkquest.org/pls/html/think.library

Econopolis
Mega Money, Bill, and Dollar tour Econopolis, where you can learn all about economics.
Availability: All requesters
Suggested Grade: All ages
Order Number: not applicable
Format: Web Site
Special Notes: This URL will lead you to a subject page. Then click on the appropriate subject heading.

Source: ThinkQuest
World Wide Web URL:
http://www.thinkquest.org/pls/html/think.library

EconoStocks
Wonderful explanations of economics and stocks with tutorial and glossary and introduction to business math.
Availability: All requesters
Suggested Grade: 9-12
Order Number: not applicable
Format: Web Site
Special Notes: This URL will lead you to a subject page. Then click on the appropriate subject heading.

Source: ThinkQuest
World Wide Web URL:
http://www.thinkquest.org/pls/html/think.library

EduStock
Follow the Stock Exchange tutorial, check the glossary of terms, and learn all about investing with "virtual" money.
Availability: All requesters
Suggested Grade: 9-Adult
Order Number: not applicable
Format: Web Site
Special Notes: This URL will lead you to a subject page. Then click on the appropriate subject heading.

Source: ThinkQuest
World Wide Web URL:
http://www.thinkquest.org/pls/html/think.library

Electronic Check Conversion
Explains how electronic check conversion works. Offers tips on keeping close tabs on your accounts.
Availability: Limit of 49 copies to schools, libraries, and homeschoolers world-wide.
Suggested Grade: 9-Adult
Order Number: order by title
Format: Brochure
Special Notes: May also be downloaded from the Web site. Quantities in excess of 50 are available from Federal Trade Commission, Distribution Office, 600 Pennsylvania Avenue, NW, Washington, D. C. 20580-0001 or fax to: 1-703-739-0991.

Source: Federal Trade Commission
Consumer Response Center
600 Pennsylvania, N. W., Room H-130
Washington, DC 20580
World Wide Web URL:
http://www.ftc.gov/bcp/consumer.shtm

Encyclopedia of Banking & Finance
A complete online dictionary that defines financial terms and symbols.
Availability: All requesters
Suggested Grade: 6-Adult
Order Number: not applicable
Format: Online Glossary

Source: EagleTraders.com
World Wide Web URL:
http://www.eagletraders.com/books/int_fin_encyclopedia.htm

Escape from Knab
Written to help students develop sound financial strategies, this site offers students a fun and educational challenge.
Availability: All requesters
Suggested Grade: 6-12
Order Number: not applicable
Format: Web Site

Source: Firstar
World Wide Web URL: http://www.escapefromknab.com/

European Monetary Union
Advantages and disadvantages of the new standard currency in many European countries.
Availability: All requesters
Suggested Grade: All ages
Order Number: not applicable
Format: Web Site
Special Notes: This URL will lead you to a subject page. Then click on the appropriate subject heading.

Source: ThinkQuest
World Wide Web URL:
http://www.thinkquest.org/pls/html/think.library

Euro, The
The new common monetary unit in Europe--the Euro.

Availability: All requesters
Suggested Grade: All ages
Languages: English; German
Order Number: not applicable
Format: Web Site
Special Notes: This URL will lead you to a subject page. Then click on the appropriate subject heading.

Source: ThinkQuest
World Wide Web URL:
http://www.thinkquest.org/pls/html/think.library

Family Vacation, The
Students will take a surprise trip around the world. As they travel, they will use clues to discover where they are going. They will then figure out how much money they have spent in U.S. dollars, using exchange rates.
Availability: All requesters
Suggested Grade: 6-12
Order Number: not applicable
Format: Online Lesson Plan

Source: Michael Koren
World Wide Web URL: http://www.econedlink.org/lessons/index.php?lid=798&type=educator

Financial Planning
Financial goals, saving, investing, stocks, bonds, mutual funds, debt management, and much more.
Availability: All requesters
Suggested Grade: 9-Adult
Order Number: not applicable
Format: Web Site
Special Notes: This URL will lead you to a subject page. Then click on the appropriate subject heading.

Source: ThinkQuest
World Wide Web URL:
http://www.thinkquest.org/pls/html/think.library

Focus on Economic Data
This lesson focuses on the January 28, 2011, first (advance) estimate of U.S. real gross domestic product (real GDP) growth for the fourth quarter (Q2) of 2010, as reported by the U.S. Bureau of Economic Analysis (BEA).
Availability: All requesters
Suggested Grade: 9-Adult
Order Number:
Production Date: 2011
Format: Online Lesson Plan

Source: Douglas Haskell
World Wide Web URL: http://www.econedlink.org/lessons/index.php?lid=989&type=educator

FTC Names Its Dirty Dozen: 12 Scams Most Likely to Arrive via Bulk Email
Alerts readers to the most common scams usually emailed to your computer.
Availability: Limit of 49 copies to schools, libraries, and homeschoolers world-wide.
Suggested Grade: 6-Adult
Order Number: order by title
Format: Brochure
Special Notes: May also be downloaded from the Web site. Quantities in excess of 50 are available from Federal Trade Commission, Distribution Office, 600 Pennsylvania Avenue, NW, Washington, D. C. 20580-0001 or fax to: 1-703-739-0991.

Source: Federal Trade Commission
Consumer Response Center
600 Pennsylvania, N. W., Room H-130
Washington, DC 20580
World Wide Web URL:
http://www.ftc.gov/bcp/consumer.shtm

Generic Drugs: Saving Money at the Pharmacy
Information to help you determine if you should select generic drugs.
Availability: Limit of 49 copies to schools, libraries, and homeschoolers world-wide.
Suggested Grade: 10-Adult
Languages: English; Spanish
Order Number: order by title
Format: Brochure
Special Notes: May also be downloaded from the Web site. Quantities in excess of 50 are available from Federal Trade Commission, Distribution Office, 600 Pennsylvania Avenue, NW, Washington, D. C. 20580-0001 or fax to: 1-703-739-0991.

Source: Federal Trade Commission
Consumer Response Center
600 Pennsylvania, N. W., Room H-130
Washington, DC 20580
World Wide Web URL:
http://www.ftc.gov/bcp/consumer.shtm

Holiday Shopping Online: Plan Ahead for Secure Surfing
Explains how to protect your privacy while shopping via the Internet as well as how to make sure you are going to receive your purchases.
Availability: Limit of 49 copies to schools, libraries, and homeschoolers world-wide.
Suggested Grade: 9-Adult
Order Number: order by title
Format: Brochure
Special Notes: May also be downloaded from the Web site. Quantities in excess of 50 are available from Federal Trade Commission, Distribution Office, 600 Pennsylvania Avenue, NW, Washington, D. C. 20580-0001 or fax to: 1-703-739-0991.

Source: Federal Trade Commission
Consumer Response Center
600 Pennsylvania, N. W., Room H-130
Washington, DC 20580
World Wide Web URL:
http://www.ftc.gov/bcp/consumer.shtm

Identity Crisis...What to Do If Your Identity Is Stolen
Tips to follow if this ever-increasing crime should happen to you or a member of your family.
Availability: Limit of 49 copies to schools, libraries, and homeschoolers world-wide.
Suggested Grade: 6-Adult
Order Number: order by title
Format: Brochure
Special Notes: May also be downloaded from the Web site. Quantities in excess of 50 are available from Federal Trade Commission, Distribution Office, 600 Pennsylvania Avenue, NW, Washington, D. C. 20580-0001 or fax to: 1-703-739-0991.
Source: Federal Trade Commission
Consumer Response Center
600 Pennsylvania, N. W., Room H-130
Washington, DC 20580
World Wide Web URL:
http://www.ftc.gov/bcp/consumer.shtm

Internet Auctions--A Guide for Buyers and Sellers
Explains the smart way to "do" Internet auctions.
Availability: Limit of 49 copies to schools, libraries, and homeschoolers world-wide.
Suggested Grade: 6-Adult
Order Number: order by title
Format: Brochure
Special Notes: May also be downloaded from the Web site. Quantities in excess of 50 are available from Federal Trade Commission, Distribution Office, 600 Pennsylvania Avenue, NW, Washington, D. C. 20580-0001 or fax to: 1-703-739-0991.
Source: Federal Trade Commission
Consumer Response Center
600 Pennsylvania, N. W., Room H-130
Washington, DC 20580
World Wide Web URL:
http://www.ftc.gov/bcp/consumer.shtm

Investing for Kids
Kid-friendly investment ideas for both beginner and intermediate investors.
Availability: All requesters
Suggested Grade: 4-10
Order Number: not applicable
Format: Web Site
Special Notes: This URL will lead you to a subject page. Then click on the appropriate subject heading.
Source: ThinkQuest
World Wide Web URL:
http://www.thinkquest.org/pls/html/think.library

Investing Glossary
Defines many of the terms used in this field.
Availability: All requesters
Suggested Grade: 6-Adult
Order Number: not applicable
Format: Online Glossary
Source: InvestorWords.com
World Wide Web URL: http://www.investorwords.com/

Investing in Your Future
Become familiar with stocks and bonds, mutual funds, or retirement investments.
Availability: All requesters
Suggested Grade: 9-Adult
Order Number: not applicable
Format: Web Site
Special Notes: This URL will lead you to a subject page. Then click on the appropriate subject heading.
Source: ThinkQuest
World Wide Web URL:
http://www.thinkquest.org/pls/html/think.library

InvestSmart
Covers investment basics, and provides market simulations, where students can get hands-on experience investing $100,000 of fantasy money.
Availability: All requesters
Suggested Grade: 9-Adult
Order Number: not applicable
Format: Web Site
Special Notes: This URL will lead you to a subject page. Then click on the appropriate subject heading.
Source: ThinkQuest
World Wide Web URL:
http://www.thinkquest.org/pls/html/think.library

It All Adds Up
A web-based interactive program designed to help high school teachers and students understand responsible personal financial skills and the proper care and use of credit.
Availability: All requesters
Suggested Grade: 9-12
Order Number: not applicable
Format: Web Site
Source: ItAllAddsUp.org
World Wide Web URL: http://www.italladdsup.org/

Kid's Consumer Corner
Explores different things one can do with money, from smart buying to investing.
Availability: All requesters
Suggested Grade: 4-10
Order Number: not applicable
Format: Web Site
Special Notes: This URL will lead you to a subject page. Then click on the appropriate subject heading.
Source: ThinkQuest
World Wide Web URL:
http://www.thinkquest.org/pls/html/think.library

Math Models and Economics Projects
The completion of these four WebQuests should teach

students a lot about economics.
Availability: All requesters
Suggested Grade: 9-Adult
Order Number: not applicable
Format: WebQuest
Source: Beau Zennadi and Doug James
World Wide Web URL:
http://www.amaisd.org/sites/nheights/math_models_&_economics_project.htm

Mint, The
An integrated web site designed for middle school and high school students as well as their teachers and parents, that teaches about economics.
Availability: All requesters
Suggested Grade: 5-12
Order Number: not applicable
Format: Web Site
Source: Northwestern Mutual Life Insurance Company, The
World Wide Web URL: http://themint.org/

Money
Details the history of money in the United States.
Availability: All requesters
Suggested Grade: All ages
Order Number: not applicable
Format: Web Site
Special Notes: This URL will lead you to a subject page. Then click on the appropriate subject heading.
Source: ThinkQuest
World Wide Web URL:
http://www.thinkquest.org/pls/html/think.library

Money Cent$ for Kids
Help learning tips about money and how to make (earn) it--for all ages.
Availability: All requesters
Suggested Grade: All ages
Order Number: not applicable
Format: Web Site
Special Notes: This URL will lead you to a subject page. Then click on the appropriate subject heading.
Source: ThinkQuest
World Wide Web URL:
http://www.thinkquest.org/pls/html/think.library

Money from Around the World
Info on different money used around the world.
Availability: All requesters
Suggested Grade: All ages
Order Number: not applicable
Format: Web Site
Special Notes: This URL will lead you to a subject page. Then click on the appropriate subject heading.
Source: ThinkQuest
World Wide Web URL:
http://www.thinkquest.org/pls/html/think.library

MoneySKILL
A highly interactive, reality based Internet curriculum designed to teach personal finance. Consists of 36 modules that students complete in approximately 40 minutes per module.
Availability: All requesters
Suggested Grade: 9-12
Order Number: not applicable
Format: Online Curriculum
Special Notes: Registration is required, but is free.
Source: AFSA Education Foundation
World Wide Web URL: http://www.moneyskill.org/

Money, The Root of All Savings
Learn what you need to know about smart stock investing.
Availability: All requesters
Suggested Grade: 6-Adult
Order Number: not applicable
Format: Web Site
Special Notes: This URL will lead you to a subject page. Then click on the appropriate subject heading.
Source: ThinkQuest
World Wide Web URL:
http://www.thinkquest.org/pls/html/think.library

Our Money
Examines how money is produced and what attempts are made to prevent counterfeiting. Also tells the history of United States currency.
Availability: All requesters
Suggested Grade: 6-12
Order Number: not applicable
Format: Online Articles
Source: Federal Reserve Bank of Minneapolis
World Wide Web URL:
http://www.minneapolisfed.org/community_education/teacher/money.cfm

Peanuts & Crackerjacks
An interactive baseball simulation that gives students a chance to test their knowledge of economics and sports trivia. Includes a teacher's guide with more than 50 activities.
Availability: All requesters
Suggested Grade: 6-12
Order Number: not applicable
Format: Online Game
Source: Federal Reserve Bank of Boston
World Wide Web URL:
http://www.bos.frb.org/peanuts/leadpgs/intro.htm

Propaganda Techniques
Students will learn to identify the different techniques that commercials use to convince us to buy certain products.
Availability: All requesters
Suggested Grade: 5-12
Order Number: not applicable
Format: Online Lesson Plan

Source: Lorraine Tanaka
World Wide Web URL:
http://youth.net/cec/ceclang/ceclang.25.txt

Sense & Dollars

Learn good money management with these interactive activities.

Availability: All requesters
Suggested Grade: 9-12
Order Number: not applicable
Format: Web Site

Source: Maryland Public Television
World Wide Web URL:
http://senseanddollars.thinkport.org/

Should LeBron James Mow His Own Lawn?

This lesson will discuss absolute advantage, comparative advantage, specialization and trade with an example using professional basketball player LeBron James.

Availability: All requesters
Suggested Grade: 9-12
Order Number: not applicable
Format: Online Lesson Plan

Source: Scott Niederjohn
World Wide Web URL: http://www.econedlink.org/lessons/index.php?lid=794&type=educator

66 Ways to Save Money

Practical ways to cut everyday costs on transportation, insurance, banking, credit, housing, utilities, food, and more.

Availability: All requesters
Suggested Grade: 6-Adult
Order Number: not applicable
Production Date: 2002
Format: Online Article; 4 pages
Special Notes: Use the on-site search engine to easily find this title. You may request a printed copy mailed to you for a fee.

Source: Federal Citizen Information Center
World Wide Web URL: http://www.pueblo.gsa.gov/

Story of Banks, The

Traces the functions, purposes, and historical roles of banks in the United States.

Availability: Limit of 34 copies to schools, libraries, and homeschoolers in the United States and Canada. Make request on a postcard.
Suggested Grade: 8-12
Order Number: order by title
Production Date: 2007
Format: Comic Book
Special Notes: May also be downloaded from the web site.

Source: Federal Reserve Bank of New York
World Wide Web URL: https://www.newyorkfed.org/publications/result.cfm?comics=1

Story of Monetary Policy, The

Uses non-technical language and lively illustrations to explain the meaning and purpose of monetary policy, how the Federal Reserve makes monetary policy, what factors are considered, and the tools of monetary policy.

Availability: Limit of 34 copies to schools, libraries, and homeschoolers in the United States and Canada. Make request on a postcard.
Suggested Grade: 8-12
Order Number: order by title
Production Date: 2007
Format: Comic Book
Special Notes: May also be downloaded from the web site.

Source: Federal Reserve Bank of New York
World Wide Web URL:
https://www.newyorkfed.org/publications/result.cfm?comics=1

Story of the Federal Reserve System

Discusses the operations of the Federal Reserve System.

Availability: Limit of 34 copies to schools, libraries, and homeschoolers in the United States and Canada. Make request on a postcard.
Suggested Grade: 8-12
Order Number: order by title
Production Date: 2007
Format: Comic Book
Special Notes: May also be downloaded from website.

Source: Federal Reserve Bank of New York
World Wide Web URL:
https://www.newyorkfed.org/publications/result.cfm?comics=1

Taking Control of Your Finances

A handy guide geared towards young adults--including those just starting a career or a family and others still in school. Learn the right ways to save and manage money, including the mistakes people make with their money and how to avoid them.

Availability: All requesters
Suggested Grade: 9-Adult
Order Number: not applicable
Production Date: 2005
Format: Online Booklet; 12 pages
Special Notes: Use the on-site search engine to easily find this title. You may request a printed copy mailed to you for a fee.

Source: Federal Citizen Information Center
World Wide Web URL: http://www.pueblo.gsa.gov/

Teen Investing

Investment information for teenagers.

Availability: All requesters
Suggested Grade: 6-12
Order Number: not applicable
Format: Web Site
Special Notes: This URL will lead you to a subject page. Then click on the appropriate subject heading.

Source: ThinkQuest
World Wide Web URL:
http://www.thinkquest.org/pls/html/think.library

Test Your Investment IQ

A test to determine if you know what a good investment is.

Availability: Limit of 49 copies to schools, libraries, and homeschoolers world-wide.
Suggested Grade: 6-Adult
Order Number: order by title
Format: Brochure
Special Notes: May also be downloaded from the Web site. Quantities in excess of 50 are available from Federal Trade Commission, Distribution Office, 600 Pennsylvania Avenue, NW, Washington, D. C. 20580-0001 or fax to: 1-703-739-0991.

Source: Federal Trade Commission
Consumer Response Center
600 Pennsylvania, N. W., Room H-130
Washington, DC 20580
World Wide Web URL:
http://www.ftc.gov/bcp/consumer.shtm

Too Much, Too Little

Presents a history of the United States monetary system and events leading to the establishment of the Federal Reserve System.

Availability: Limit of 34 copies to schools, libraries, and homeschoolers in the United States and Canada. Make request on a postcard.
Suggested Grade: 8-12
Order Number: order by title
Production Date: 2007
Format: Comic Book
Special Notes: May also be downloaded from website.

Source: Federal Reserve Bank of New York
World Wide Web URL:
https://www.newyorkfed.org/publications/result.cfm?comics=1

Understanding Vehicle Financing

Explains dealership financing and can serve as a guide for evaluating your own financial situation.

Availability: All requesters
Suggested Grade: 9-Adult
Order Number:
Format: Booklet

Source: AFSA Education Foundation
919 18th Street, N. W., 3rd Floor
Washington, DC 20006
Phone: 1-202-466-8611
Fax: 1-202-223-0321
World Wide Web URL:
www.afsaef.orghttp://www.afsaef.org
Email Address: susie@afsamail.org

World Currency

Tells the history of money and even lets kids design their own. Information is included for all ages.

Availability: All requesters
Suggested Grade: All ages
Order Number: not applicable
Format: Web Site
Special Notes: This URL will lead you to a subject page. Then click on the appropriate subject heading.

Source: ThinkQuest
World Wide Web URL:
http://www.thinkquest.org/pls/html/think.library

World of Coins

Discusses the many choices in coins, including the fifty state quarters that are being issued today.

Availability: All requesters
Suggested Grade: All ages
Order Number: not applicable
Format: Web Site
Special Notes: This URL will lead you to a subject page. Then click on the appropriate subject heading.

Source: ThinkQuest
World Wide Web URL:
http://www.thinkquest.org/pls/html/think.library

Adult Learning In and Through the Arts
Discusses adult learning in the arts and addresses current issues in adult arts education.
Availability: All requesters
Suggested Grade: Teacher Reference
Order Number: not applicable
Production Date: 2002
Format: Online Article
Source: Sandra Kerka
World Wide Web URL:
http://www.ericdigests.org/2003-2/adult.html

Animation 101
Claymation, computer animation and hand drawn animation with tips and tricks.
Availability: All requesters
Suggested Grade: All ages
Order Number: not applicable
Format: Web Site
Special Notes: This URL will lead you to a subject page. Then click on the appropriate subject heading.
Source: ThinkQuest
World Wide Web URL:
http://www.thinkquest.org/pls/html/think.library

Animation Sensation
Walks you through creating your own animation, details the history of animation, and quizzes you to test your animation knowledge.
Availability: All requesters
Suggested Grade: All ages
Order Number: not applicable
Format: Web Site
Special Notes: This URL will lead you to a subject page. Then click on the appropriate subject heading.
Source: ThinkQuest
World Wide Web URL:
http://www.thinkquest.org/pls/html/think.library

Art Access
Lesson plans, activities, maps, and more about the multicultural art collections found in this museum.
Availability: All requesters
Suggested Grade: 3-Adult
Order Number: not applicable
Format: Web Site
Source: Art Institute of Chicago, The
World Wide Web URL: http://www.artic.edu/artaccess/

Art and Science of Theater, The
Learn how to stage a theatrical production.
Availability: All requesters
Suggested Grade: 6-12
Order Number: not applicable
Format: Web Site
Special Notes: This URL will lead you to a subject page. Then click on the appropriate subject heading.
Source: ThinkQuest
World Wide Web URL:
http://www.thinkquest.org/pls/html/think.library

Art and the Shaping of Identity
Explores how art and the discourses surrounding its production and presentation participate in the shaping of a wide range of identities.
Availability: All requesters
Suggested Grade: 9-12
Order Number: not applicable
Format: Online Lesson Plan
Source: Sue Luftschein and David Jaffee
World Wide Web URL:
http://historymatters.gmu.edu/d/6875

Artist Research Poster Lesson
Create a poster about a well-known contemporary artist.
Availability: All requesters
Suggested Grade: 5-12
Order Number: not applicable
Format: Online Lesson Plan
Source: Dorothy Morris
World Wide Web URL:
http://www.princetonol.com/groups/iad/lessons/high/Dorothy-poster.htm

ArtMagick
A gallery of paintings and poetry from the 19th and 20th centuries.
Availability: All requesters
Suggested Grade: 6-Adult
Order Number: not applicable
Format: Web Site
Source: Frances Rawnsley
World Wide Web URL:
http://www.artmagick.com/default.aspx

Art of Taiko, The
Music and instruments of Taiko.
Availability: All requesters
Suggested Grade: All ages
Order Number: not applicable
Format: Web Site
Special Notes: This URL will lead you to a subject page. Then click on the appropriate subject heading.
Source: ThinkQuest
World Wide Web URL:
http://www.thinkquest.org/pls/html/think.library

Art Projects
Art projects for students of all ages.
Availability: All requesters
Suggested Grade: All ages
Order Number: not applicable
Format: Online Lesson Plans

Source: Barbara Sonek
World Wide Web URL:
http://accessarts.org/ArtKids/Crafts/lessonsnow.html

ArtQuest
Art information for the young student.
Availability: All requesters
Suggested Grade: 4-12
Order Number: not applicable
Format: Web Site
Special Notes: This URL will lead you to a subject page. Then click on the appropriate subject heading.
Source: ThinkQuest
World Wide Web URL:
http://www.thinkquest.org/pls/html/think.library

Art Revolution, The
Artists from the Renaissance period through modern times, with a glimpse of future art.
Availability: All requesters
Suggested Grade: 6-12
Order Number: not applicable
Format: Web Site
Special Notes: This URL will lead you to a subject page. Then click on the appropriate subject heading.
Source: ThinkQuest
World Wide Web URL:
http://www.thinkquest.org/pls/html/think.library

Artsonia
A site that allows students to display artwork for others to view.
Availability: All requesters
Suggested Grade: All ages
Order Number: not applicable
Format: Web Site
Source: Artsonia LLC
World Wide Web URL: http://www.artsonia.com/

Berklee Shares: Free Music Lessons
Free music lessons for all sorts of instruments.
Availability: All requesters
Suggested Grade: All ages
Order Number: not applicable
Format: Downloadable Music Lessons
Source: Berklee College of Music
World Wide Web URL: http://www.berkleeshares.com/

Brush with Wildlife, A
Introduce yourself to the animated principles of art, then create your own composition.
Availability: All requesters
Suggested Grade: 7-Adult
Order Number: not applicable
Format: Online Art Lessons
Source: Carl Rungius
World Wide Web URL:
http://www.wildlifeart.org/Rungius/

Chopin Early Editions
Digitized images of more than 400 first and early printed editions of musical compositions by Frederic Chopin.
Availability: All requesters
Suggested Grade: 4-12
Order Number: not applicable
Format: Online Musical Scores
Source: University of Chicago Library
World Wide Web URL: http://chopin.lib.uchicago.edu/

Comic Strip WebQuest
Students will learn how to create their own comic strip.
Availability: All requesters
Suggested Grade: 6-12
Order Number: not applicable
Format: WebQuest
Source: Edie Aldridge
World Wide Web URL:
http://education.iupui.edu/webquests/comic/comic.htm

Composers, ThinkQuest Junior 1998
Learn about four great composers in history, then test your knowledge.
Availability: All requesters
Suggested Grade: 6-12
Order Number: not applicable
Format: Web Site
Special Notes: This URL will lead you to a subject page. Then click on the appropriate subject heading.
Source: ThinkQuest
World Wide Web URL:
http://www.thinkquest.org/pls/html/think.library

Composers, ThinkQuest Junior 1999
A study of various composers.
Availability: All requesters
Suggested Grade: 6-12
Order Number: not applicable
Format: Web Site
Special Notes: This URL will lead you to a subject page. Then click on the appropriate subject heading.
Source: ThinkQuest
World Wide Web URL:
http://www.thinkquest.org/pls/html/think.library

Craftplace
Here are the instructions for making a number of craft projects.
Availability: All requesters
Suggested Grade: All ages
Order Number: not applicable
Format: Web Site
Source: Craft & Hobby Association
World Wide Web URL: http://www.craftplace.org/

Creative Drama & Theatre Education Resource Site
Here's a collection of teaching ideas and suggestions for drama teachers.

Availability:	All requesters
Suggested Grade:	3-12
Order Number:	not applicable
Format:	Online Lesson Plans

Source: Janine Moyer Buesgen
World Wide Web URL: http://www.creativedrama.com/

Drama for Those Who Do Not Like or Understand Drama
Lessons to help students study drama even when they are not fans of reading.

Availability:	All requesters
Suggested Grade:	11-12
Order Number:	not applicable
Format:	Online Lesson Plans

Source: Edward D. Cohen
World Wide Web URL:
http://www.yale.edu/ynhti/curriculum/units/1983/5/83.05.03.x.html

Drum Lesson Database, A
Presents over 400 free drum lessons and drum tabs.

Availability:	All requesters
Suggested Grade:	2-12
Order Number:	not applicable
Format:	Web Site

Source: DrumBum.com
World Wide Web URL: http://drumbum.com/lessons/

Early American Weaving
Experience the Native American and Colonial American art of weaving with this activity.

Availability:	All requesters
Suggested Grade:	2-12
Order Number:	not applicable
Format:	Online Lesson Plan

Source: TeachersFirst
World Wide Web URL:
http://www.teachersfirst.com/summer/weaving.htm

Evidence of Protest in African American Art
Students will gain a new appreciation of the struggles encountered by African Americans from the time of slavery through modern times.

Availability:	All requesters
Suggested Grade:	9-12
Order Number:	not applicable
Format:	WebQuest

Source: Greg Bulger
World Wide Web URL:
http://www.towson.edu/heartfield/lessons/lppolitical.html

FastMIDI Player
Automatically plays MIDI files in a user-selected directory.

Availability:	All requesters
Suggested Grade:	All ages
Platform:	Windows
Order Number:	not applicable
Format:	Downloadable FULL PROGRAM

Source: DynoTech Software
World Wide Web URL:
http://www.dynotech.com/other.htm

First Impressions: The Post-Impressionist Art of Van Gogh, Vauguin, and Toulouse-Lautrec
Larn about these post-impressionist artists and their art.

Availability:	All requesters
Suggested Grade:	6-12
Order Number:	not applicable
Format:	Web Site
Special Notes:	This URL will lead you to a subject page. Then click on the appropriate subject heading.

Source: ThinkQuest
World Wide Web URL:
http://www.thinkquest.org/pls/html/think.library

!Fortissimo! A Program for Musical Development
Learn all about music and musical instruments.

Availability:	All requesters
Suggested Grade:	All ages
Order Number:	not applicable
Format:	Web Site
Special Notes:	This URL will lead you to a subject page. Then click on the appropriate subject heading.

Source: ThinkQuest
World Wide Web URL:
http://www.thinkquest.org/pls/html/think.library

HymnSite.Com
This site presents a large number of MIDI music for downloading--all songs are religious.

Availability:	All requesters
Suggested Grade:	4-12
Order Number:	not applicable
Format:	Downloadable MIDI music

Source: HymnSite
World Wide Web URL: http://hymnsite.com/

Jazz in America
Here are lesson plans and other resources regarding the history of jazz as a part of culture in America.

Availability:	All requesters
Suggested Grade:	11
Order Number:	not applicable
Format:	Web Site

Source: Thelonious Monk Institute of Jazz
World Wide Web URL: http://www.jazzinamerica.org/

Leather Mardi Gras Mask
Students will learn more about Mardi Gras and create a typical mask used on this occasion.

Availability:	All requesters
Suggested Grade:	9-12
Order Number:	not applicable
Format:	Online Lesson Plan

Source: Christina Salinas
World Wide Web URL:
http://www.princetonol.com/groups/iad/lessons/high/Christina-leather.htm

Lesson 29: Textured Pottery Using Self-Hardening Clay and Multicultural Designs

Learn how to create clay vessels that pay tribute to other cultures.

Availability: All requesters
Suggested Grade: Teacher Reference
Order Number: not applicable
Format: Online Lesson Plan

Source: American Art Clay Co., Inc.
Sales Support
6060 Guion Road
Indianapolis, IN 46254
Phone: 1-800-374-1600
Fax: 1-317-248-9300
World Wide Web URL: http://www.amaco.com
Email Address: salessupport@amaco.com

Let's Dance Latin Style!

Explores 3 different types of Latin Dances--the Samba, Mambo, and Tango.

Availability: All requesters
Suggested Grade: 6-12
Order Number: not applicable
Format: Web Site
Special Notes: This URL will lead you to a subject page. Then click on the appropriate subject heading.

Source: ThinkQuest
World Wide Web URL:
http://www.thinkquest.org/pls/html/think.library

Lift Every Voice: Music in American Life

A collection of information about ballads, hymns, spirituals, patriotic odes, protest songs and more that reflect upon American history. Includes numerous audio clips.

Availability: All requesters
Suggested Grade: 6-Adult
Order Number: not applicable
Format: Web Site

Source: University of Virginia Library
World Wide Web URL:
http://www.lib.virginia.edu/speccol/exhibits/music/

Make a Splash with Color

Students will learn more about color and how our eyes view it.

Availability: All requesters
Suggested Grade: 4-12
Order Number: not applicable
Format: Web Site

Source: Adobe Systems
World Wide Web URL:
http://www.thetech.org/exhibits/online/color/intro/

Muralism, Muralists and Murals

Students will research murals, the muralist movement, and the muralists themselves.

Availability: All requesters
Suggested Grade: 7-12
Order Number: not applicable
Format: WebQuest

Source: Carol Sparks
World Wide Web URL:
http://www.clta.net/lessons/spanish/level1/mural.html

Music Theory for Songwriters

Explains music theory.

Availability: All requesters
Suggested Grade: 6-Adult
Order Number: not applicable
Format: Online Articles

Source: Steve Mugglin
World Wide Web URL: http://chordmaps.com/

Music UZIT

Shows how to read music and explains different kinds of music.

Availability: All requesters
Suggested Grade: All ages
Order Number: not applicable
Format: Web Site
Special Notes: This URL will lead you to a subject page. Then click on the appropriate subject heading.

Source: ThinkQuest
World Wide Web URL:
http://www.thinkquest.org/pls/html/think.library

Music World

Explains four different types of music: classical, jazz, MIDI, and trumpet. Includes sound.

Availability: All requesters
Suggested Grade: All ages
Order Number: not applicable
Format: Web Site
Special Notes: This URL will lead you to a subject page. Then click on the appropriate subject heading.

Source: ThinkQuest
World Wide Web URL:
http://www.thinkquest.org/pls/html/think.library

Native American Technology and Art

Presents articles on the many types of art crafted by Native Americans.

Availability: All requesters
Suggested Grade: 4-Adult
Order Number: not applicable
Format: Web Site

Source: Tara Prindle
World Wide Web URL: http://www.nativetech.org/

Performing Medieval Narrative Today: A Video Showcase
A database of video clips of contemporary performances of medieval narrative.
Availability: All requesters
Suggested Grade: 6-12
Order Number: not applicable
Format: Online Video Performances
Source: Evelyn Birge Vitz, Nancy Freeman Regalado, and Marilyn Lawrence
World Wide Web URL:
http://www.nyu.edu/projects/mednar/index.php

Pieces and Creases--A Fun Guide to Origami
Gives directions for making origami objects and explains the history of this ancient art.
Availability: All requesters
Suggested Grade: All ages
Order Number: not applicable
Format: Web Site
Special Notes: This URL will lead you to a subject page. Then click on the appropriate subject heading.
Source: ThinkQuest
World Wide Web URL:
http://www.thinkquest.org/pls/html/think.library

Pysanky Eggs
Students will learn the history behind these Ukranian eggs and how to make them.
Availability: All requesters
Suggested Grade: 9-12
Order Number: not applicable
Format: Online Lesson Plan
Source: Sue Stevens
World Wide Web URL:
http://www.princetonol.com/groups/iad/lessons/high/Sue-Pysanky.htm

Restoring the Nike
Learn about this famous sculpture (not the shoe).
Availability: All requesters
Suggested Grade: 9-12
Order Number: not applicable
Format: WebQuest
Source: Sean Patrick Drummond
World Wide Web URL:
http://oncampus.richmond.edu/academics/education/projects/webquests/restorenike/

Salt Crystal Growth Directions
Instructions for growing salt crystals from table salt and other household ingredients. Also known as a "salt crystal garden" or a "depression garden." Excellent science project for rock/mineral units and for aiding in understanding evaporation.
Availability: One copy to schools, libraries, homeschoolers, and others in the United States and Canada. May be copied.
Suggested Grade: K-12
Order Number: order by title
Format: Flyer
Special Notes: May also be downloaded from the web site.
Source: Mrs. Stewart's Bluing
P. O. Box 201405
Bloomington, MN 55420
Phone: 1-800-325-7785
Fax: 1-952-881-1873
World Wide Web URL: http://www.mrsstewart.com
Email Address: msb@mrsstewart.com

SARA: South Africa Resistance Art
Four artists chose to resist the Apartheid system through their art. Find background info and examples of their work.
Availability: All requesters
Suggested Grade: 6-12
Order Number: not applicable
Format: Web Site
Special Notes: This URL will lead you to a subject page. Then click on the appropriate subject heading.
Source: ThinkQuest
World Wide Web URL:
http://www.thinkquest.org/pls/html/think.library

SoundJunction
Learn all about music.
Availability: All requesters
Suggested Grade: All ages
Order Number: not applicable
Format: Web Site
Source: Associated Board of the Royal Schools of Music
World Wide Web URL:
http://www.soundjunction.org/default.aspa

Styrofoam Sculpture
Students will create a sculpture in-the-round influenced by Jean Dubuffet sculptures.
Availability: All requesters
Suggested Grade: 9-12
Order Number: not applicable
Format: Online Lesson Plan
Source: Tim Hunt
World Wide Web URL:
http://www.princetonol.com/groups/iad/lessons/high/Tim-sculpt.htm

Technomusic
Different styles of Technomusic, people who create it, and the history of it.
Availability: All requesters
Suggested Grade: 6-12
Order Number: not applicable
Format: Web Site
Special Notes: This URL will lead you to a subject page. Then click on the appropriate subject heading.
Source: ThinkQuest
World Wide Web URL:
http://www.thinkquest.org/pls/html/think.library

1200 Years of Italian Sculpture
While the text is almost all in Italian, this image gallery of Italian sculpture can be understood just by viewing the works of art.
Availability: All requesters
Suggested Grade: All ages
Language: Italian
Order Number: not applicable
Format: Web Site
Source: Anonymous
World Wide Web URL:
http://www.thais.it/scultura/scultura.htm

Uffizi Gallery
Can't make it to this museum in Italy? Visit this web site and you'll see it all.
Availability: All requesters
Suggested Grade: 9-Adult
Order Number: not applicable
Format: Web Site
Source: Uffizi Gallery
World Wide Web URL: http://www.virtualuffizi.com/uffizi/

Using Drama and Theatre to Promote Literacy Development: Some Basic Classroom Applications
Explores some readily applicable strategies for classroom application.
Availability: All requesters
Suggested Grade: Teacher Reference
Order Number: not applicable
Format: Online Article
Source: Ping-Yun Sun
World Wide Web URL:
http://www.ericdigests.org/2004-1/drama.htm

Vintage Radio Script Library Page
Reprints of famous radio scripts can be found here.
Availability: All requesters
Suggested Grade: 4-Adult
Order Number: not applicable
Format: Online Radio Scripts
Source: Generic Radio Workshop
World Wide Web URL: http://www.genericradio.com/

Welcome to the Renaissance Art World
Michelangelo, Leonardo da Vinci, and Raphael, are featured with biographical info and examples of their work. Brueghel and Holbein are also considered.
Availability: All requesters
Suggested Grade: 6-12
Order Number: not applicable
Format: Web Site
Special Notes: This URL will lead you to a subject page. Then click on the appropriate subject heading.
Source: ThinkQuest
World Wide Web URL:
http://www.thinkquest.org/pls/html/think.library

Western Music History - The Romantic Period
Explains romantic music by explaining it systematically.
Availability: All requesters
Suggested Grade: 6-12
Order Number: not applicable
Format: Web Site
Special Notes: This URL will lead you to a subject page. Then click on the appropriate subject heading.
Source: ThinkQuest
World Wide Web URL:
http://www.thinkquest.org/pls/html/think.library

Why Is Mona Lisa Smiling?
An interesting theory about the genius of Leonardo Da Vinci with original music composed by Da Vinci.
Availability: All requesters
Suggested Grade: 6-12
Order Number: not applicable
Format: Web Site
Special Notes: This URL will lead you to a subject page. Then click on the appropriate subject heading.
Source: ThinkQuest
World Wide Web URL:
http://www.thinkquest.org/pls/html/think.library

Woodwind Fingering Guide, The
Fingering charts for virtually every woodwind instrument.
Availability: All requesters
Suggested Grade: 4-12
Order Number: not applicable
Format: Web Site
Source: Tim Reichard
World Wide Web URL:
http://www.wfg.woodwind.org/index.html

World of Music, The
People in all countries express themselves through music. Find out about the history of music in other parts of the world.
Availability: All requesters
Suggested Grade: 6-12
Order Number: not applicable
Format: Web Site
Special Notes: This URL will lead you to a subject page. Then click on the appropriate subject heading.
Source: ThinkQuest
World Wide Web URL:
http://www.thinkquest.org/pls/html/think.library

Young Composers
Presents music composed by young people and offers information on how to submit your own.
Availability: All requesters
Suggested Grade: 6-Adult
Order Number: not applicable
Format: Web Site
Source: Able Minds, Inc.
World Wide Web URL: http://www.youngcomposers.com/

Advising the President: A Simulated Cabinet Meeting
Challenges students to assume the role of the head of a federal government agency.
Availability: All requesters
Suggested Grade: 12
Order Number: not applicable
Format: WebQuest
Source: Bob O'Connor
World Wide Web URL:
http://score.rims.k12.ca.us/activity/cabinet/index.html

Ben's Guide to U. S. Government for Kids
Information for all ages, including games and activities, about how the U. S. Government works.
Availability: All requesters
Suggested Grade: All ages
Order Number: not applicable
Format: Web Site
Source: U. S. Government Printing Office
World Wide Web URL: http://bensguide.gpo.gov/

Citizenship and the Constitution
This lesson helps students be informed citizens on a local, state, and national level.
Availability: All requesters
Suggested Grade: 7-12
Order Number: not applicable
Format: Online Lesson Plan
Source: Tana Carney Preciado
World Wide Web URL:
http://youth.net/cec/cecsst/cecsst.92.txt

Constitution Finder
Offers constitutions, charters, amendments, and other related documents for countries from Albania to Zambia.
Availability: All requesters
Suggested Grade: 6-12
Order Number: not applicable
Format: Web Site
Source: John Paul Jones
World Wide Web URL: http://confinder.richmond.edu/

Constitution, The: Counter Revolution or National Salvation?
Students will access primary documents, identify arguments for and against the ratification of the Constitution, and produce a broadside in which they take a position on whether their state should ratify the Constitution.
Availability: All requesters
Suggested Grade: 11
Order Number: not applicable
Format: Online Lesson Plan
Source: Claudia Argyres and Jim Smith
World Wide Web URL:
http://www.loc.gov/teachers/classroommaterials/lessons/constitution/

Constitution, The: Our Plan for Government
A lesson on the Constitution of the United States.
Availability: All requesters
Suggested Grade: 8-9
Order Number: not applicable
Format: Online Lesson Plan
Source: Willie Jefferson
World Wide Web URL:
http://www.eduref.org/Virtual/Lessons/Social_Studies/US_Government/GOV0005.html

Due Process: Search and Seizure
Students observe first hand a simulation of the court case New Jersey vs. T.L.O.
Availability: All requesters
Suggested Grade: 11-12
Order Number: not applicable
Format: Online Lesson Plan
Source: Bill Cairns
World Wide Web URL:
http://youth.net/cec/cecsst/cecsst.01.txt

Ethics in American Government
Students analyze the statement "Those who govern in a democracy hold a 'public trust'."
Availability: All requesters
Suggested Grade: 12
Order Number: not applicable
Format: Online Lesson Plan
Source: Riki Dewey
World Wide Web URL:
http://www.eduref.org/Virtual/Lessons/Social_Studies/US_Government/GOV0008.html

Evaluating Crimes
Students will learn that a crime is something that one does or fails to do in violation of law.
Availability: All requesters
Suggested Grade: 9-12
Order Number: not applicable
Format: Online Lesson Plan
Source: Frances Troyer Glenn
World Wide Web URL:
http://youth.net/cec/cecsst/cecsst.33.txt

Fourth Amendment and Judicial Review, The
This lesson is on the Fourth Amendment and how court cases have looked at the meaning of the rights granted within the Amendment.
Availability: All requesters
Suggested Grade: 7-11
Order Number: not applicable
Format: Online Lesson Plan
Source: Paul G. Sutliff
World Wide Web URL:
http://www.eduref.org/Virtual/Lessons/Social_Studies/US_Government/GOV0205.html

Full Text of Supreme Court Decisions Issued Between 1937 and 1975
Contains 7,407 decisions from 1937 to 1975.
Availability: All requesters
Suggested Grade: 9-Adult
Order Number: not applicable
Format: Web Site
Source: National Technical Information Service
World Wide Web URL: http://supcourt.ntis.gov/

Government & Economics: The Ties That Bind
The purpose of this activity is to expand the understanding of students in the areas of both economics and government.
Availability: All requesters
Suggested Grade: 11-12
Order Number: not applicable
Format: Online Lesson Plan
Source: Mary J. Williams
World Wide Web URL:
http://youth.net/cec/cecsst/cecsst.15.txt

Home-Made Political Parties
This activity provides students with an understanding of the role of political parties in our democracy, by offering them an opportunity to participate.
Availability: All requesters
Suggested Grade: 9-12
Order Number: not applicable
Format: Online Lesson Plan
Source: Joanne Flint
World Wide Web URL:
http://www.col-ed.org/cur/sst/sst51.txt

How an Idea Becomes a Law
Gives students a chance to visualize the step-by-step process of how an idea becomes a law and how involved the process is.
Availability: All requesters
Suggested Grade: 6-9
Order Number: not applicable
Format: Online Lesson Plan
Source: Wanda Kehl
World Wide Web URL:
http://youth.net/cec/cecsst/cecsst.87.txt

Introduction of Restrictions on Freedom of Speech
This lesson helps students see the limits to freedom of speech.
Availability: All requesters
Suggested Grade: 10-12
Order Number: not applicable
Format: Online Lesson Plan
Source: Van Hadley
World Wide Web URL:
http://youth.net/cec/cecsst/cecsst.85.txt

Introduction to Law, An
Introduces the wide ranging effect that law has on citizens daily.
Availability: All requesters
Suggested Grade: 9-12
Order Number: not applicable
Format: Online Lesson Plan
Source: Dave Snook
World Wide Web URL:
http://youth.net/cec/cecsst/cecsst.98.txt

Inviting Candidates to Class
Explains why you may want to have political candidates visit your classroom and how to speak to them.
Availability: All requesters
Suggested Grade: 9-12
Order Number: not applicable
Format: Online Lesson Plan
Source: Ronald W. Ryckman
World Wide Web URL:
http://www.eduref.org/Virtual/Lessons/Social_Studies/US_Government/GOV0020.html

Iron Triangles
One of the most effective blocks to presidential power has developed from a three-sided combination of members of Congress, bureaucrats, and interest groups.
Availability: All requesters
Suggested Grade: 7-12
Order Number: not applicable
Format: Online Lesson Plan
Source: John Vincent Balistere
World Wide Web URL:
http://youth.net/cec/cecsst/cecsst.95.txt

Law in the Future
Students will be able to identify the problems associated with applying the U.S. laws and history to an international situation.
Availability: All requesters
Suggested Grade: 11-12
Order Number: not applicable
Format: Online Lesson Plan
Source: Carl Dearden
World Wide Web URL:
http://www.eduref.org/Virtual/Lessons/Social_Studies/US_Government/GOV0025.html

Laws--Who Needs Them?
Illustrates why laws and rules are needed.
Availability: All requesters
Suggested Grade: 7-9
Order Number: not applicable
Format: Online Lesson Plan
Source: Deb Gehrman
World Wide Web URL:
http://www.col-ed.org/cur/sst/sst16.txt

Middle East Information Brochure
Working with groups of three to four, students create an

information brochure for the United States government.
Availability: All requesters
Suggested Grade: 9-12
Order Number: not applicable
Format: Online Lesson Plan
Source: Les Morse
World Wide Web URL:
http://www.col-ed.org/cur/sst/sst249.txt

Mock Congress
This activity gets students involved in the legislative process of law-making by assuming different roles.
Availability: All requesters
Suggested Grade: 9-12
Order Number: not applicable
Format: Online Lesson Plan
Source: Rosella S. Campos
World Wide Web URL:
http://www.teachersdesk.com/lessons/government/Mock%20Congress.htm

National Assessment of Educational Progress in Civics, The
Discusses the framework, assessment procedures, and findings of this 1998 study.
Availability: All requesters
Suggested Grade: Teacher Reference
Order Number: not applicable
Production Date: 2000
Format: Online Article
Source: John J. Patrick
World Wide Web URL:
http://www.indiana.edu/%7Essdc/naepc2dig.htm

National Budget Simulation
A game (long or short) to give you a better feel for the trade-offs which policy makers need to make in creating federal budgets and dealing with deficits.
Availability: All requesters
Suggested Grade: 7-Adult
Order Number: not applicable
Format: Online Game
Source: Nathan Newman and Anders Schneiderman
World Wide Web URL:
http://www.nathannewman.org/nbs/

Nineteenth Amendment, The
Stimulates analytical thinking skills and class discussion by learning how different groups of people received the right to vote before women received that same right.
Availability: All requesters
Suggested Grade: 9-12
Order Number: not applicable
Format: Online Lesson Plan
Source: Larry W. Rowley
World Wide Web URL:
http://youth.net/cec/cecsst/cecsst.28.txt

Oyez Baseball
This game compares Supreme Court justices from the United States with baseball players--learn more about our highest court and the people who have served on it.
Availability: All requesters
Suggested Grade: 7-Adult
Order Number: not applicable
Format: Online Game
Source: Jerry Goldman and Paul Manna
World Wide Web URL: http://baseball.oyez.org/

Political Issues and Opinions
Students choose a stance on several political issues and based on their responses align themselves with a political faction.
Availability: All requesters
Suggested Grade: 8-12
Order Number: not applicable
Format: Online Lesson Plan
Source: Glenn Hall
World Wide Web URL:
http://youth.net/cec/cecsst/cecsst.31.txt

Political Polls
Students must know that polls are statements of short-term probability that may easily be skewed. They are a tool to help man make rational decisions.
Availability: All requesters
Suggested Grade: 9-12
Order Number: not applicable
Format: Online Lesson Plan
Source: Rob Bishop
World Wide Web URL:
http://youth.net/cec/cecsst/cecsst.105.txt

Presidential Campaign Game, The
This political game gives students experience in working within the political process and managing a political campaign.
Availability: All requesters
Suggested Grade: 11-12
Order Number: not applicable
Format: Online Lesson Plan
Source: Denton S. Gehr, II
World Wide Web URL:
http://youth.net/cec/cecsst/cecsst.42.txt

Presidential Elections: A Simulation
Through this activity, students come to better recognize and understand the intricacies of U. S. presidential elections.
Availability: All requesters
Suggested Grade: 12
Order Number: not applicable
Format: Online Lesson Plan
Source: Randolph Burns
World Wide Web URL:
http://youth.net/cec/cecsst/cecsst.43.txt

Role of the Government
The intent of this activity is to introduce students to the meaning of the word "government."
Availability: All requesters
Suggested Grade: 9-12
Order Number: not applicable
Format: Online Lesson Plan
Source: Mark W. Dean
World Wide Web URL:
http://www.eduref.org/Virtual/Lessons/Social_Studies/US_Government/GOV0034.html

Search & Seizure
Engage students in a search and seizure activity that allows an exploration of students' rights within a school setting, leading to issues of individual freedoms.
Availability: All requesters
Suggested Grade: 7-12
Order Number: not applicable
Format: Online Lesson Plan
Source: Lynn MacAusland
World Wide Web URL:
http://youth.net/cec/cecsst/cecsst.26.txt

Search for a Meaningful Dialectic, The
Introduces students to a framework of political and social values which may be used to evaluate the validity of any public policy debate, bill, law, etc.
Availability: All requesters
Suggested Grade: 12
Order Number: not applicable
Format: Online Lesson Plan
Source: Dwayne Blackwell
World Wide Web URL:
http://youth.net/cec/cecsst/cecsst.84.txt

Separation of Powers Between the Three Branches of Government
By understanding the development of the three branches of government, students will better understand the decision making process by which our government lives.
Availability: All requesters
Suggested Grade: 10-12
Order Number: not applicable
Format: Online Lesson Plan
Source: Tim Brennan
World Wide Web URL:
http://youth.net/cec/cecsst/cecsst.102.txt

Staffing Exercise, The: A Lesson Cluster for Civics
A lesson that will help students identify federal laws and regulations dealing with gender bias, stereotyping, and discrimination and identify career areas which are non-traditional for their gender.
Availability: All requesters
Suggested Grade: 7-12
Order Number: not applicable
Format: Online Lesson Plan
Source: Dr. Milburn Stone
World Wide Web URL:
http://www.ricw.state.ri.us/lessons/296.htm

Supreme Court Decisions and Their Effect on Us
The purpose of this activity is to help students understand how Supreme Court decisions affect all of us and what the Supreme Court bases its decisions on.
Availability: All requesters
Suggested Grade: 11-12
Order Number: not applicable
Format: Online Lesson Plan
Source: Glen Bradshaw
World Wide Web URL:
http://www.col-ed.org/cur/sst/sst154.txt

ThisNation.com
A repository of basic information, resources and historical documents related to American government and politics.
Availability: All requesters
Suggested Grade: 6-Adult
Order Number: not applicable
Format: Web Site
Source: Jonathan Mott
World Wide Web URL: http://www.thisnation.com/

U. S. Constitution Power Grab Game
The highest law of the land in the United States is the Constitution. This is the basic principle we want young people to understand.
Availability: All requesters
Suggested Grade: 10-12
Order Number: not applicable
Format: Online Lesson Plan
Source: Don M. Carlson
World Wide Web URL:
http://youth.net/cec/cecsst/cecsst.52.txt

User's Guide to the Declaration of Independence, A
Features a large collection of writings from early America and provides a complete explanation of the Declaration through hyperlinks.
Availability: All requesters
Suggested Grade: 6-12
Order Number: not applicable
Format: Web Site
Source: Claremont Institute
World Wide Web URL:
http://www.founding.com/the_guide/

Vocabulary in the Content Area
Ideas for teaching secondary students to really grasp the meaning of words used in government or social studies classes rather than just memorize the definition.
Availability: All requesters
Suggested Grade: 9-12
Order Number: not applicable

Format: Online Lesson Plan

Source: Suzanne Gaffney
World Wide Web URL:
http://youth.net/cec/cecsst/cecsst.88.txt

Voting: A Privilege Through Registration

A lesson on how to properly register to vote.

Availability: All requesters
Suggested Grade: 11-12
Order Number: not applicable
Format: Online Lesson Plan

Source: Donnalee Eisenhaut
World Wide Web URL:
http://www.eduref.org/Virtual/Lessons/Social_Studies/US_Government/GOV0047.html

Who Gets the Job?

The purpose of this lesson is for students to understand that even though Senate approval is needed for presidential Cabinet appointments, there are no qualifications or standards set for each position.

Availability: All requesters
Suggested Grade: 9-12
Order Number: not applicable
Format: Online Lesson Plan

Source: Jeanette Jackson
World Wide Web URL:
http://www.eduref.org/Virtual/Lessons/Social_Studies/US_Government/GOV0051.html

Advanced Placement Science or Mathematics--What to Do Between AP Exams and Semester Finals
Students work together to prepare a final examination, understanding comprehensive topics covered during the entire school year.
Availability: All requesters
Suggested Grade: 10-12
Order Number: not applicable
Format: Online Lesson Plan
Source: Bud Stephen
World Wide Web URL:
http://youth.net/cec/cecmisc/cecmisc.56.txt

Argumentation and Critical Thinking Tutorial
Intended to help students in college level critical thinking classes learn some of the basic concepts of the formal logical structure of arguments and informal fallacies.
Availability: All requesters
Suggested Grade: Adult
Order Number: not applicable
Format: Online Tutorial
Source: Jay VerLinden
World Wide Web URL:
http://www.humboldt.edu/act/HTML/

Character Education Teaching Guides
Three teacher's guides packed with discussion questions, writing assignments, and student activities for developing good character in students.
Availability: All requesters
Suggested Grade: All ages
Order Number: not applicable
Format: Online Teacher's Guides
Source: GoodCharacter.com
World Wide Web URL: http://www.goodcharacter.com

Choosing a Major
Tips on how to choose a major before "one chooses you."
Availability: All requesters
Suggested Grade: Adult
Order Number: not applicable
Format: Online Article
Source: CollegePrep-101
World Wide Web URL:
http://frontpage.okstate.edu/COE/cp101/Majors.htm

Christopher News Notes
A rich source of inspiration materials, these newsletters are published ten times a year on a variety of topics.
Availability: Limit of 25 copies to schools, libraries, and homeschoolers in the United States; limit of 10 available in Canada. Make request on official stationery.
Suggested Grade: 6-Adult
Order Number: order by title
Format: Newsletter subscription
Special Notes: Also available for download via the web site.
Source: Christophers, The
5 Hanover Square, 11th Floor
New York, NY 10004
Phone: 1-212-759-4050
Fax: 1-212-838-5073
World Wide Web URL: http://www.christophers.org
Email Address: mail@christophers.org

Conflict Management Techniques
Identify personal conflict management styles and develop an awareness of strategies of each style.
Availability: All requesters
Suggested Grade: 4-12
Order Number: not applicable
Format: Online Lesson Plan
Source: Christy Hornung
World Wide Web URL:
http://youth.net/cec/cecmisc/cecmisc.33.txt

Cultural Diversity and Teamwork
Examines cultural beliefs, attitudes, and practices as they influence communication style.
Availability: All requesters
Suggested Grade: Teacher Reference
Order Number: not applicable
Production Date: 1994
Format: Online Article
Source: Bettina Lankard Brown
World Wide Web URL:
http://www.ericdigests.org/1995-2/teamwork.htm

Do You Need Money for College: FSA at a Glance
Contains highlights about federal student aid such as what it is, who gets aid, and how to apply. It also provides a chart of federal aid programs. Students and parents seeking information on financial aid can use this handout as a reference tool.
Availability: Single copies to schools, libraries, and homeschoolers in the United States.
Suggested Grade: 9-Adult
Order Number: EN0995P
Production Date: 2011
Format: Handout
Special Notes: May also be downloaded from the web site.
Source: ED Pubs
P. O. Box 1398
Jessup, MD 20794-1398
Phone: 1-877-4-ED-PUBS
Fax: 1-301-470-1244
World Wide Web URL:
http://www.edpubs.org/webstore/Content/search.asp

Dynamics of Relationships
This lesson shows that it is important to recognize unique contributions and attributes of each individual, including yourself.
Availability: All requesters
Suggested Grade: 9-12

Order Number: not applicable
Format: Online Lesson Plan

Source: Gloria Fastabend
World Wide Web URL:
http://youth.net/cec/cecmisc/cecmisc.36.txt

Effective Study Skills

This web page on study skills is designed to help you improve your learning and understanding, and ultimately your grades.

Availability: All requesters
Suggested Grade: 9-Adult
Order Number: not applicable
Format: Online Article

Source: Bob Kizlik
World Wide Web URL:
http://www.adprima.com/studyout.htm

Embark

Produced by a company that supplies application management software to universities and provides this free resource on the web for students pursuing their educational dreams.

Availability: All requesters
Suggested Grade: 9-12
Order Number: not applicable
Format: Web Site

Source: Embark
World Wide Web URL:
http://www.embark.com/Pages/default.aspx

Equal Treatment, Equal Access

The lessons included in this curriculum unit seek to challenge myths and stereotypes about people with disabilities and to promote awareness of various forms of disability

Availability: All requesters
Suggested Grade: 9-Adult
Order Number: not applicable
Format: Online Lesson Plans

Source: Anti-Defamation League
World Wide Web URL:
http://www.adl.org/education/curriculum_connections/fall_2005/

Experiencing Prejudice and Discrimination

An activity geared to helping students understand what it feels like to be picked out and experience discrimination and prejudice that is so apparent in our world.

Availability: All requesters
Suggested Grade: 6-12
Order Number: not applicable
Format: Online Lesson Plan

Source: Kim Stickel
World Wide Web URL:
http://eduref.org/Virtual/Lessons/Social_Studies/World_History/WRH0019.html

Experiment in Unfair Treatment/Prejudice, An

Students will experience some of the feelings associated with prejudice/bias and unfair treatment.

Availability: All requesters
Suggested Grade: 3-12
Order Number: not applicable
Format: Online Lesson Plan

Source: Pauline Finlay
World Wide Web URL:
http://www.educationworld.com/a_tsl/archives/04-1/lesson006.shtml

Family Newscast

Allows students to experience what takes place in the production of a newscast or newsmagazine while relating this information to American family life.

Availability: All requesters
Suggested Grade: 10-12
Order Number: not applicable
Format: Online Lesson Plan

Source: Thomas E. Collins
World Wide Web URL:
http://www.teachersdesk.com/lessons/family_science/Family%20Newscast.htm

Funny Money

Students bid funny money for prizes with objectives of improving attendance and rewarding good attitude and responsibility.

Availability: All requesters
Suggested Grade: 11-12
Order Number: not applicable
Format: Online Lesson Plan

Source: Cheryl McGilbray
World Wide Web URL:
http://youth.net/cec/cecmisc/cecmisc.21.txt

Gender Role Assignment

Students will learn to recognize gender bias, stereotyping, and discrimination in school materials and activities.

Availability: All requesters
Suggested Grade: 7-Adult
Order Number: not applicable
Format: Online Lesson Plan

Source: Dr. Betty J. Rauhe
World Wide Web URL:
http://www.ricw.state.ri.us/lessons/358.htm

If You Think Saying "No" Is Tough, Just Wait 'til You Say "Yes"

Explains how wrong the statement, "Giving in and saying yes to sex will solve all your problems."

Availability: Classroom quantities to schools, libraries, and homeschoolers in the United States; limit of 10 elsewhere.
Suggested Grade: 7-Adult
Languages: English; Spanish
Order Number: English FP-110003; Spanish FP-110006

Format: Brochure
Special Notes: May also be downloaded from the web site.

Source: Office of Population Affairs Clearinghouse
P. O. Box 30686
Bethesda, MD 20824-0686
Phone: 1-866-640-7827
Fax: 1-866-592-3299
World Wide Web URL:
http://opa.osophs.dhhs.gov/pubs/publications.html
Email Address: clearinghouse@dhhsopa.net

Listening Skills

Study these tips to improve your listening skills.

Availability: All requesters
Suggested Grade: 9-Adult
Order Number: not applicable
Format: Online Articles

Source: University of Minnesota Duluth
World Wide Web URL:
http://www.d.umn.edu/student/loon/acad/strat/ss_listening.html

Looking Into the Mirror

Written to deliver a vivid portrayal of intolerance and inequality as well as provoke a response to the various types of intolerance that exist in our multicultural society.

Availability: All requesters
Suggested Grade: 7-12
Order Number: not applicable
Format: Online Lesson Plan

Source: Tony L. Talbert
World Wide Web URL:
http://youth.net/cec/cecsst/cecsst.80.txt

Making Binding Agreements

Students thoroughly explore "offer" and "acceptance" in relationship to making binding agreements and contracts.

Availability: All requesters
Suggested Grade: 11-12
Order Number: not applicable
Format: Online Lesson Plan

Source: Boyd Whitesides
World Wide Web URL:
http://youth.net/cec/cecsst/cecsst.96.txt

Mental Edge Online

Allows students to practice what they learn in class or to prepare for taking standardized tests. Nearly all grade levels and all subject areas are covered.

Availability: All requesters
Suggested Grade: 3-12
Order Number: not applicable
Format: Web Site

Source: Short Cuts, Inc.
World Wide Web URL: http://www.learningshortcuts.com/

Paragon Learning Style Inventory

Here is a 48-item general version of the Paragon Learning Style Inventory.

Availability: All requesters
Suggested Grade: 4-Adult
Order Number: not applicable
Format: Online Test
Special Notes: The 52-item version may be purchased.

Source: Dr. John Shindler
World Wide Web URL: http://www.oswego.edu/plsi/

Peer Pressure Refusal

Recognize signs of trouble among peers by observation and instinct.

Availability: All requesters
Suggested Grade: 9-12
Order Number: not applicable
Format: Online Lesson Plan

Source: Jessie L. Halton
World Wide Web URL:
http://youth.net/cec/cecmisc/cecmisc.10.txt

RACE: A Teacher's Guide

This teacher's guide serves as a teaching tool to assist educators in addressing race and human variation in the classroom.

Availability: All requesters
Suggested Grade: 5-8; 9-12
Order Number: not applicable
Format: Downloadable Teacher's Guide

Source: American Anthropological Association
World Wide Web URL:
http://www.understandingrace.org/resources/for_teachers.html

Smart Saving for College--Better Buy Degrees

Provides information to help you save and invest wisely for college.

Availability: All requesters
Suggested Grade: 9-Adult
Order Number: not applicable
Production Date: Booklet; 24 pages
Format: Downloadable Booklet
Special Notes: Use the on-site search engine to easily find this title. You may request a printed copy mailed to you for a fee.

Source: Federal Citizen Information Center
World Wide Web URL: http://www.pueblo.gsa.gov/

Stop the Hate

Presents the writings of many people who have been affected by hate and discrimination, along with a large number of links to web sites working to stop hate crimes.

Availability: All requesters
Suggested Grade: 4-Adult
Order Number: not applicable
Format: Web Site

Source: Stop-the-hate.org
World Wide Web URL: http://stop-the-hate.org

Study Guides and Strategies
A large assortment of articles for learning proper study habits, how to prepare for and take tests, and much more.
Availability: All requesters
Suggested Grade: 6-12
Order Number: not applicable
Format: Online Study Guides
Source: Joe Landsberger
World Wide Web URL: http://www.studygs.net/

Teaching the Thinking Skill of Compare and Contrast
Often you will be asked to use the skill of compare and contrast in writing essays and reports, as well as in your personal life. This activity teaches those skills.
Availability: All requesters
Suggested Grade: 9-12
Order Number: not applicable
Format: Online Lesson Plan
Source: Donna Cawiezell
World Wide Web URL:
http://www.col-ed.org/cur/misc/misc80.txt

Teen Central.Net
Allows teens to share their own stories, read stories by others, and get feedback from trained professionals who can help them.
Availability: All requesters
Suggested Grade: 6-12
Order Number: not applicable
Format: Web Site
Source: KidsPeace
World Wide Web URL: http://www.teencentral.net/

Test of Applied Creativity, Logic, and Reasoning
While this "test" might at first seem to be a joke, it will help students to think logically and with common sense. Sample question: There are 12 one-cent stamps in a dozen. How many two-cent stamps are in a dozen?
Availability: All requesters
Suggested Grade: All ages
Order Number: not applicable
Format: Online Lesson Plan
Source: Paul T. Williams (reason)
World Wide Web URL:
http://youth.net/cec/cecmisc/cecmisc.53.txt

Tolerance Wins Friends Game
Students will discover how tolerant of others they really are.
Availability: All requesters
Suggested Grade: All ages
Order Number: not applicable
Format: Downloadable Game
Source: Unesco (friends)
World Wide Web URL:
http://web.macam.ac.il/~suki/Paderborn/game1eng.htm

Truth and Lies Game
A fun, get-acquainted activity to learn more about all class members.
Availability: All requesters
Suggested Grade: 4-12
Order Number: not applicable
Format: Online Lesson Plan
Source: Elizabeth Hardin
World Wide Web URL:
http://youth.net/cec/cecmisc/cecmisc.04.txt

Using Stories About Heroes to Teach Values
Explains what and how to use heroes to teach values to students.
Availability: All requesters
Suggested Grade: Teacher Reference
Order Number: not applicable
Production Date: 1998
Format: Online Article
Source: Tony R. Sanchez
World Wide Web URL:
http://www.indiana.edu/~ssdc/valdig.htm

What Influences Our Perception of Gender Roles?
Attempts to help students answer this question.
Availability: All requesters
Suggested Grade: 7-Adult
Order Number: not applicable
Format: Online Lesson Plan
Source: Dr. Betty J. Rauhe
World Wide Web URL:
http://www.ricw.state.ri.us/lessons/166.htm

What Is Self-Esteem
Students differentiate between traits of low self-esteem and high self-esteem and decide where their self-esteem is.
Availability: All requesters
Suggested Grade: 4-12
Order Number: not applicable
Format: Online Lesson Plan
Source: Nykki L. Holton
World Wide Web URL:
http://youth.net/cec/cecmisc/cecmisc.74.txt

What Kids Can Do
Shows examples of students working to improve their community so that others may adopt these actions and attitudes.
Availability: All requesters
Suggested Grade: 6-Adult
Order Number: not applicable
Format: Web Site
Source: What Kids Can Do, Inc.
World Wide Web URL: http://www.whatkidscando.org/

You Didn't Get Pregnant, You Didn't Get AIDS...

Tells why the fear of pregnancy or the fear of AIDS are not the only reasons to avoid having premarital sex as a teenager.

Availability:	Classroom quantities to schools, libraries, and homeschoolers in the United States; limit of 10 elsewhere.
Suggested Grade:	7-Adult
Languages:	English; Spanish
Order Number:	English FP-110004; Spanish FP-110007
Format:	Brochure
Special Notes:	May also be downloaded from the web site.

Source: Office of Population Affairs Clearinghouse
P. O. Box 30686
Bethesda, MD 20824-0686
Phone: 1-866-640-7827
Fax: 1-866-592-3299
World Wide Web URL:
http://opa.osophs.dhhs.gov/pubs/publications.html
Email Address: clearinghouse@dhhsopa.net

Alcohol--A Potent Drug
Provides the history of alcohol and discusses the effect it has on the body--both temporary and permanent.
Availability: Single copies to schools, libraries, and homeschoolers world-wide. A stamped, self-addressed envelope is appreciated.
Suggested Grade: 2-12
Order Number: order by title
Format: Flyer
Source: Narcotic Educational Foundation of America
28245 Avenue Crocker, Suite 230
Santa Clarita, CA 91355-1201
Phone: 1-661-775-6968
Fax: 1-661-775-1648
World Wide Web URL: http://www.cnoa.org
Email Address: lwhite@cnoa.org

Am I Addicted or Dependent?
Explains what a drug is, why people use drugs, and more.
Availability: Single copies to schools, libraries, and homeschoolers world-wide. A stamped, self-addressed envelope is appreciated.
Suggested Grade: 2-12
Order Number: order by title
Format: Flyer
Source: Narcotic Educational Foundation of America
28245 Avenue Crocker, Suite 230
Santa Clarita, CA 91355-1201
Phone: 1-661-775-6968
Fax: 1-661-775-1648
World Wide Web URL: http://www.cnoa.org
Email Address: lwhite@cnoa.org

Black Lungs: The Danger of Smoking
Discusses the dangers of smoking not only cigarettes but anything that goes into your lungs.
Availability: All requesters
Suggested Grade: All ages
Order Number: not applicable
Format: Web Site
Special Notes: This URL will lead you to a subject page. Then click on the appropriate subject heading.
Source: ThinkQuest
World Wide Web URL:
http://www.thinkquest.org/pls/html/think.library

Butts & Ashtrays
Click on the interactive body tour for a picture of how smoking affects the body from head to toe.
Availability: All requesters
Suggested Grade: All ages
Order Number: not applicable
Format: Web Site
Special Notes: This URL will lead you to a subject page. Then click on the appropriate subject heading.
Source: ThinkQuest
World Wide Web URL:
http://www.thinkquest.org/pls/html/think.library

Clearing the Air: Quit Smoking Today
Offers a variety of approaches to quitting smoking; for the motivated person.
Availability:
Suggested Grade: 6-Adult
Order Number: not applicable
Production Date: 2010
Format: Downloadable Booklet
Special Notes: May also be downloaded from the web site.
Source: National Cancer Institute
World Wide Web URL: http://cancer.gov/publications

Creating Safe and Drug-Free Schools: An Action Guide
A complete guide to schools, students, parents, and community and business groups for creating schools that are safe.
Availability: All requesters
Suggested Grade: Teacher Reference
Order Number: not applicable
Format: Online Book
Source: United States Department of Education
World Wide Web URL:
http://www.ed.gov/offices/OSDFS/actguid/index.html

Dear Mom & Dad
Letters from youth addressing the drinking problems of their parents. Designed to help adolescents explain their membership in an Alateen group.
Availability: Limit of 10 copies to schools, libraries, and homeschoolers in the United States and Canada. Make request on official stationery.
Suggested Grade: 6-Adult
Languages: English; French; Spanish
Order Number: order by title
Format: Brochure
Source: Al-Anon Family Group Headquarters, Inc.
Attn: Public Outreach Department
1600 Corporate Landing Parkway
Virginia Beach, VA 23454-5617
Phone: 1-888-425-2666
Fax: 1-757-563-1655
World Wide Web URL: http://www.al-anon.alateen.org
Email Address: wso@al-anon.org

Drugs and Alcohol: What You Need to Know...
Provides lots of information relating to the hazards of drugs and alcohol.
Availability: All requesters
Suggested Grade: All ages
Order Number: not applicable
Format: Web Site
Special Notes: This URL will lead you to a subject page. Then click on the appropriate subject heading.
Source: ThinkQuest
World Wide Web URL:
http://www.thinkquest.org/pls/html/think.library

Drugs and Your Health
Discusses drug and alcohol dependency.
Availability: All requesters
Suggested Grade: 6-Adult
Order Number: not applicable
Format: Web Site
Special Notes: This URL will lead you to a subject page. Then click on the appropriate subject heading.
Source: ThinkQuest
World Wide Web URL:
http://www.thinkquest.org/pls/html/think.library

Effects of Marijuana on the Lung and Its Immune Defenses
Explores the effects of this drug on parts of the human body.
Availability: All requesters
Suggested Grade: 6-Adult
Order Number: not applicable
Format: Online Article
Special Notes: Reprinted from Secretary's Youth Substance Abuse Prevention Initiative: Resource Papers.
Source: Donald P. Tashkin
World Wide Web URL: http://www.ukcia.org/research/EffectsOfMarijuanaOnLungAndImmuneDefenses.html

Factline
Here are a number of facts sheets about various drugs of abuse as well as tobacco.
Availability: All requesters
Suggested Grade: 6-Adult
Order Number: not applicable
Format: Online Fact Sheets
Source: Indiana Prevention Resource Center
World Wide Web URL:
http://www.drugs.indiana.edu/library-factline.html

Heroin Story, The
Presents the history of the creation of heroin and the dangerous effects of this drug.
Availability: Single copies to schools, libraries, and homeschoolers world-wide. A stamped, self-addressed envelope is appreciated.
Suggested Grade: 2-12
Order Number: order by title
Format: Flyer
Source: Narcotic Educational Foundation of America
28245 Avenue Crocker, Suite 230
Santa Clarita, CA 91355-1201
Phone: 1-661-775-6968
Fax: 1-661-775-1648
World Wide Web URL: http://www.cnoa.org
Email Address: lwhite@cnoa.org

Joe Chemo
Designed to reduce teen smoking, this site is a takeoff on the Joe Camel advertisements.
Availability: All requesters
Suggested Grade: 6-12
Order Number: not applicable
Format: Web Site
Source: Professor Scott Plous
World Wide Web URL: http://www.joechemo.org/

Marijuana: Facts for Teens
Defines and explores the effects of marijuana on adolescents.
Availability: All requesters
Suggested Grade: 6-12
Order Number: not applicable
Format: Online Article
Source: National Institute on Drug Abuse
World Wide Web URL:
http://www.nida.nih.gov/MarijBroch/MarijIntro.html

Marijuana: Facts Parents Need to Know
Informs parents about the effects of this drug and presents statistics concerning its use.
Availability: All requesters
Suggested Grade: Adult
Order Number: not applicable
Format: Online Article
Source: National Institute on Drug Abuse
World Wide Web URL:
http://www.nida.nih.gov/MarijBroch/MarijIntro.htmlParents

Rohypnol: "The Date Rape Drug"
Explains the effects of this drug which is being used to sedate women so that they may be sexually abused.
Availability: Single copies to schools, libraries, and homeschoolers world-wide. A stamped, self-addressed envelope is appreciated.
Suggested Grade: 2-12
Order Number: order by title
Format: Flyer
Source: Narcotic Educational Foundation of America
28245 Avenue Crocker, Suite 230
Santa Clarita, CA 91355-1201
Phone: 1-661-775-6968
Fax: 1-661-775-1648
World Wide Web URL: http://www.cnoa.org
Email Address: lwhite@cnoa.org

Smoking and Your Digestive System
Think smoking only affects your lungs? Read these article to find out how smoking affects all parts of the body, including the digestive system.
Availability: All requesters
Suggested Grade: 7-Adult
Order Number: not applicable
Format: Online Article

Source: National Digestive Diseases Information Clearinghouse
World Wide Web URL:
http://digestive.niddk.nih.gov/ddiseases/pubs/smoking/index.htm

Spit Tobacco: A Guide for Quitting

Information to tell you how and why to quit.

Availability: Limit of 50 copies to schools, libraries, and homeschoolers in the United States and Canada.
Suggested Grade: 6-12
Order Number: NIH Pub. No. 06-3270
Production Date: 2006
Format: Booklet

Source: National Institute of Dental and Craniofacial Research
National Oral Health Information Clearinghouse
1 NOHIC Way
Bethesda, MD 20892-3500
Phone: 1-301-232-4528
Fax: 1-301-480-4098
World Wide Web URL: http://www.nidcr.nih.gov
Email Address: nidcrinfo@mail.nih.gov

Story of Cocaine, The

Tells about this drug and the effects it has on the human body.

Availability: Single copies to schools, libraries, and homeschoolers world-wide. A stamped, self-addressed envelope is appreciated.
Suggested Grade: 2-12
Order Number: order by title
Format: Flyer

Source: Narcotic Educational Foundation of America
28245 Avenue Crocker, Suite 230
Santa Clarita, CA 91355-1201
Phone: 1-661-775-6968
Fax: 1-661-775-1648
World Wide Web URL: http://www.cnoa.org
Email Address: lwhite@cnoa.org

Substance Abuse Fact Sheets

The fact sheets discuss alcohol, marijuana, tobacco, and many other drugs.

Availability: All requesters
Suggested Grade: 6-12
Order Number:
Format: Downloadable Fact Sheets

Source: Oakland County Michigan Health Division
World Wide Web URL:
http://www.oakgov.com/health/info_pub/fs_index.html

Tobacco--Smoke or Chew

Discusses the dangers of tobacco.

Availability: Single copies to schools, libraries, and homeschoolers world-wide. A stamped, self-addressed envelope is appreciated.
Suggested Grade: 2-12
Order Number: order by title
Format: Flyer

Source: Narcotic Educational Foundation of America
28245 Avenue Crocker, Suite 230
Santa Clarita, CA 91355-1201
Phone: 1-661-775-6968
Fax: 1-661-775-1648
World Wide Web URL: http://www.cnoa.org
Email Address: lwhite@cnoa.org

Urban School-Community Parent Programs to Prevent Drug Use

Discusses this issue.

Availability: All requesters
Suggested Grade: Teacher Reference
Order Number: not applicable
Production Date: 1997
Format: Online Article

Source: Wendy Schwartz
World Wide Web URL:
http://www.ericdigests.org/1999-3/drug.htm

Valium & Other Depressants

Useful in moderate amounts, these drugs are being abused--here is more information.

Availability: Single copies to schools, libraries, and homeschoolers world-wide. A stamped, self-addressed envelope is appreciated.
Suggested Grade: 2-12
Order Number: order by title
Format: Flyer

Source: Narcotic Educational Foundation of America
28245 Avenue Crocker, Suite 230
Santa Clarita, CA 91355-1201
Phone: 1-661-775-6968
Fax: 1-661-775-1648
World Wide Web URL: http://www.cnoa.org
Email Address: lwhite@cnoa.org

What About Marijuana?

Information about this commonly smoked drug.

Availability: Single copies to schools, libraries, and homeschoolers world-wide. A stamped, self-addressed envelope is appreciated.
Suggested Grade: 2-12
Order Number: order by title
Format: Flyer

Source: Narcotic Educational Foundation of America
28245 Avenue Crocker, Suite 230
Santa Clarita, CA 91355-1201
Phone: 1-661-775-6968
Fax: 1-661-775-1648
World Wide Web URL: http://www.cnoa.org
Email Address: lwhite@cnoa.org

Acne--Questions and Answers
Information about this skin condition.

Availability: Single copies to schools, libraries, and homeschoolers in the United States and Canada.
Suggested Grade: 5-Adult
Order Number: AR-80 QA
Production Date: 1997
Format: Fact Sheet
Special Notes: May also be downloaded from the web site.

Source: National Institute of Arthritis and Musculoskeletal and Skin Diseases Information Clearinghouse
National Institutes of Health
1 AMS Circle
Bethesda, MD 20892-3675
Phone: 1-877-226-4267
Fax: 1-301-718-6366
World Wide Web URL: http://www.niams.nih.gov
Email Address: NIAMSInfo@mail.nih.gov

Acute Lymphocytic Leukemia
Very complete information about this disease.

Availability: Limit of 25 copies to schools, libraries, and homeschoolers in the United States.
Suggested Grade: 6-Adult
Order Number: PS33
Format: Booklet; 48 pages
Special Notes: Order via web site only. May also be downloaded from the web site.

Source: Leukemia & Lymphoma Society, The
World Wide Web URL: http://www.lls.org//resourcecenter/freeeducationmaterials/leukemia/

Acute Myeloid Leukemia
This booklet provides information about acute myeloid leukemia (AML) for patients and their families.

Availability: One copy to schools, libraries, and homeschoolers world-wide.
Suggested Grade: 6-Adult
Order Number: order by title
Format: Booklet
Special Notes: Order via web site only. May also be downloaded from the web site.

Source: Leukemia & Lymphoma Society, The
World Wide Web URL: http://www.lls.org//resourcecenter/freeeducationmaterials/leukemia/

Age-Related Macular Degeneration
Discusses macular degeneration and low vision resources.

Availability: All requesters
Suggested Grade: 7-Adult
Order Number: not applicable
Format: Downloadable Article

Source: American Academy of Ophthalmology
World Wide Web URL: http://www.geteyesmart.org/eyesmart/

Asthma & Allergy Medications
Provides information on antihistamines, decongestants, and more.

Availability: Limit of one copy to non-profit schools, libraries, and homeschoolers world-wide.
Suggested Grade: 7-Adult
Languages: English; Spanish
Order Number: order by title
Format: Brochure
Special Notes: Requests must be made via web site or email ONLY.

Source: American Academy of Allergy, Asthma & Immunology
Attn: Membership Assistant
555 East Wells Street, Suite 1100
Milwaukee, WI 53202
Fax: 1-414-276-3349
World Wide Web URL: http://www.aaaai.org
Email Address: info@aaaai.org

Asthma and Physical Activity in the School
This easy-to-read booklet is a perfect companion for teachers and coaches who want to help students with asthma participate in sports and physical activities.

Availability: One copy is free to schools, libraries, and homeschoolers world-wide. Shipping charges will apply if more than one publication is requested.
Suggested Grade: 4-12
Order Number: 05-3651
Format: Booklet

Source: National Heart, Lung, and Blood Institute Information Center
P. O. Box 30105
Bethesda, MD 20824-0105
Phone: 1-301-592-8573
Fax: 1-240-629-3246
World Wide Web URL: http://www.nhlbi.nih.gov/
Email Address: nhlbiinfo@nhlbi.nih.gov

Atopic Dermatitis--Handout on Health
Discusses atopic dermatitis, often called eczema.

Availability: Single copies to schools, libraries, and homeschoolers in the United States and Canada.
Suggested Grade: 6-Adult
Order Number: AR-68HH
Production Date: 2003
Format: Booklet
Special Notes: May also be downloaded from the web site.

Source: National Institute of Arthritis and Musculoskeletal and Skin Diseases Information Clearinghouse
National Institutes of Health
1 AMS Circle
Bethesda, MD 20892-3675
Phone: 1-877-226-4267
Fax: 1-301-718-6366
World Wide Web URL: http://www.niams.nih.gov
Email Address: NIAMSInfo@mail.nih.gov

Back Pain, Handout on Health

Describes causes, diagnosis, and treatments for back pain as well as discussing research efforts to learn more about it.

Availability: Single copies to schools, libraries, and homeschoolers in the United States and Canada.
Suggested Grade: 6-Adult
Order Number: AR-79 HH
Production Date: 2006
Format: Booklet
Special Notes: May also be downloaded from the web site.

Source: National Institute of Arthritis and Musculoskeletal and Skin Diseases Information Clearinghouse
National Institutes of Health
1 AMS Circle
Bethesda, MD 20892-3675
Phone: 1-877-226-4267
Fax: 1-301-718-6366
World Wide Web URL: http://www.niams.nih.gov
Email Address: NIAMSInfo@mail.nih.gov

Bone Health for Life

Easy to read information about bone health.

Availability: Single copies to schools, libraries, and homeschoolers in the United States and Canada.
Suggested Grade: 6-Adult
Order Number: AR-740
Production Date: 2008
Format: Booklet
Special Notes: May also be downloaded from the web site.

Source: National Institute of Arthritis and Musculoskeletal and Skin Diseases Information Clearinghouse
National Institutes of Health
1 AMS Circle
Bethesda, MD 20892-3675
Phone: 1-877-226-4267
Fax: 1-301-718-6366
World Wide Web URL: http://www.niams.nih.gov
Email Address: NIAMSInfo@mail.nih.gov

Breast Cancer and Mammograms

Describes who is at risk for breast cancer, what you can do, and how a mammogram can help.

Availability: All requesters
Suggested Grade: 7-Adult
Order Number: not applicable
Format: Online Article; 5 pages
Special Notes: Use the on-site search engine to easily find this title. You may request a printed copy mailed to you for a fee.

Source: Federal Citizen Information Center
World Wide Web URL: http://www.pueblo.gsa.gov/

Bursitis andTendinitis

Information about this condition.

Availability: Single copies to schools, libraries, and homeschoolers in the United States and Canada.
Suggested Grade: 6-Adult
Order Number: AR-166 QA
Production Date: 2002
Format: Fact sheet
Special Notes: May also be downloaded from the web site.

Source: National Institute of Arthritis and Musculoskeletal and Skin Diseases Information Clearinghouse
National Institutes of Health
1 AMS Circle
Bethesda, MD 20892-3675
Phone: 1-877-226-4267
Fax: 1-301-718-6366
World Wide Web URL: http://www.niams.nih.gov
Email Address: NIAMSInfo@mail.nih.gov

Cancer and the Environment: What You Need to Know, What You Can Do

Focuses on the agents in the environment that cause cancer and what we can do to lower our cancer risk.

Availability:
Suggested Grade: Adult
Order Number: P011
Production Date: 2003
Format: Downloadable Booklet

Source: National Cancer Institute
World Wide Web URL: http://cancer.gov/publications

Childhood Asthma

Includes tips for parents, caregivers, and school personnel.

Availability: Limit of one copy to non-profit schools, libraries, and homeschoolers world-wide.
Suggested Grade: Teacher Reference
English; Spanish
Order Number: order by title
Format: Brochure
Special Notes: Requests must be made via web site or email ONLY.

Source: American Academy of Allergy, Asthma & Immunology
Attn: Membership Assistant
555 East Wells Street, Suite 1100
Milwaukee, WI 53202
World Wide Web URL: http://www.aaaai.org
Email Address: info@aaaai.org

Chronic Lymphocytic Leukemia

This booklet provides information about chronic lymphocytic leukemia (CLL) for patients and their families.

Availability: One copy to schools, libraries, and homeschoolers world-wide.
Suggested Grade: 6-Adult
Order Number:
Format: Booklet
Special Notes: Order via web site only. May also be downloaded from the web site.

Source: Leukemia & Lymphoma Society, The
World Wide Web URL:
http://www.lls.org//resourcecenter/freeeducationmaterials/leukemia/

Chronic Myelogenous Leukemia

Very complete information about this disease.

Availability: Limit of 25 copies to schools, libraries, and homeschoolers in the United States.
Suggested Grade: 6-Adult
Order Number: CML
Format: Booklet
Special Notes: Order via web site only. May also be downloaded from the web site.

Source: Leukemia & Lymphoma Society, The
World Wide Web URL:
http://www.lls.org//resourcecenter/freeeducationmaterials/leukemia/

Communicable Diseases Fact Sheets

From anthrax to VRSA and all sorts of communicable diseases in between.

Availability: All requesters
Suggested Grade: 6-12
Order Number: not applicable
Format: Downloadable Fact Sheets

Source: Oakland County Michigan Health Division
World Wide Web URL:
http://www.oakgov.com/health/info_pub/fs_index.html

Diet, Nutrition and Prostate Cancer

Discusses the connection between diet, nutrition, and cancer of this male gland.

Availability: Limit of 1 copy to schools, libraries, and homeschoolers in the United States and Canada.
Suggested Grade: 10-Adult
Order Number: order by title
Format: Booklet

Source: American Institute for Cancer Research
Publication Orders
1759 R Street, N. W.
Washington, DC 20009
Phone: 1-800-843-8114
Fax: 1-202-328-7226
World Wide Web URL: http://www.aicr.org
Email Address: aicrweb@aicr.org

Dry Mouth

Discusses the causes of dry mouth, the importance of saliva to oral health, and steps to follow to relieve dryness.

Availability: Limit of 50 copies to schools, libraries, and homeschoolers in the United States and Canada.
Suggested Grade: 6-Adult
Languages: English; Spanish
Order Number: English NIH Pub. No. 08-3174; Spanish NIH Pub. No. 08-3174S
Format: Booklet

Source: National Institute of Dental and Craniofacial Research
National Oral Health Information Clearinghouse
1 NOHIC Way
Bethesda, MD 20892-3500
Phone: 1-301-232-4528
Fax: 1-301-480-4098
World Wide Web URL: http://www.nidcr.nih.gov
Email Address: nidcrinfo@mail.nih.gov

Everything You Need to Know About...Asthma & Food

Discusses what foods can trigger an asthma attack.

Availability: All requesters
Suggested Grade: 4-12
Order Number: not applicable
Production Date: 1997
Format: Downloadable Leaflet

Source: International Food Information Council Foundation
World Wide Web URL:
http://ific.org/publications/brochures/index.cfm

Facts About Angina

Describes how this disease affects the body and includes information on symptoms, causes, diagnoses, and treatments. Reproducible.

Availability: One copy is free to schools, libraries, and homeschoolers world-wide. Shipping charges will apply if more than one publication is requested.
Suggested Grade: 4-12
Order Number: 04-5685
Format: Fact Sheet
Special Notes: May also be downloaded from the web site.

Source: National Heart, Lung, and Blood Institute
Information Center
P. O. Box 30105
Bethesda, MD 20824-0105
Phone: 1-301-592-8573
Fax: 1-240-629-3246
World Wide Web URL: http://www.nhlbi.nih.gov/
Email Address: nhlbiinfo@nhlbi.nih.gov

Facts About Arrhythmias/Rhythm Disorders

Describes how this disease affects the body and includes information on symptoms, causes, diagnoses, and treatments. Reproducible.

Availability: One copy is free to schools, libraries, and homeschoolers world-wide. Shipping charges will apply if more than one publication is requested.
Suggested Grade: 4-12
Order Number: 07-5826
Format: Fact Sheet
Special Notes: May also be downloaded from the web site.

Source: National Heart, Lung, and Blood Institute
Information Center
P. O. Box 30105
Bethesda, MD 20824-0105
Phone: 1-301-592-8573
Fax: 1-240-629-3246
World Wide Web URL: http://www.nhlbi.nih.gov/
Email Address: nhlbiinfo@nhlbi.nih.gov

Facts About Heart Failure

Discusses this affliction and how it can be diagnosed.

Availability: One copy is free to schools, libraries, and homeschoolers world-wide. Shipping charges will apply if more than one publication is requested.
Suggested Grade: 4-12
Order Number: 04-5694
Format: Fact Sheet
Special Notes: May also be downloaded from the web site.

Source: National Heart, Lung, and Blood Institute
Information Center
P. O. Box 30105
Bethesda, MD 20824-0105
Phone: 1-301-592-8573
Fax: 1-240-629-3246
World Wide Web URL: http://www.nhlbi.nih.gov/
Email Address: nhlbiinfo@nhlbi.nih.gov

Facts About Heart Transplant

Facts about this life-saving procedure.

Availability: One copy is free to schools, libraries, and homeschoolers world-wide. Shipping charges will apply if more than one publication is requested.
Suggested Grade: 4-12
Order Number: 08-6169
Format: Fact Sheet
Special Notes: May also be downloaded from the web site.

Source: National Heart, Lung, and Blood Institute
Information Center
P. O. Box 30105
Bethesda, MD 20824-0105
Phone: 1-301-592-8573
Fax: 1-240-629-3246
World Wide Web URL: http://www.nhlbi.nih.gov/
Email Address: nhlbiinfo@nhlbi.nih.gov

Facts About Insomnia

Explains this sleep disorder.

Availability: One copy is free to schools, libraries, and homeschoolers world-wide. Shipping charges will apply if more than one publication is requested.
Suggested Grade: 4-12
Order Number: 07-5824
Format: Leaflet
Special Notes: May also be downloaded from the web site.

Source: National Heart, Lung, and Blood Institute
Information Center
P. O. Box 30105
Bethesda, MD 20824-0105
Phone: 1-301-592-8573
Fax: 1-240-629-3246
World Wide Web URL: http://www.nhlbi.nih.gov/
Email Address: nhlbiinfo@nhlbi.nih.gov

Facts About Pesticides and Food Additives, The

There is no convincing evidence that foods with pesticide residues or additives increase cancer risk--here is more information.

Availability: Limit of 1 copy to schools, libraries, and homeschoolers in the United States and Canada.
Suggested Grade: 10-Adult
Order Number: order by title
Format: Brochure

Source: American Institute for Cancer Research
Publication Orders
1759 R Street, N. W.
Washington, DC 20009
Phone: 1-800-843-8114
Fax: 1-202-328-7226
World Wide Web URL: http://www.aicr.org
Email Address: aicrweb@aicr.org

Facts About Raynaud's Phenomenon

Discusses this disorder of the small blood vessels that feed the skin.

Availability: One copy is free to schools, libraries, and homeschoolers world-wide. Shipping charges will apply if more than one publication is requested.
Suggested Grade: 4-12
Order Number: 06-5814
Production Date: 1993
Format: Article
Special Notes: May also be downloaded from the web site.

Source: National Heart, Lung, and Blood Institute
Information Center
P. O. Box 30105
Bethesda, MD 20824-0105
Phone: 1-301-592-8573
Fax: 1-240-629-3246
World Wide Web URL: http://www.nhlbi.nih.gov/
Email Address: nhlbiinfo@nhlbi.nih.gov

Facts About Restless Legs Syndrome

Explains this sleep disorder.

Availability: One copy is free to schools, libraries, and homeschoolers world-wide. Shipping charges will apply if more than one publication is requested.
Suggested Grade: 4-12
Order Number: 06-5822
Format: Leaflet
Special Notes: May also be downloaded from the web site.

Source: National Heart, Lung, and Blood Institute
Information Center
P. O. Box 30105
Bethesda, MD 20824-0105
Phone: 1-301-592-8573
Fax: 1-240-629-3246
World Wide Web URL: http://www.nhlbi.nih.gov/
Email Address: nhlbiinfo@nhlbi.nih.gov

Facts About Sleep Apnea

Explains this potentially deadly sleep disorder.

Availability:	One copy is free to schools, libraries, and homeschoolers world-wide. Shipping charges will apply if more than one publication is requested.
Suggested Grade:	4-12
Order Number:	05-5680
Format:	Leaflet
Special Notes:	May also be downloaded from the web site.

Source: National Heart, Lung, and Blood Institute Information Center
P. O. Box 30105
Bethesda, MD 20824-0105
Phone: 1-301-592-8573
Fax: 1-240-629-3246
World Wide Web URL: http://www.nhlbi.nih.gov/
Email Address: nhlbiinfo@nhlbi.nih.gov

Fibromyalgia--Questions and Answers

A collection of articles about this condition.

Availability:	Single copies to schools, libraries, and homeschoolers in the United States and Canada.
Suggested Grade:	6-Adult
Order Number:	AR-91QA
Production Date:	2004
Format:	Booklet
Special Notes:	May also be downloaded from the web site.

Source: National Institute of Arthritis and Musculoskeletal and Skin Diseases Information Clearinghouse
National Institutes of Health
1 AMS Circle
Bethesda, MD 20892-3675
Phone: 1-877-226-4267
Fax: 1-301-718-6366
World Wide Web URL: http://www.niams.nih.gov
Email Address: NIAMSInfo@mail.nih.gov

Glossary of HIV/AIDS Related Terms

Defines commonly used words to describe the HIV virus, its pathogenesis, its associated treatments, and the medical management of related conditions.

Availability:	All requesters
Suggested Grade:	9-Adult
Order Number:	not applicable
Format:	Online Glossary

Source: D. Sander
World Wide Web URL:
http://www.virology.net/ATVHIVGlossary.html

Health Finder

A searchable database of health topics.

Availability:	All requesters
Suggested Grade:	All ages
Order Number:	not applicable
Format:	Web Site

Source: U. S. Department of Health & Human Services
World Wide Web URL: http://www.healthfinder.gov/

Hepatitis C

Explains how this serious blood-borne infection is spread, diagnosed, and treated.

Availability:	All requesters
Suggested Grade:	6-Adult
Order Number:	not applicable
Production Date:	1999
Format:	Online Article; 6 pages
Special Notes:	Use the on-site search engine to easily find this title. You may request a printed copy mailed to you for a fee.

Source: Federal Citizen Information Center
World Wide Web URL: http://www.pueblo.gsa.gov/

How Asthma-Friendly Is Your School?

Parents and school staff will find this resource useful for determining how well their school accommodates children with asthma.

Availability:	One copy is free to schools, libraries, and homeschoolers world-wide. Shipping charges will apply if more than one publication is requested.
Suggested Grade:	4-12
Order Number:	55-830
Production Date:	1997
Format:	Leaflet
Special Notes:	May also be downloaded from the web site.

Source: National Heart, Lung, and Blood Institute Information Center
P. O. Box 30105
Bethesda, MD 20824-0105
Phone: 1-301-592-8573
Fax: 1-240-629-3246
World Wide Web URL: http://www.nhlbi.nih.gov/
Email Address: nhlbiinfo@nhlbi.nih.gov

How to Hold Your Own Against Colds and Flu

Get the facts on lowering your chance of infection, treating difficult cold and flu symptoms and make lifestyle changes to reduce your risk.

Availability:	All requesters
Suggested Grade:	4-Adult
Order Number:	not applicable
Production Date:	2001
Format:	Online Article; 6 pages
Special Notes:	Use the on-site search engine to easily find this title. You may request a printed copy mailed to you for a fee.

Source: Federal Citizen Information Center
World Wide Web URL: http://www.pueblo.gsa.gov/

Juvenile Arthritis--Questions and Answers

Answers general questions about arthritis and exercise.

Availability:	Single copies to schools, libraries, and homeschoolers in the United States and Canada.
Suggested Grade:	6-Adult
Order Number:	AR-112QA
Production Date:	2001

Format: Booklet
Special Notes: May also be downloaded from the web site.

Source: National Institute of Arthritis and Musculoskeletal and Skin Diseases Information Clearinghouse
National Institutes of Health
1 AMS Circle
Bethesda, MD 20892-3675
Phone: 1-877-226-4267
Fax: 1-301-718-6366
World Wide Web URL: http://www.niams.nih.gov
Email Address: NIAMSInfo@mail.nih.gov

Keloids and Hypertrophic Scars

A collection of articles about this condition.

Availability: Single copies to schools, libraries, and homeschoolers in the United States and Canada.
Suggested Grade: 6-Adult
Order Number: AR-144IP
Production Date: 2003
Format: Packet of Materials
Special Notes: May also be downloaded from the web site.

Source: National Institute of Arthritis and Musculoskeletal and Skin Diseases Information Clearinghouse
National Institutes of Health
1 AMS Circle
Bethesda, MD 20892-3675
Phone: 1-877-226-4267
Fax: 1-301-718-6366
World Wide Web URL: http://www.niams.nih.gov
Email Address: NIAMSInfo@mail.nih.gov

Kidney Disease of Diabetes Fact Sheet

Defines the stages of this progressive disease and describes the preventive measures that can forestall kidney failure for many years.

Availability: Single copies to schools, libraries, and homeschoolers in the United States and Canada.
Suggested Grade: 5-12
Order Number: KU-93
Production Date: 1995
Format: Fact Sheet
Special Notes: May also be downloaded from the web site.

Source: National Institute of Diabetes and Digestive and Kidney Diseases
5 Information Way
Bethesda, MD 20892-3568
Phone: 1-800-891-5390
Fax: 1-703-738-4929
World Wide Web URL: http://www.niddk.nih.gov/
Email Address: nkudidc@info.niddk.nih.gov

Live Healthier, Live Longer

Explains coronary heart disease and how to avoid it.

Availability: All requesters
Suggested Grade: 6-12
Order Number: not applicable
Format: Web Site

Source: National Institutes of Health
World Wide Web URL: http://rover.nhlbi.nih.gov/chd/

Lowe Syndrome Association

Provides brief information about this genetic condition that affects only males.

Availability: One copy to schools, libraries, and homeschoolers world-wide.
Suggested Grade: 8-Adult
Order Number: order by title
Format: Brochure
Special Notes: May also be downloaded from the web site.

Source: Lowe Syndrome Association, Inc.
P. O. Box 864346
Plano, TX 75086-4346
Phone: 1-972-733-1338
World Wide Web URL: http://www.lowesyndrome.org

Lyme Disease--The Facts, The Challenge

Presents the most recently available information on the diagnosis, treatment, and prevention of Lyme disease.

Availability: Single copies to schools, libraries, and homeschoolers in the United States and Canada.
Suggested Grade: 6-Adult
Order Number: AR-655
Format: Booklet
Special Notes: May also be downloaded from the web site.

Source: National Institute of Arthritis and Musculoskeletal and Skin Diseases Information Clearinghouse
National Institutes of Health
1 AMS Circle
Bethesda, MD 20892-3675
Phone: 1-877-226-4267
Fax: 1-301-718-6366
World Wide Web URL: http://www.niams.nih.gov
Email Address: NIAMSInfo@mail.nih.gov

Managing Chronic Pain

Learn more about how to cope with chronic pain.

Availability: All requesters
Suggested Grade: 6-Adult
Order Number: not applicable
Production Date: 2004
Format: Online Article
Special Notes: Use the on-site search engine to easily find this title. You may request a printed copy mailed to you for a fee.

Source: Federal Citizen Information Center
World Wide Web URL: http://www.pueblo.gsa.gov/

Myths About Stuttering

Dispels myths about people who stutter.

Availability: Single copies to schools, libraries, and homeschoolers world-wide. May be copied.
Suggested Grade: 6-Adult
Order Number: order by title
Production Date: 2006
Format: Fact Card

Source: Stuttering Foundation of America
P. O. Box 11749
Memphis, TN 38111-0749
Phone: 1-800-992-9392
World Wide Web URL: http://www.stutteringhelp.org
Email Address: info@stutteringhelp.org

Oral Cancer Pamphlet

Presents possible signs and symptoms of this disease.

Availability: Limit of 50 copies to schools, libraries, and homeschoolers in the United States and Canada.
Suggested Grade: 6-12
Order Number: NIH Pub. No. 08-5032
Production Date: 2008
Format: Card

Source: National Institute of Dental and Craniofacial Research
National Oral Health Information Clearinghouse
1 NOHIC Way
Bethesda, MD 20892-3500
Phone: 1-301-232-4528
Fax: 1-301-480-4098
World Wide Web URL: http://www.nidcr.nih.gov
Email Address: nidcrinfo@mail.nih.gov

Osteoporosis

A collection of articles about this condition.

Availability: Single copies to schools, libraries, and homeschoolers in the United States and Canada.
Suggested Grade: 6-Adult
Order Number: AR-28IP
Production Date: 2000
Format: Packet of Materials
Special Notes: May also be downloaded from the web site.

Source: National Institute of Arthritis and Musculoskeletal and Skin Diseases Information Clearinghouse
National Institutes of Health
1 AMS Circle
Bethesda, MD 20892-3675
Phone: 1-877-226-4267
Fax: 1-301-718-6366
World Wide Web URL: http://www.niams.nih.gov
Email Address: NIAMSInfo@mail.nih.gov

Periodontal (Gum) Disease

Discusses the causes, risk factors, diagnosis, and treatment options.

Availability: Limit of 50 copies to schools, libraries, and homeschoolers in the United States and Canada.
Suggested Grade: 6-Adult
Languages: English; Spanish
Order Number: English NIH Pub. No. 08-1142; Spanish NIH Pub. No. 08-1142S
Production Date: 2008
Format: Brochure

Source: National Institute of Dental and Craniofacial Research
National Oral Health Information Clearinghouse
1 NOHIC Way
Bethesda, MD 20892-3500
Phone: 1-301-232-4528
Fax: 1-301-480-4098
World Wide Web URL: http://www.nidcr.nih.gov
Email Address: nidcrinfo@mail.nih.gov

Psoriasis--Questions and Answers

Answers general questions about this skin condition.

Availability: Single copies to schools, libraries, and homeschoolers in the United States and Canada.
Suggested Grade: 6-Adult
Order Number: AR-97QA
Production Date: 2003
Format: Booklet
Special Notes: May also be downloaded from the web site.

Source: National Institute of Arthritis and Musculoskeletal and Skin Diseases Information Clearinghouse
National Institutes of Health
1 AMS Circle
Bethesda, MD 20892-3675
Phone: 1-877-226-4267
Fax: 1-301-718-6366
World Wide Web URL: http://www.niams.nih.gov
Email Address: NIAMSInfo@mail.nih.gov

Raynaud's Phenomenon--Questions and Answers

Answers commonly asked questions about this disorder that affects the blood vessels in the fingers, toes, ears, and nose.

Availability: Single copies to schools, libraries, and homeschoolers in the United States and Canada.
Suggested Grade: 6-Adult
Order Number: AR-125QA
Production Date: 2001
Format: Booklet
Special Notes: May also be downloaded from the web site.

Source: National Institute of Arthritis and Musculoskeletal and Skin Diseases Information Clearinghouse
National Institutes of Health
1 AMS Circle
Bethesda, MD 20892-3675
Phone: 1-877-226-4267
Fax: 1-301-718-6366
World Wide Web URL: http://www.niams.nih.gov
Email Address: NIAMSInfo@mail.nih.gov

Reducing Your Risk of Skin Cancer

Explains how to reduce the chances you will get this most common type of cancer in the United States.

Availability: Limit of 1 copy to schools, libraries, and homeschoolers in the United States and Canada.
Suggested Grade: 10-Adult
Languages: English; Spanish

Order Number: order by title
Format: Brochure
Special Notes: May also be downloaded from the web site.

Source: American Institute for Cancer Research
Publication Orders
1759 R Street, N. W.
Washington, DC 20009
Phone: 1-800-843-8114
Fax: 1-202-328-7226
World Wide Web URL: http://www.aicr.org
Email Address: aicrweb@aicr.org

Refractive Errors

Explains how we see and what causes the need for eyeglasses.

Availability: All requesters
Suggested Grade: 7-Adult
Order Number: not applicable
Format: Downloadable Article

Source: American Academy of Ophthalmology
World Wide Web URL:
http://www.geteyesmart.org/eyesmart/

Rheumatoid Arthritis--Handout on Health

Describes how rheumatoid arthritis develops, how it is diagnosed, and how it is treated.

Availability: Single copies to schools, libraries, and homeschoolers in the United States and Canada.
Suggested Grade: 6-Adult
Order Number: AR-13HH
Production Date: 2004
Format: Booklet
Special Notes: May also be downloaded from the web site.

Source: National Institute of Arthritis and Musculoskeletal and Skin Diseases Information Clearinghouse
National Institutes of Health
1 AMS Circle
Bethesda, MD 20892-3675
Phone: 1-877-226-4267
Fax: 1-301-718-6366
World Wide Web URL: http://www.niams.nih.gov
Email Address: NIAMSInfo@mail.nih.gov

Rhinitis

Describes what is also known as "hay fever."

Availability: Limit of one copy to non-profit schools, libraries, and homeschoolers world-wide.
Suggested Grade: 7-Adult
Languages: English; Spanish
Order Number: order by title
Format: Brochure
Special Notes: Requests must be made via web site or email ONLY.

Source: American Academy of Allergy, Asthma & Immunology
Attn: Membership Assistant
555 East Wells Street, Suite 1100
Milwaukee, WI 53202
orld Wide Web URL: http://www.aaaai.org
Email Address: info@aaaai.org

6 Tips for Speaking with Someone Who Stutters

Simple advice to help you when speaking with someone who stutters.

Availability: Single copies to schools, libraries, and homeschoolers world-wide. May be copied.
Suggested Grade: K-Adult
Order Number: order by title
Production Date: 2006
Format: Fact Card

Source: Stuttering Foundation of America
P. O. Box 11749
Memphis, TN 38111-0749
Phone: 1-800-992-9392
World Wide Web URL: http://www.stutteringhelp.org
Email Address: info@stutteringhelp.org

Sweating Disorders

A collection of articles about this condition.

Availability: Single copies to schools, libraries, and homeschoolers in the United States and Canada.
Suggested Grade: 6-Adult
Order Number: AR-77 IP
Production Date: 2004
Format: Packet of Materials
Special Notes: May also be downloaded from the web site.

Source: National Institute of Arthritis and Musculoskeletal and Skin Diseases Information Clearinghouse
National Institutes of Health
1 AMS Circle
Bethesda, MD 20892-3675
Phone: 1-877-226-4267
Fax: 1-301-718-6366
World Wide Web URL: http://www.niams.nih.gov
Email Address: NIAMSInfo@mail.nih.gov

Toxoplasmosis

Learn about a disease that pregnant women and immune-deficient people should be especially concerned about protecting themselves against.

Availability: Single copies to schools, libraries, and homeschoolers in the United States and Canada.
Suggested Grade: 6-Adult
Languages: English; Spanish
Order Number: order by title
Format: Brochure
Special Notes: May also be downloaded from the web site.

Source: American Veterinary Medical Association
Attn: Order Dept.
1931 North Meacham Road, Suite 100
Schaumburg, IL 60173-4360
Phone: 1-847-285-6655
Fax: 1-847-925-1329
World Wide Web URL: http://www.avma.org
Email Address: productorders@avma.org

Understanding Leukemia
Explains the four main types of leukemia, how leukemia is diagnosed, general methods of treatment, and how this organization can help.
Availability: One copy to schools, libraries, and homeschoolers world-wide.
Suggested Grade: 6-Adult
Order Number: PS70
Format: Booklet; 28 pages
Special Notes: Order via web site only. May also be downloaded from the web site.
Source: Leukemia & Lymphoma Society, The
World Wide Web URL:
http://www.lls.org//resourcecenter/freeeducationmaterials/leukemia/

Use of Inhaled Asthma Medications
Details various classes of inhaled asthma medications.
Availability: Limit of one copy to non-profit schools, libraries, and homeschoolers world-wide.
Suggested Grade: 7-Adult
Languages: English; Spanish
Order Number: order by title
Format: Brochure
Special Notes: Requests must be made via web site or email ONLY.
Source: American Academy of Allergy, Asthma & Immunology
Attn: Membership Assistant
555 East Wells Street, Suite 1100
Milwaukee, WI 53202
World Wide Web URL: http://www.aaaai.org
Email Address: info@aaaai.org

What I Need to Know About Eating and Diabetes
Reviews diabetes nutrition basics, including what, when, and how much a person with diabetes should eat.
Availability: Single copies to schools, libraries, and homeschoolers in the United States and Canada.
Suggested Grade: 9-Adult
Languages: English; Spanish
Order Number: English DM-226; Spanish DM-233
Format: Booklet
Special Notes: May also be downloaded from the web site.
Source: National Institute of Diabetes and Digestive and Kidney Diseases
5 Information Way
Bethesda, MD 20892-3568
Phone: 1-800-891-5390
Fax: 1-703-738-4929
World Wide Web URL: http://www.niddk.nih.gov/
Email Address: nkudidc@info.niddk.nih.gov

What Is Allergy Testing?
Describes how these tests are conducted.
Availability: Limit of one copy to non-profit schools, libraries, and homeschoolers world-wide.
Suggested Grade: 7-Adult
Languages: English; Spanish
Order Number: order by title
Format: Brochure
Special Notes: Requests must be made via web site or email ONLY.
Source: American Academy of Allergy, Asthma & Immunology
Attn: Membership Assistant
555 East Wells Street, Suite 1100
Milwaukee, WI 53202
World Wide Web URL: http://www.aaaai.org
Email Address: info@aaaai.org

What You Need to Know About Cancer
Discusses symptoms, diagnosis, treatment, emotional issues, and questions to ask the doctor.
Availability: Limit of 20 copies TOTAL, in any combination, to schools, libraries, homeschoolers and others world-wide.
Suggested Grade: 7-Adult
Order Number: P018
Production Date: 2006
Format: Pamphlet
Special Notes: May also be downloaded from the web site.
Source: National Cancer Institute
Publications Ordering Service
P. O. Box 24128
Baltimore, MD 21227
Phone: 1-800-4-CANCER
Fax: 1-301-330-7968
World Wide Web URL: http://cancer.gov/publications

What You Need to Know About Cancer--Colon & Rectum
Discusses symptoms, diagnosis, treatment, emotional issues, and questions to ask the doctor.
Availability: Limit of 20 copies TOTAL, in any combination, to schools, libraries, homeschoolers and others world-wide.
Suggested Grade: 7-Adult
Order Number: P020
Production Date: 2006
Format: Pamphlet
Special Notes: May also be downloaded from the web site.
Source: National Cancer Institute
Publications Ordering Service
P. O. Box 24128
Baltimore, MD 21227
Phone: 1-800-4-CANCER
Fax: 1-301-330-7968
World Wide Web URL: http://cancer.gov/publications

What You Need to Know About Cancer--Esophagus
Discusses symptoms, diagnosis, treatment, emotional issues, and questions to ask the doctor.
Availability: Limit of 20 copies TOTAL, in any combination, to schools, libraries, homeschoolers and others world-wide.
Suggested Grade: 7-Adult

Order Number: P021
Production Date: 2008
Format: Pamphlet
Special Notes: May also be downloaded from the web site.

Source: National Cancer Institute
Publications Ordering Service
P. O. Box 24128
Baltimore, MD 21227
Phone: 1-800-4-CANCER
Fax: 1-301-330-7968
World Wide Web URL: http://cancer.gov/publications

What You Need to Know About Cancer--Kidney

Discusses symptoms, diagnosis, treatment, emotional issues, and questions to ask the doctor.

Availability: Limit of 20 copies TOTAL, in any combination, to schools, libraries, homeschoolers and others world-wide.
Suggested Grade: 7-Adult
Order Number: P023
Production Date: 2010
Format: Pamphlet
Special Notes: May also be downloaded from the web site.

Source: National Cancer Institute
Publications Ordering Service
P. O. Box 24128
Baltimore, MD 21227
Phone: 1-800-4-CANCER
Fax: 1-301-330-7968
World Wide Web URL: http://cancer.gov/publications

What You Need to Know About Cancer--Melanoma

Discusses symptoms, diagnosis, treatment, emotional issues, and questions to ask the doctor.

Availability: Limit of 20 copies TOTAL, in any combination, to schools, libraries, homeschoolers and others world-wide.
Suggested Grade: 7-Adult
Order Number: P027
Production Date: 2002
Format: Pamphlet
Special Notes: May also be downloaded from the web site.

Source: National Cancer Institute
Publications Ordering Service
P. O. Box 24128
Baltimore, MD 21227
Phone: 1-800-4-CANCER
Fax: 1-301-330-7968
World Wide Web URL: http://cancer.gov/publications

What You Need to Know About Cancer--Prostate

Discusses symptoms, diagnosis, treatment, emotional issues, and questions to ask the doctor.

Availability: Limit of 20 copies TOTAL, in any combination, to schools, libraries, homeschoolers and others world-wide.
Suggested Grade: 7-Adult
Order Number: P035
Production Date: 2008
Format: Pamphlet
Special Notes: May also be downloaded from the web site.

Source: National Cancer Institute
Publications Ordering Service
P. O. Box 24128
Baltimore, MD 21227
Phone: 1-800-4-CANCER
Fax: 1-301-330-7968
World Wide Web URL: http://cancer.gov/publications

What You Need to Know About Oral Cancer

Discusses the cause and treatment of this disease.

Availability: Limit of 50 copies to schools, libraries, and homeschoolers in the United States and Canada.
Suggested Grade: 6-Adult
Order Number: NIH Pub. 03-1574
Production Date: 2003
Format: Booklet; 48 pages

Source: National Institute of Dental and Craniofacial Research
National Oral Health Information Clearinghouse
1 NOHIC Way
Bethesda, MD 20892-3500
Phone: 1-301-232-4528
Fax: 1-301-480-4098
World Wide Web URL: http://www.nidcr.nih.gov
Email Address: nidcrinfo@mail.nih.gov

When Cancer Returns

Details the different types of recurrence, types of treatment, and coping with cancer's return.

Availability: Limit of 20 copies TOTAL, in any combination, to schools, libraries, homeschoolers and others world-wide.
Suggested Grade: Adult
Order Number: P129
Production Date: 2010
Format: Booklet
Special Notes: May also be downloaded from the web site.

Source: National Cancer Institute
Publications Ordering Service
P. O. Box 24128
Baltimore, MD 21227
Phone: 1-800-4-CANCER
Fax: 1-301-330-7968
World Wide Web URL: http://cancer.gov/publications

Why Speech Therapy?

An important tool for all those trying to find the therapist who is right for them, and for setting realistic goals for therapy.

Availability: Single copies to schools, libraries, and homeschoolers world-wide. May be copied.
Suggested Grade: 6-Adult
Order Number: order by title
Production Date: 2006
Format: Brochure

Source: Stuttering Foundation of America
P. O. Box 11749
Memphis, TN 38111-0749
Phone: 1-800-992-9392
World Wide Web URL: http://www.stutteringhelp.org
Email Address: info@stutteringhelp.org

Anxiety Disorders
Discusses treatments available and resources to contact for more information on panic phobias, stress, obsessive compulsive, and other disorders.
Availability: All requesters
Suggested Grade: 4-Adult
Order Number: not applicable
Format: Online Article; 24 pages
Special Notes: Use the on-site search engine to easily find this title. You may request a printed copy mailed to you for a fee.
Source: Federal Citizen Information Center
World Wide Web URL: http://www.pueblo.gsa.gov/

Anxiety--Fact Sheet
Describes different types of anxiety disorders and what you can do if you recognize these symptoms in yourself or a loved one.
Availability: All requesters
Suggested Grade: 4-Adult
Order Number: not applicable
Production Date: 2001
Format: Online Article; 4 pages
Special Notes: Use the on-site search engine to easily find this title. You may request a printed copy mailed to you for a fee.
Source: Federal Citizen Information Center
World Wide Web URL: http://www.pueblo.gsa.gov/

Bodies in Motion Minds at Rest
Sensible recommendations for diet and exercise, self esteem, parental divorce, and school stress.
Availability: All requesters
Suggested Grade: 6-12
Order Number: not applicable
Format: Web Site
Special Notes: This URL will lead you to a subject page. Then click on the appropriate subject heading.
Source: ThinkQuest
World Wide Web URL:
http://www.thinkquest.org/pls/html/think.library

Depression and Disability in Children and Adolescents
Focuses on major depressive disorder, dysthymic disorder, and bipolar disorder as they are exhibited in childhood and adolescence. Discusses their symptoms, casual factors, and treatment.
Availability: All requesters
Suggested Grade: Teacher Reference
Order Number: not applicable
Production Date: 2003
Format: Online Article
Source: Eleanor Guetzloe
World Wide Web URL:
http://www.ericdigests.org/2005-1/depression.htm

Eating Disorder Awareness Website
Develop insight and power against diseases of Anorexia, Binge eating and Bulimia.
Availability: All requesters
Suggested Grade: 6-12
Order Number: not applicable
Format: Web Site
Special Notes: This URL will lead you to a subject page. Then click on the appropriate subject heading.
Source: ThinkQuest
World Wide Web URL:
http://www.thinkquest.org/pls/html/think.library

Eating Disorders
Recognize the symptoms of different eating disorders, who is most likely to be affected, and various treatment options.
Availability: All requesters
Suggested Grade: 4-Adult
Order Number: not applicable
Production Date: 2001
Format: Online Article; 8 pages
Special Notes: Use the on-site search engine to easily find this title. You may request a printed copy mailed to you for a fee.
Source: Federal Citizen Information Center
World Wide Web URL: http://www.pueblo.gsa.gov/

Eating Disorders Awareness and Prevention Materials
Presents a number of articles on what eating disorders are and how you can help yourself--and others--who suffer from this problem.
Availability: All requesters
Suggested Grade: 4-Adult
Order Number: not applicable
Format: Web Site
Source: Eating Disorders Awareness and Prevention, Inc.
World Wide Web URL: http://nationaleatingdisorders.org/

Eating Disorders for Teens
Explains eating disorders and presents information designed to help prevent them.
Availability: All requesters
Suggested Grade: 6-12
Order Number: not applicable
Format: Web Site
Special Notes: This URL will lead you to a subject page. Then click on the appropriate subject heading.
Source: ThinkQuest
World Wide Web URL:
http://www.thinkquest.org/pls/html/think.library

I Can't Stand It! - Phobias
Explores and explains phobias.
Availability: All requesters
Suggested Grade: All ages
Order Number: not applicable
Format: Web Site
Special Notes: This URL will lead you to a subject page. Then click on the appropriate subject heading.

Source: ThinkQuest
World Wide Web URL:
http://www.thinkquest.org/pls/html/think.library

Something Fishy Website on Eating Disorders, The

This website provides lots of information on eating disorders--what they are, who suffers from them, how to help others as well as yourself, and more.

Availability: All requesters
Suggested Grade: 6-12
Order Number: not applicable
Format: Web Site

Source: Something Fishy Music & Publishing
World Wide Web URL: http://www.something-fishy.org/

Stress Double Dealer

Learn tips to cope with stress, as well as illnesses caused or made worse by stress.

Availability: All requesters
Suggested Grade: 4-12
Languages: English; Japanese
Order Number: not applicable
Format: Web Site
Special Notes: This URL will lead you to a subject page. Then click on the appropriate subject heading.

Source: ThinkQuest
World Wide Web URL:
http://www.thinkquest.org/pls/html/think.library

Striking Out Stress: A "Gallery Walk" Activity

Teaches about stress and how to cope with its effects.

Availability: All requesters
Suggested Grade: 6-12
Order Number: not applicable
Format: Online Lesson Plan

Source: Andrea Petho
World Wide Web URL:
http://www.educationworld.com/a_tsl/archives/02-1/lesson045.shtml

Teens and Stress

Learn about the causes and results of stress and ways to prevent it.

Availability: All requesters
Suggested Grade: 6-12
Languages: English; Dutch; French; Spanish
Order Number: not applicable
Format: Web Site
Special Notes: This URL will lead you to a subject page. Then click on the appropriate subject heading.

Source: ThinkQuest
World Wide Web URL:
http://www.thinkquest.org/pls/html/think.library

About Safety & Regulations
A complete water safety lesson plan.
Availability: All requesters
Suggested Grade: 4-12
Order Number: not applicable
Format: Online Lesson Plan
Source: City of San Diego, The
World Wide Web URL:
http://www.sandiego.gov/lifeguards/safety/lesson.shtml

Bikeability Checklist
Written for adult and child bicyclists to help them assess the conditions they encounter when biking.
Availability: All requesters
Suggested Grade: 4-Adult
Order Number: not applicable
Format: Downloadable Brochure
Source: National Highway Traffic Safety Administration
World Wide Web URL: http://www.nhtsa.dot.gov/

California Poison Control System Consumer Information
Articles, posters, a coloring book, and much more about protecting you and your family from all types of poisons.
Availability: All requesters
Suggested Grade: All ages
Order Number: not applicable
Format: Web Site
Source: California Poison Control System
World Wide Web URL:
http://www.calpoison.org/public/home.html

Common Sense About Kids and Guns
This site offers common sense solutions for reducing gun-related injuries and deaths to children and teens.
Availability: All requesters
Suggested Grade: All ages
Order Number: not applicable
Format: Web Site
Source: Common Sense About Kids and Guns
World Wide Web URL: http://www.kidsandguns.org/

First Aid
Find out how to react in an emergency.
Availability: All requesters
Suggested Grade: 5-Adult
Order Number: not applicable
Format: Online Course
Source: BBC Learning
World Wide Web URL:
http://www.bbc.co.uk/health/first_aid_action/

For Kids Sake, Think Toy Safety
Explains why, and how, to make sure a child's toys are not hazardous to them.
Availability: Limit of 50 copies to schools, libraries, and homeschoolers in the United States and Canada. May be copied.
Suggested Grade: Adult
Languages: English; Spanish
Order Number: English 281; Spanish 281S
Format: Sheet of Paper
Special Notes: May also be downloaded from the web site.
Source: U. S. Consumer Product Safety Commission
Order by email or web site
World Wide Web URL: http://www.cpsc.gov
Email Address: info@cpsc.gov

High School Safety Web Pages
Here are several articles on safe procedures to follow in the high school chemistry laboratory.
Availability: All requesters
Suggested Grade: 9-Adult
Order Number: not applicable
Format: Online Articles
Source: Department of Chemistry, University of Nebraska-Lincoln
World Wide Web URL:
http://www.chem.unl.edu/safety/hslabcon.html

Know the Rules Brochure
Describes four basic safety messages for teens.
Availability: Limit of 50 copies to schools, libraries, and homeschoolers world-wide.
Suggested Grade: 6-12
Languages: English; Spanish
Order Number: English 54; Spanish 61
Production Date: 1998
Format: Brochure
Special Notes: Additional copies are 10 cents each.
Source: National Center for Missing & Exploited Children
Administrative Services
Charles B. Wang International Children's Building
699 Prince Street
Alexandria, VA 22314-3175
Phone: 1-703-274-3900
Fax: 1-703-274-2200
World Wide Web URL: http://www.missingkids.com

Know the Rules Package
Presents in-depth safety messages for teens relating to a number of different situations.
Availability: One copy to schools, libraries, and homeschoolers world-wide.
Suggested Grade: 6-12
Order Number: 55
Production Date: 1998
Format: Booklet
Special Notes: Additional copies are $2.00 each.
Source: National Center for Missing & Exploited Children
Administrative Services
Charles B. Wang International Children's Building
699 Prince Street
Alexandria, VA 22314-3175
Phone: 1-703-274-3900
Fax: 1-703-274-2200
World Wide Web URL: http://www.missingkids.com

Ladders, Lifting and Falls

Students will learn how to properly use and ladder as well as how to lift properly to avoid injury.

Availability: All requesters
Suggested Grade: 6-Adult
Order Number: not applicable
Format: Online Lesson Plan

Source: Dawna L. Cyr and Steven B. Johnson
World Wide Web URL:
http://nasdonline.org/document/1032/d000826/ladders-lifting-and-falls.html

Operation Lifesaver Lesson Plans

Lessons plans for teaching railroad safety--reinforces the theme, "Stay Off! Stay Away! Stay Alive!"

Availability: All requesters
Suggested Grade: K-5; 6-8; 9-12
Order Number: not applicable
Format: Online Lesson Plans

Source: Operation Lifesaver, Inc.
World Wide Web URL: http://www.oli.org/

OSHA Fact Sheets

Lots of fact sheets pertaining to workplace safety.

Availability: All requesters
Suggested Grade: 6-Adult
Order Number: not applicable
Format: Downloadable Fact Sheets

Source: United States Department of Labor, OSHA
World Wide Web URL:
http://www.osha.gov/OshDoc/toc_fact.html

Plants That Poison

Indicates which plants are poisonous when ingested.

Availability: Single copies to schools, libraries, and homeschoolers in the United States and Canada. Send a stamped, self-addressed envelope for reply.
Suggested Grade: All ages
Order Number: order by title
Format: Brochure

Source: Bronson Methodist Hospital Pharmacy
Attn: Nancy
601 John Street, 56
Kalamazoo, MI 49007

Product Safety Publications

Here are a number of articles about accident prevention when using certain items.

Availability: All requesters
Suggested Grade: All ages
Order Number: not applicable
Format: Online Articles

Source: Consumer Product Safety Commission
World Wide Web URL:
http://www.cpsc.gov/cpscpub/pubs/pub_idx.html

Safety & Health Fact Sheets

Lots of fact sheets covering weather safety, driving safety, agricultural safety, and safety inside and outside the home.

Availability: All requesters
Suggested Grade: 4-Adult
Order Number: not applicable
Format: Downloadable Fact Sheets

Source: National Safety Council
World Wide Web URL:
http://www.nsc.org/news_resources/Resources/Pages/SafetyHealthFactsheets.aspx

Using a Case Study to Teach Preservice Educators to Plan Violence Prevention Programs

Details this concept for planning a violence prevention program.

Availability: All requesters
Suggested Grade: Teacher Reference
Order Number: not applicable
Format: Online Lesson Plan

Source: Brian F. Geiger
World Wide Web URL:
http://eduref.org/Virtual/Lessons/Health/Safety/SFY0015.html

Action Guide for Healthy Eating
Gives helpful hints to help you include more low fat, high-fiber foods in your diet.
Availability: All requesters
Suggested Grade: 4-Adult
Order Number: not applicable
Format: Online Article; 17 pages
Special Notes: Use the on-site search engine to easily find this title. You may request a printed copy mailed to you for a fee.
Source: Federal Citizen Information Center
World Wide Web URL: http://www.pueblo.gsa.gov/

Arielle's Recipe Archives
Here are more than 35,000 recipes from African and appetizers to vegetables and vegetarian.
Availability: All requesters
Suggested Grade: All ages
Order Number: not applicable
Format: Web Site
Source: Stephanie da Silva
World Wide Web URL: http://recipes2.alastra.com/

Aunt Edna's Kitchen
A web site that provides all sorts of information useful in teaching, and learning about, cooking skills and nutrition.
Availability: All requesters
Suggested Grade: 6-12
Order Number: not applicable
Format: Web Site
Source: Aunt Edna's Kitchen
World Wide Web URL: http://www.auntedna.com/

Beef Recipes
Here is a searchable archive of recipes using beef.
Availability: All requesters
Suggested Grade: 4-Adult
Order Number: not applicable
Format: Web Site
Source: Nebraska Beef Council
World Wide Web URL:
http://www.nebeef.org/recipe_search.asp

Cajun Recipes
Here are recipes for Cajun dishes, popular on the Gulf coast.
Availability: All requesters
Suggested Grade: All ages
Order Number: not applicable
Format: Web Site
Source: RecipeSource
World Wide Web URL: http://www.recipesource.com/

Canadian Recipes
Recipes for dishes commonly served in Canada.
Availability: All requesters
Suggested Grade: All ages
Order Number: not applicable
Format: Web Site
Source: RecipeSource
World Wide Web URL: http://www.recipesource.com/

Chesapeake Treasure
Recipes as well as nutritional information, fish safety tips, and handling guidelines.
Availability: Classroom quantities to schools, libraries, and homeschoolers in the United States and Canada.
Suggested Grade: 6-Adult
Order Number: order by title
Format: Leaflet
Source: Maryland Department of Agriculture
Seafood Marketing Program
50 Harry S. Truman Parkway
Annapolis, MD 21401
Phone: 1-410-841-5820
Fax: 1-410-841-5970
World Wide Web URL:
Email Address: eberlynl@mda.state.md.us

Chocolate Glossary
Defines the many terms that relate to that wonderful food--chocolate.
Availability: All requesters
Suggested Grade: 6-Adult
Order Number: not applicable
Format: Online Glossary
Source: ChocolateSource.com
World Wide Web URL:
http://www.chocolatesource.com/glossary/index.asp

Chow Down...Down Under
Recipes for preparing authentic Australian cuisine.
Availability: All requesters
Suggested Grade: All ages
Order Number: not applicable
Format: Web Site
Source: Linda
World Wide Web URL:
http://members.tripod.com/~damsel2_2/ChowDown.html

Closer Look at Phytochemicals, A
Explains what phytochemicals are (naturally occurring chemicals in plant-based foods), where they occur and why they help make plant-based foods such an important part of a healthy diet.
Availability: Limit of 1 copy to schools, libraries, and homeschoolers in the United States and Canada.
Suggested Grade: 10-Adult
Order Number: order by title
Format: Brochure
Special Notes: May also be downloaded from the web site.

Source: American Institute for Cancer Research
Publication Orders
1759 R Street, N. W.
Washington, DC 20009
Phone: 1-800-843-8114
Fax: 1-202-328-7226
World Wide Web URL: http://www.aicr.org
Email Address: aicrweb@aicr.org

Diabetes Recipes

Five tasty and easy-to-follow recipes for people with diabetes.

Availability: All requesters
Suggested Grade: 4-Adult
Languages: English; Spanish
Order Number: not applicable
Production Date: 2005
Format: Online Article; 5 pages
Special Notes: Use the on-site search engine to easily find this title. You may request a printed copy mailed to you for a fee.

Source: Federal Citizen Information Center
World Wide Web URL: http://www.pueblo.gsa.gov/

Dietary Guidelines for Americans

Discusses how to choose a diet that will taste good, be nutritious, and reduce chronic disease risks.

Availability: All requesters
Suggested Grade: 4-Adult
Order Number: not applicable
Production Date: 2000
Format: Online Article; 44 pages
Special Notes: Use the on-site search engine to easily find this title. You may request a printed copy mailed to you for a fee.

Source: Federal Citizen Information Center
World Wide Web URL: http://www.pueblo.gsa.gov/

Down Home Healthy Cookin'

Provides 12 recipes that are low-fat, high-fiber versions of traditional favorites of black Americans.

Availability: Limit of 20 copies TOTAL, in any combination, to schools, libraries, homeschoolers and others world-wide.
Suggested Grade: 6-Adult
Order Number: P886
Production Date: 2010
Format: Booklet
Special Notes: May also be downloaded from the web site.

Source: National Cancer Institute
Publications Ordering Service
P. O. Box 24128
Baltimore, MD 21227
Phone: 1-800-4-CANCER
Fax: 1-301-330-7968
World Wide Web URL: http://cancer.gov/publications

Dried Plum and Prune Recipes

lots of recipes using plums and prunes.

Availability: All requesters
Suggested Grade: 4-Adult
Order Number: not applicable
Format: Online Recipes

Source: California Dried Plum Board
World Wide Web URL:
http://www.californiadriedplums.org/recipes

Durum Wheat Sample

A small bag of durum wheat with an information card.

Availability: Single copies to schools, libraries, and homeschoolers in the United States.
Suggested Grade: 2-12
Order Number: order by title
Format: Sample of Wheat

Source: North Dakota Wheat Commission
2401 46th Avenue SE, Suite 104
Mandan, ND 58554-4829
Phone: 1-701-328-5111
Fax: 1-701-663-5787
World Wide Web URL: http://www.ndwheat.com
Email Address: ndwheat@ndwheat.com

Dutch Recipes

Recipes commonly prepared by the Dutch peoples.

Availability: All requesters
Suggested Grade: All ages
Order Number: not applicable
Format: Web Site

Source: RecipeSource
World Wide Web URL: http://www.recipesource.com/

Easy French Food

French recipes and cultural information.

Availability: All requesters
Suggested Grade: 6-Adult
Order Number: not applicable
Format: Web Site

Source: Easy French Food
World Wide Web URL: http://www.easy-french-food.com/

Ethnic Dishes

Recipes for dishes ranging from Ancient Rome to Australia and France.

Availability: All requesters
Suggested Grade: All ages
Order Number: not applicable
Format: Web Site

Source: Michael Witbrock
World Wide Web URL:
http://www-2.cs.cmu.edu/~mjw/recipes/ethnic/

Fabulous Fruits...Versatile Vegetables

Get tips on new ways to serve fruits and vegetables--you need 5 to 9 daily servings in your diet.

Availability: All requesters
Suggested Grade: 6-Adult
Order Number: not applicable

Production Date: 2003
Format: Online Article; 6 pages
Special Notes: Use the on-site search engine to easily find this title. You may request a printed copy mailed to you for a fee.

Source: Federal Citizen Information Center
World Wide Web URL: http://www.pueblo.gsa.gov/

Facts About Fats, The

Explains good fat versus bad fat in your diet and how knowing these can lower your risk for cancer.

Availability: Limit of 1 copy to schools, libraries, and homeschoolers in the United States and Canada.
Suggested Grade: 10-Adult
Order Number: order by title
Format: Brochure

Source: American Institute for Cancer Research
Publication Orders
1759 R Street, N. W.
Washington, DC 20009
Phone: 1-800-843-8114
Fax: 1-202-328-7226
World Wide Web URL: http://www.aicr.org
Email Address: aicrweb@aicr.org

Facts About Fiber, The

Explains why fiber is beneficial to your health and explains how to increase the amount of fiber in your diet.

Availability: Limit of 1 copy to schools, libraries, and homeschoolers in the United States and Canada.
Suggested Grade: 10-Adult
Order Number: order by title
Production Date: 2005
Format: Brochure
Special Notes: May also be downloaded from the web site.

Source: American Institute for Cancer Research
Publication Orders
1759 R Street, N. W.
Washington, DC 20009
Phone: 1-800-843-8114
Fax: 1-202-328-7226
World Wide Web URL: http://www.aicr.org
Email Address: aicrweb@aicr.org

Fight BAC!: Four Simple Steps to Food Safety

Gives advice on how to handle food safely to avoid bacteria.

Availability: All requesters
Suggested Grade: 4-Adult
Order Number: not applicable
Production Date: 1998
Format: Online Article; 5 pages
Special Notes: Use the on-site search engine to easily find this title. You may request a printed copy mailed to you for a fee.

Source: Federal Citizen Information Center
World Wide Web URL: http://www.pueblo.gsa.gov/

Food Guide Pyramid

This easy guide can help you select the nutrients you need (without too many calories) and reduce the fat, cholesterol, sugar, sodium, or alcohol in your diet.

Availability: All requesters
Suggested Grade: 4-Adult
Order Number: not applicable
Production Date: 1996
Format: Online Article; 29 pages
Special Notes: Use the on-site search engine to easily find this title. You may request a printed copy mailed to you for a fee.

Source: Federal Citizen Information Center
World Wide Web URL: http://www.pueblo.gsa.gov/

Food Safety at Home

Explains the four easy ways to keep food from spoiling.

Availability: All requesters
Suggested Grade: 7-Adult
Order Number: not applicable
Format: Online Article; 2 pages
Special Notes: Use the on-site search engine to easily find this title. You may request a printed copy mailed to you for a fee.

Source: Federal Citizen Information Center
World Wide Web URL: http://www.pueblo.gsa.gov/

Food Safety Fact Sheets

Fact sheets on safe food handling and more.

Availability: All requesters
Suggested Grade: 4-12
Order Number: not applicable
Format: Downloadable Fact Sheets

Source: U. S. Department of Agriculture, Food Safety and Inspection Service
World Wide Web URL: http://www.fsis.usda.gov/factsheets/

Free Gourmet Recipes

A selection of recipes which taste gourmet but are easy to prepare.

Availability: All requesters
Suggested Grade: All ages
Order Number: not applicable
Format: Web Site

Source: Free-Gourmet-Recipes.com
World Wide Web URL:
http://www.free-gourmet-recipes.com

French Cheese

Learn about French cheese--there are more than 400 types,

Availability: All requesters
Suggested Grade: 6-12
Order Number: not applicable
Format: Online Article

Source: Franceway.com
World Wide Web URL:
http://www.franceway.com/cheese/intro.htm

French Food and Cook
French menus and recipes as well as tips and tools.
Availability: All requesters
Suggested Grade: 6-Adult
Order Number: not applicable
Format: Web Site
Source: French Food and Cook
World Wide Web URL: http://www.ffcook.com/

Guide to Healthy Dining Out
Shows you how to make healthy choices in restaurants by understanding how to order, and by having a clearer idea of which foods represent the healthier choices.
Availability: Limit of 1 copy to schools, libraries, and homeschoolers in the United States and Canada.
Suggested Grade: 5-Adult
Order Number: order by title
Format: Brochure
Special Notes: May also be downloaded from the web site.
Source: American Institute for Cancer Research
Publication Orders
1759 R Street, N. W.
Washington, DC 20009
Phone: 1-800-843-8114
Fax: 1-202-328-7226
World Wide Web URL: http://www.aicr.org
Email Address: aicrweb@aicr.org

Hard Red Spring Wheat Sample
A small bag of hard red spring wheat with an information card.
Availability: Single copies to schools, libraries, and homeschoolers in the United States.
Suggested Grade: 2-12
Order Number: order by title
Format: Sample of Wheat
Source: North Dakota Wheat Commission
2401 46th Avenue SE, Suite 104
Mandan, ND 58554-4829
Phone: 1-701-328-5111
Fax: 1-701-663-5787
World Wide Web URL: http://www.ndwheat.com
Email Address: ndwheat@ndwheat.com

Heart Healthy Eating Tips
Shows how to follow a vegetarian diet--which is ideal for your heart.
Availability: Classroom quantities to schools, libraries, and homeschoolers world-wide. Send a stamped, self-addressed envelope for reply.
Suggested Grade: 6-Adult
Languages: English; Spanish
Order Number: order by title
Format: Brochure
Source: Vegetarian Resource Group, The
P. O. Box 1463
Baltimore, MD 21203
Phone: 1-410-366-8343
Fax: 1-410-366-8804
World Wide Web URL: http://www.vrg.org
Email Address: vrg@vrg.org

Home Economics Lesson Plans
An assortment of different lesson plans for creating healthy, tasty foods.
Availability: All requesters
Suggested Grade: 6-Adult
Order Number: not applicable
Format: Online Lesson Plans
Source: Clabber Girl
World Wide Web URL:
http://www.clabbergirl.com/consumer/baking_fun/lesson_plans/

Jewish Recipes
Recipes that are enjoyed by this group of people.
Availability: All requesters
Suggested Grade: All ages
Order Number: not applicable
Format: Web Site
Source: RecipeSource
World Wide Web URL: http://www.recipesource.com/

Keep Your Food Safe
Provides tips on the safe handling, cooking and storage of food in order to avoid food-borne illness.
Availability: All requesters
Suggested Grade: 4-Adult
Order Number: not applicable
Format: Online Article; 20 pages
Special Notes: Use the on-site search engine to easily find this title. You may request a printed copy mailed to you for a fee.
Source: Federal Citizen Information Center
World Wide Web URL: http://www.pueblo.gsa.gov/

Kidnetic.com
Designed to help kids tap into their own energy through good nutrition and regular physical activity, this fun site presents activities and ideas.
Availability: All requesters
Suggested Grade: All ages
Order Number: not applicable
Format: Web Site
Source: International Food Information Council Foundation
World Wide Web URL: http://www.kidnetic.com/

Lessons and Activities
Lots of activities for students about health and nutrition.
Availability: All requesters
Suggested Grade: 5-12
Order Number: not applicable
Format: Online Activities
Source: New England Dairy & Food Council
World Wide Web URL:
http://www.newenglanddairycouncil.org/page/educators

Maryland Seafood--Aquaculture
Recipes for bass, tilapia, crayfish, trout, and catfish.
Availability: Classroom quantities to schools, libraries, and homeschoolers in the United States and Canada.
Suggested Grade: 6-Adult
Order Number: order by title
Format: Leaflet

Source: Maryland Department of Agriculture
Seafood Marketing Program
50 Harry S. Truman Parkway
Annapolis, MD 21401
Phone: 1-410-841-5820
Fax: 1-410-841-5970
Email Address: eberlynl@mda.state.md.us

Maryland Seafood--Clams
A variety of recipes using clams.
Availability: Classroom quantities to schools, libraries, and homeschoolers in the United States and Canada.
Suggested Grade: 6-Adult
Order Number: order by title
Format: Leaflet

Source: Maryland Department of Agriculture
Seafood Marketing Program
50 Harry S. Truman Parkway
Annapolis, MD 21401
Phone: 1-410-841-5820
Fax: 1-410-841-5970
Email Address: eberlynl@mda.state.md.us

Maryland Seafood--Cuisine
Several recipes for preparing oyster and crab appetizers.
Availability: Classroom quantities to schools, libraries, and homeschoolers in the United States and Canada.
Suggested Grade: 6-Adult
Order Number: order by title
Format: Leaflet

Source: Maryland Department of Agriculture
Seafood Marketing Program
50 Harry S. Truman Parkway
Annapolis, MD 21401
Phone: 1-410-841-5820
Fax: 1-410-841-5970
Email Address: eberlynl@mda.state.md.us

Maryland Seafood--Finfish
Several recipes for various finfish including monkfish, bluefish, flounder, and sea trout.
Availability: Classroom quantities to schools, libraries, and homeschoolers in the United States and Canada.
Suggested Grade: 6-Adult
Order Number: order by title
Format: Leaflet

Source: Maryland Department of Agriculture
Seafood Marketing Program
50 Harry S. Truman Parkway
Annapolis, MD 21401
Phone: 1-410-841-5820
Fax: 1-410-841-5970
Email Address: eberlynl@mda.state.md.us

Native American Recipes
Students experience a taste of Native American foods. Students prepare some foods, including journey cake (a kind of corn bread), that are popular in some Native American cultures.
Availability: All requesters
Suggested Grade: All ages
Order Number: not applicable
Format: Online Lesson Plan

Source: Lois Lewis
World Wide Web URL:
http://www.educationworld.com/a_lesson/00-2/lp2211.shtml

New American Plate for Breakfast, The
Describes what a healthful breakfast should supply and why it is so important to have one. Includes recipes.
Availability: Limit of 1 copy to schools, libraries, and homeschoolers in the United States and Canada.
Suggested Grade: 10-Adult
Order Number: order by title
Format: Booklet
Special Notes: May also be downloaded from the web site.

Source: American Institute for Cancer Research
Publication Orders
1759 R Street, N. W.
Washington, DC 20009
Phone: 1-800-843-8114
Fax: 1-202-328-7226
World Wide Web URL: http://www.aicr.org
Email Address: aicrweb@aicr.org

New American Plate, The--One-Pot Meals
Explains how to reshape your diet to prevent cancer and maintain a healthy weight--with simple to prepare recipes that involve only one pot!
Availability: Limit of 1 copy to schools, libraries, and homeschoolers in the United States and Canada.
Suggested Grade: 10-Adult
Order Number: order by title
Format: Booklet
Special Notes: May also be downloaded from the web site.

Source: American Institute for Cancer Research
Publication Orders
1759 R Street, N. W.
Washington, DC 20009
Phone: 1-800-843-8114
Fax: 1-202-328-7226
World Wide Web URL: http://www.aicr.org
Email Address: aicrweb@aicr.org

New American Plate, The--Veggies
Information about the health benefits of vegetables as well as tips on how to select, store, and prepare them. Includes recipes.
Availability: Limit of 1 copy to schools, libraries, and homeschoolers in the United States and Canada.
Suggested Grade: 10-Adult
Order Number: order by title
Format: Booklet
Special Notes: May also be downloaded from the web site.
Source: American Institute for Cancer Research
Publication Orders
1759 R Street, N. W.
Washington, DC 20009
Phone: 1-800-843-8114
Fax: 1-202-328-7226
World Wide Web URL: http://www.aicr.org
Email Address: aicrweb@aicr.org

Nutrition After Fifty
Tips and recipes for staying fit and healthy after reaching this milestone.
Availability: Limit of 1 copy to schools, libraries, and homeschoolers in the United States and Canada.
Suggested Grade: Adult
Order Number: order by title
Format: Booklet
Special Notes: May also be downloaded from the web site.
Source: American Institute for Cancer Research
Publication Orders
1759 R Street, N. W.
Washington, DC 20009
Phone: 1-800-843-8114
Fax: 1-202-328-7226
World Wide Web URL: http://www.aicr.org
Email Address: aicrweb@aicr.org

Nutrition Guide for Teenage Vegetarians, A
Addresses how nutrition needs of teenagers can be met with a vegetarian diet.
Availability: Classroom quantities to schools, libraries, and homeschoolers world-wide. Send a stamped, self-addressed envelope for reply.
Suggested Grade: 6-12
Languages: English; Spanish
Order Number: order by title
Format: Brochure
Source: Vegetarian Resource Group, The
P. O. Box 1463
Baltimore, MD 21203
Phone: 1-410-366-8343
Fax: 1-410-366-8804
World Wide Web URL: http://www.vrg.org
Email Address: vrg@vrg.org

Peruvian Recipes
Recipes from Peru.
Availability: All requesters
Suggested Grade: All ages
Order Number: not applicable
Format: Web Site
Source: RecipeSource
World Wide Web URL: http://www.recipesource.com/

Pesticides and Food: What You and Your Family Need to Know
Information about the levels of exposure to pesticides in food which can cause health problems.
Availability: All requesters
Suggested Grade: 4-Adult
Order Number: not applicable
Format: Online Article; 4 pages
Special Notes: Use the on-site search engine to easily find this title. You may request a printed copy mailed to you for a fee.
Source: Federal Citizen Information Center
World Wide Web URL: http://www.pueblo.gsa.gov/

Pizza Explorer, The
Learn more about food chemistry, food processing, nutrition, and the health benefits of this food favorite.
Availability: All requesters
Suggested Grade: 6-12
Order Number: not applicable
Format: Web Site
Source: Purdue Research Foundation
World Wide Web URL:
http://www.omega3learning.purdue.edu/learning/activities/pizzaexplorer/

Produce Oasis
Just click on a letter of the alphabet and find out about nutrition information for the produce that begins with that letter.
Availability: All requesters
Suggested Grade: 4-12
Order Number: not applicable
Format: Web Site
Source: Produce Oasis
World Wide Web URL:
http://www.produceoasis.com/Alpha_Folder/Alpha.html

Recipe Archive Index
An enormous collection of recipes--from appetizers to vegetable recipes.
Availability: All requesters
Suggested Grade: All ages
Order Number: not applicable
Format: Web Site
Source: Michael Witbrock
World Wide Web URL:
http://www-2.cs.cmu.edu/~mjw/recipes/

Recipe Book Online.com
Lots of recipes and a feature that allows you to submit your

own.
Availability: All requesters
Suggested Grade: 4-Adult
Order Number: not applicable
Format: Web Site

Source: Recipe Book Online.com
World Wide Web URL: http://www.recipebookonline.com/

Recipe Cottage

Over 35,000 recipes can be found here.
Availability: All requesters
Suggested Grade: All ages
Order Number: not applicable
Format: Web Site
Special Notes: Not updated recently, but, of course, recipes are timeless.

Source: Recipe Cottage
World Wide Web URL: http://www.recipecottage.com/

Recipe Dude, The

Not only will you find recipes here, but you will also find a dedicated search engine that will try to find the recipe you're looking for from other web sites.
Availability: All requesters
Suggested Grade: All ages
Order Number: not applicable
Format: Web Site

Source: Recipe Dude, The
World Wide Web URL: http://www.recipedude.com/

Recipe E-Book--Volume I--Beef

A complete downloadable recipe book that runs on your computer.
Availability: All requesters
Suggested Grade: 6-Adult
Platform: Windows
Order Number: not applicable
Format: Downloadable FULL PROGRAM

Source: All Family Resources
World Wide Web URL:
http://www.familymanagement.com/recipe.download.html

RecipeLand.com

More recipes than you can possibly make or consume.
Availability: All requesters
Suggested Grade: All ages
Order Number: not applicable
Format: Web Site

Source: Sean Wenzel
World Wide Web URL: http://www.recipeland.com/

Sports and Nutrition: The Winning Connection

Explores the relationship between sports and exercise and the food you need to supply the energy needed.
Availability: All requesters
Suggested Grade: 6-Adult
Order Number: not applicable
Format: Web Site

Source: University of Illinois Extension Urban Programs Resource Network
World Wide Web URL:
http://www.urbanext.uiuc.edu/hsnut/index.html

Stay Young at Heart Recipes

A multitude of recipes for preparing delicious foods low in cholesterol.
Availability: One copy is free to schools, libraries, and homeschoolers world-wide. Shipping charges will apply if more than one publication is requested.
Suggested Grade: 4-12
Order Number: 55-648
Format: Booklet
Special Notes: May also be downloaded from the web site.

Source: National Heart, Lung, and Blood Institute Information Center
P. O. Box 30105
Bethesda, MD 20824-0105
Phone: 1-301-592-8573
Fax: 1-240-629-3246
World Wide Web URL: http://www.nhlbi.nih.gov/
Email Address: nhlbiinfo@nhlbi.nih.gov

Swiss Recipes

Recipes enjoyed by the people in Switzerland.
Availability: All requesters
Suggested Grade: All ages
Order Number: not applicable
Format: Web Site

Source: RecipeSource
World Wide Web URL: http://www.recipesource.com/

Teens Health, Food & Fitness

Lots of articles about eating, dieting, strength training, and more, specifically targeted to teens.
Availability: All requesters
Suggested Grade: 7-12
Order Number: not applicable
Format: Online Articles

Source: Nemours Foundation, The
World Wide Web URL:
http://teenshealth.org/teen/food_fitness/

Tibetan Recipes

Recipes from Tibet.
Availability: All requesters
Suggested Grade: All ages
Order Number: not applicable
Format: Web Site

Source: RecipeSource
World Wide Web URL: http://www.recipesource.com/

Turkish Recipes

A selection of recipes popular in this country.
Availability: All requesters
Suggested Grade: All ages

Order Number: not applicable
Format: Web Site
Source: RecipeSource
World Wide Web URL: http://www.recipesource.com/

Using the Dietary Guidelines for Americans
How to choose a diet that tastes good, is nutritious, and will reduce chronic disease risks.
Availability: All requesters
Suggested Grade: 6-Adult
Order Number: not applicable
Format: Online Article; 2 pages
Special Notes: Use the on-site search engine to easily find this title. You may request a printed copy mailed to you for a fee.
Source: Federal Citizen Information Center
World Wide Web URL: http://www.pueblo.gsa.gov/

After a Disaster: Repairing Your Home

It's unfortunate when disaster hits--but here are some tips to help you make your home more energy efficient when rebuilding.

Availability: Limit of 49 copies to schools, libraries, and homeschoolers world-wide.
Suggested Grade: 6-Adult
Order Number: order by title
Format: Brochure
Special Notes: May also be downloaded from the Web site. Quantities in excess of 50 are available from Federal Trade Commission, Distribution Office, 600 Pennsylvania Avenue, NW, Washington, D. C. 20580-0001 or fax to: 1-703-739-0991.

Source: Federal Trade Commission
Consumer Response Center
600 Pennsylvania, N. W., Room H-130
Washington, DC 20580
World Wide Web URL:
http://www.ftc.gov/bcp/consumer.shtm

Before Disaster Strikes

Suggests ways to be financially prepared to deal with a natural disaster.

Availability: All requesters
Suggested Grade: 9-Adult
Order Number: not applicable
Production Date: 1997
Format: Online Article; 8 pages
Special Notes: Use the on-site search engine to easily find this title. You may request a printed copy mailed to you for a fee.

Source: Federal Citizen Information Center
World Wide Web URL: http://www.pueblo.gsa.gov/

Budgeting for Home Ownership

Walks you through the budgeting process.

Availability: All requesters
Suggested Grade: 6-Adult
Order Number: not applicable
Format: Online Article
Special Notes: This is a PDF file which will automatically open on your computer.

Source: North Carolina Cooperative Extension Service
World Wide Web URL:
http://www.ces.ncsu.edu/depts/fcs/pdfs/fcs432.pdf

Child Care Consumer Education on the Internet

Discusses how consumer educators can use the Internet to help families find high-quality child care.

Availability: All requesters
Suggested Grade: Teacher Reference
Order Number: not applicable
Production Date: 1998
Format: Online Article

Source: Anne Goldstein
World Wide Web URL:
http://www.ericdigests.org/1999-3/care.htm

Choosing the Best Mortgage

Explains the variety of home mortgages available and tells how to pick the best one for your needs.

Availability: All requesters
Suggested Grade: 6-Adult
Order Number: not applicable
Format: Online Article
Special Notes: This is a PDF file which will open automatically on your computer.

Source: North Carolina Cooperative Extension Service
World Wide Web URL:
http://www.ces.ncsu.edu/depts/fcs/pdfs/fcs437.pdf

Creating Holiday Fun for Children

Students in child care class will gather resources that will help families and caregivers ideas on celebrating or establishing traditions for different holidays.

Availability: All requesters
Suggested Grade: 9-12
Order Number: not applicable
Format: Online Lesson Plan

Source: Christine Miller
World Wide Web URL: http://www.lessonplanspage.com/OMDSSHolidayFunForKids912.htm

Creative Homemaking E-Books

Recipe books, decorating books, craft books, and more all to be downloaded on your computer.

Availability: All requesters
Suggested Grade: 4-Adult
Order Number: not applicable
Format: Downloadable Books

Source: Creative Homemaking, LLC
World Wide Web URL:
http://www.creativehomemaking.com/download.shtml

Energy Guide to Home Heating & Cooling

Indicates how much energy the heating and cooling of your home consumes.

Availability: Limit of 49 copies to schools, libraries, and homeschoolers world-wide.
Suggested Grade: 6-Adult
Order Number: order by title
Format: Brochure
Special Notes: May also be downloaded from the Web site. Quantities in excess of 50 are available from Federal Trade Commission, Distribution Office, 600 Pennsylvania Avenue, NW, Washington, D. C. 20580-0001 or fax to: 1-703-739-0991.

Source: Federal Trade Commission
Consumer Response Center
600 Pennsylvania, N. W., Room H-130
Washington, DC 20580
World Wide Web URL:
http://www.ftc.gov/bcp/consumer.shtm

Energy Savers: Tips on Saving Energy & Money at Home
A practical guide on reducing your home energy use, with tips on insulation, weatherization, heating, and more.
Availability: All requesters
Suggested Grade: 4-Adult
Order Number: not applicable
Production Date: 1998
Format: Online Article; 36 pages
Special Notes: Use the on-site search engine to easily find this title. You may request a printed copy mailed to you for a fee.
Source: Federal Citizen Information Center
World Wide Web URL: http://www.pueblo.gsa.gov/

Firearms Responsibility in the Home
Explains the responsibilities all firearms users must accept when they bring a gun into the home.
Availability: Limit of 100 copies to schools, libraries, and homeschoolers in the United States and Canada. Make request on official stationery.
Suggested Grade: 6-Adult
Order Number: 080
Format: Leaflet
Source: National Shooting Sports Foundation
Council for Wildlife Conservation and Education
11 Mile Hill Road
Newtown, CT 06470-2359
Phone: 1-203-426-1320
Fax: 1-203-426-1245
World Wide Web URL: http://www.nssf.org
Email Address: literature@nssf.org

Fun Play, Safe Play
Teaches the importance of play and explains how to buy safe toys.
Availability: All requesters
Suggested Grade: 4-Adult
Order Number: not applicable
Production Date: 2004
Format: Online Article; 18 pages
Special Notes: Use the on-site search engine to easily find this title. You may request a printed copy mailed to you for a fee.
Source: Federal Citizen Information Center
World Wide Web URL: http://www.pueblo.gsa.gov/

Help Yourself to a Healthy Home: Protect Your Children's Health
Find out about potentially harmful products in your home and follow the easy action steps to keep your house healthy.
Availability: All requesters
Suggested Grade: 4-Adult
Order Number: not applicable
Format: Online Article; 24 pages
Special Notes: Use the on-site search engine to easily find this title. You may request a printed copy mailed to you for a fee.
Source: Federal Citizen Information Center
World Wide Web URL: http://www.pueblo.gsa.gov/

Homeowner's Glossary of Building Terms
Designed to help you keep up with the terms of this trade.
Availability: All requesters
Suggested Grade: 6-Adult
Order Number: not applicable
Format: Online Article; 12 pages
Special Notes: Use the on-site search engine to easily find this title. You may request a printed copy mailed to you for a fee.
Source: Federal Citizen Information Center
World Wide Web URL: http://www.pueblo.gsa.gov/

Just in Case...You Need A Babysitter
Includes information on finding a babysitter and safety tips.
Availability: Limit of 50 copies to schools, libraries, and homeschoolers world-wide.
Suggested Grade: 10-Adult
Languages: English; Spanish
Order Number: English 12; Spanish 14
Production Date: 1986
Format: Brochure
Special Notes: Additional copies are 10 cents each.
Source: National Center for Missing & Exploited Children
Administrative Services
Charles B. Wang International Children's Building
699 Prince Street
Alexandria, VA 22314-3175
Phone: 1-703-274-3900
Fax: 1-703-274-2200
World Wide Web URL: http://www.missingkids.com

Mortgage Loans
Designed to assist you in identifying the terms of a mortgage loan, and provides much more information of vital importance in today's economy.
Availability: Limit of 30 copies to to schools, libraries, and homeschoolers.
Suggested Grade: 6-Adult
Order Number: order by title
Format: Booklet
Special Notes: May also be downloaded from the web site.
Source: AFSA Education Foundation
919 18th Street, N. W., 3rd Floor
Washington, DC 20006
Phone: 1-202-466-8611
Fax: 1-202-223-0321
World Wide Web URL:
www.afsaef.orghttp://www.afsaef.org
Email Address: susie@afsamail.org

100 Questions and Answers About Buying a New Home
Focuses on finances.
Availability: All requesters
Suggested Grade: 6-Adult
Order Number: not applicable
Production Date: 2005

Format: Downloadable Booklet; 40 pages
Special Notes: Use the on-site search engine to easily find this title. You may request a printed copy mailed to you for a fee.

Source: Federal Citizen Information Center
World Wide Web URL: http://www.pueblo.gsa.gov/

Renting Your First Apartment

You have finally graduated and landed your first job. Now you want to move out of your parent's house and get a place of your own. This project will help you organize all of the information needed to make a wise decision.

Availability: All requesters
Suggested Grade: 11-12
Order Number: not applicable
Format: WebQuest

Source: Catrina Eddington
World Wide Web URL:
http://www.yorkville.k12.il.us/webquests/webqeddington/webqseddington.html

ABCs of the Writing Process, The
Information to help students and teachers through each step of the writing process.
Availability: All requesters
Suggested Grade: K-12
Order Number: not applicable
Format: Web Site
Source: A. E. Lipkewich and R. S. Mazurenko
World Wide Web URL:
http://www.angelfire.com/wi/writingprocess/

African American Women Writers of the 19th Century
Presents over 50 published works by black women writers.
Availability: All requesters
Suggested Grade: All ages
Order Number: not applicable
Format: Downloadable Books
Source: New York Public Library
World Wide Web URL:
http://digital.nypl.org/schomburg/writers_aa19

Alex Catalogue of Electronic Texts
A collection of public domain documents from American and English literature as well as Western philosophy.
Availability: All requesters
Suggested Grade: 6-Adult
Order Number: not applicable
Format: Downloadable Texts
Source: Eric Lease Morgan
World Wide Web URL: http://www.infomotions.com/alex/

Anagram Genius Server
Type in any word, or combination of words, and you will get lots of anagrams in return. Be careful, however, some words may not be to your liking.
Availability: All requesters
Suggested Grade: All ages
Order Number: not applicable
Format: Web Site
Source: Anagram Genius Server
World Wide Web URL:
http://www.anagramgenius.com/server.html

Approach to Current Events, An
Students will develop critical thinking skills.
Availability: All requesters
Suggested Grade: 5-12
Order Number: not applicable
Format: Online Lesson Plan
Source: Connie Hudgeons
World Wide Web URL:
http://www.col-ed.org/cur/sst/sst49.txt

AskOxford.com
Includes searchable access to the Compact Oxford English Dictionary plus many other resources for writers and students.
Availability: All requesters
Suggested Grade: 9-Adult
Order Number: not applicable
Format: Online Glossary
Source: Oxford University Press
World Wide Web URL: http://www.askoxford.com/

Battle Bars
Students will be able to develop a thesis statement and two paragraphs which support that statement after performing this activity involving candy bars.
Availability: All requesters
Suggested Grade: 9-12
Order Number: not applicable
Format: Online Lesson Plan
Source: Mark A. Schneberger
World Wide Web URL:
http://www.buildingrainbows.com/CA/lesson/lessonid/1069811011

Big Dog's Grammar: A Bare Bones Guide to English
Basic grammar lessons along with interactive exercises.
Availability: All requesters
Suggested Grade: 9-12
Order Number: not applicable
Format: Online Lessons
Source: Scott Foll
World Wide Web URL: http://www.aliscot.com/bigdog/

BookTalks--Quick and Simple
Features information on over 600 books--listings include the title, author, and a brief description of the story.
Availability: All requesters
Suggested Grade: Teacher Reference
Order Number: not applicable
Format: Web Site
Source: Nancy J. Keane
World Wide Web URL: http://nancykeane.com/booktalks/

Buber's Basque Page
Lessons to help you learn this language.
Availability: All requesters
Suggested Grade: All ages
Order Number: not applicable
Format: Web Site
Source: Blas Uberuaga
World Wide Web URL: http://www.buber.net/Basque/

Children's Storybooks Online--Older Children
Two stories for young adults.
Availability: All requesters
Suggested Grade: 7-9
Order Number: not applicable
Format: Online Books
Source: Carol Moore
World Wide Web URL:
http://www.magickeys.com/books/index.html

Children's Storybooks Online--Young Adults
A good selection of short, illustrated stories and parables.
Availability: All requesters
Suggested Grade: 6-9
Order Number: not applicable
Format: Online Books
Source: Carol Moore
World Wide Web URL:
http://www.magickeys.com/books/index.html

Class Directory
Students will write stories about each other to "break the ice."
Availability: All requesters
Suggested Grade: 7-12
Order Number: not applicable
Format: Online Lesson Plan
Source: Jan Riley
World Wide Web URL:
http://youth.net/cec/ceclang/ceclang.36.txt

Common Errors in English
Includes a list of commonly misspelled words as well as phrases that are commonly misquoted.
Availability: All requesters
Suggested Grade: 5-9
Order Number: not applicable
Format: Web Site
Source: Paul Brian
World Wide Web URL:
http://www.wsu.edu/~brians/errors/errors.html

Creative Writing
Encourages students to be creative in their own writing, as well as being critical and analytical of another's.
Availability: All requesters
Suggested Grade: 1-12
Order Number: not applicable
Format: Online Lesson Plan
Source: Twila Chambers
World Wide Web URL:
http://youth.net/cec/ceclang/ceclang.03.txt

Culture of Spain
Students will learn more about Spanish culture.
Availability: All requesters
Suggested Grade: 10-12
Order Number: not applicable
Format: WebQuests
Source: Becky Walleen and Andrea Roberds
World Wide Web URL:
http://www.clta.net/lessons/spanish/level3/cultura.html

Deutsch Plus
A dynamic introduction to German taking you through the basics of the language.
Availability: All requesters
Suggested Grade: 7-12
Order Number: not applicable
Format: Online Course
Source: BBC Learning
World Wide Web URL:
http://www.bbc.co.uk/languages/german/dplus/

Dickinson Electronic Archives
Information and primary documents concerning Emily Dickinson.
Availability: All requesters
Suggested Grade: 6-12
Order Number: not applicable
Format: Web Site
Source: Martha Nell Smith
World Wide Web URL: http://www.emilydickinson.org/

English Lessons and Tests
Receive English lessons by email at three levels every week.
Availability: All requesters
Suggested Grade: All ages
Order Number: not applicable
Format: Email Lessons
Source: Elek Mathe
World Wide Web URL: http://www.englishlearner.com/

Euphemisms
A lesson on learning about synonyms.
Availability: All requesters
Suggested Grade: 7-9
Order Number: not applicable
Format: Online Lesson Plan
Source: Meredith Ford
World Wide Web URL:
http://youth.net/cec/ceclang/ceclang.26.txt

Family Feud
An enjoyable way to review specific material before a test--in this case "Romeo and Juliet."
Availability: All requesters
Suggested Grade: 9
Order Number: not applicable
Format: Online Lesson Plan
Source: Linda Kramer
World Wide Web URL:
http://www.col-ed.org/cur/lang/lang94.txt

Foreign Language for Travelers
Find the translation of common words used by travelers in virtually every language.
Availability: All requesters
Suggested Grade: 6-12
Order Number: not applicable
Format: Online Glossary
Source: Michael C. Martin
World Wide Web URL:
http://www.travlang.com/languages/

Four Corners Series Sample Book
A sample book from this second grade level book series is available.
Availability: One copy to professional staff of schools, libraries, and homeschoolers in the United States. Make request on official stationery.
Suggested Grade: 5-Adult
Order Number: order by title
Format: Book
Special Notes: Second grade readability
Source: High Noon Books
Attn: Customer Services
20 Commercial Boulevard
Novato, CA 94949-6191
Phone: 1-800-422-7249
Fax: 1-888-287-9975
World Wide Web URL: http://www.highnoonbooks.com
Email Address: mailatp@aol.com

French Experience, The
A series of multimedia activities for beginners.
Availability: All requesters
Suggested Grade: 3-12
Order Number: not applicable
Format: Online Course
Source: BBC Learning
World Wide Web URL:
http://www.bbc.co.uk/languages/french/experience/

French Revision
Many activities and lessons in French.
Availability: All requesters
Suggested Grade: All ages
Order Number: not applicable
Format: Online Language Lessons
Source: B. Dyer
World Wide Web URL: http://www.frenchrevision.co.uk/

French Tutorial, The
A very complete tutorial on the French language and the French way of life.
Availability: All requesters
Suggested Grade: 3-12
Order Number: not applicable
Format: Online Language Tutorial
Source: Herve Foucher
World Wide Web URL: http://www.frenchtutorial.com/

GrammarCheck
An email newsletter that will help you improve your writing and grammar skills.
Availability: All requesters
Suggested Grade: 9-Adult
Order Number: not applicable
Format: Email Newsletter
Source: GrammarCheck
World Wide Web URL: http://www.grammarcheck.com/

High School Journalism
More than 240 archived lesson plans on advertising, copy editing, editorial writing, and much more.
Availability: All requesters
Suggested Grade: 9-12
Order Number: not applicable
Format: Web Site
Source: American Society of Newspaper Editors
World Wide Web URL:
http://www.highschooljournalism.org/

History of the English Language, The
Young students learn about English.
Availability: All requesters
Suggested Grade: All ages
Order Number: not applicable
Format: Web Site
Special Notes: This URL will lead you to a subject page. Then click on the appropriate subject heading.
Source: ThinkQuest
World Wide Web URL:
http://www.thinkquest.org/pls/html/think.library

Huckleberry Finn
Presents the full text of this famous tale along with early reviews of the book and other information about the book printed 150 years ago.
Availability: All requesters
Suggested Grade: 5-12
Order Number: not applicable
Format: Web Site
Source: Virginia Cope
World Wide Web URL:
http://etext.lib.virginia.edu/twain/huckfinn.html

Indispensable Listening Skills
The purpose of this activity is to increase the students' ability to listen and understand what is being said.
Availability: All requesters
Suggested Grade: 9-12
Order Number: not applicable
Format: Online Lesson Plan
Source: Ann Douglas
World Wide Web URL:
http://youth.net/cec/ceclang/ceclang.21.txt

Inferring Character Traits
Students will learn how to identify character traits.
Availability: All requesters
Suggested Grade: All ages
Order Number: not applicable
Format: Online Lesson Plans
Source: Donna Calder
World Wide Web URL:
http://youth.net/cec/ceclang/ceclang.39.txt

Integrated Vocabulary, Creating Writing, and Listening Exercise
This lesson will increase students ability to write, listen, and increase their vocabulary bank.
Availability: All requesters
Suggested Grade: All ages
Order Number: not applicable
Format: Online Lesson Plan
Source: June Paganelli
World Wide Web URL:
http://youth.net/cec/ceclang/ceclang.19.txt

Interactive On-Line Reference Grammar, An
Lessons on the Russian language.
Availability: All requesters
Suggested Grade: 6-Adult
Order Number: not applicable
Format: Online Language Lessons
Source: Robert Beard
World Wide Web URL:
http://www.alphadictionary.com/rusgrammar/index.html

Interesting Things for ESL Students
Activities, games, and puzzles that provide lots of practice for ESL students.
Availability: All requesters
Suggested Grade: 3-12
Order Number: not applicable
Format: Web Site
Source: Charles I. Kelly and Lawrence E. Kelly
World Wide Web URL:
http://www.manythings.org/sitemap.html

Introduction to Russian, An
A tutorial designed as a beginning point for a casual learner of the Russian language.
Availability: All requesters
Suggested Grade: 3-Adult
Order Number: not applicable
Format: Online Tutorial
Source: J. David Eisenberg
World Wide Web URL:
http://www.langintro.com/rintro/index.htm

Italian Steps
Test your knowledge of Italian.
Availability: All requesters
Suggested Grade: 7-12
Order Number: not applicable
Format: Online Course
Source: BBC Learning
World Wide Web URL:
http://www.bbc.co.uk/languages/italian/lj/

Japanese Language
This site not only offers lessons in Japanese but provides links for obtaining pen pals in Japan and much more.
Availability: All requesters
Suggested Grade: 4-Adult
Order Number: not applicable
Format: Web Site
Source: Namiko Abe
World Wide Web URL: http://japanese.about.com/

Learn Spanish
An online tutorial for Spanish lessons.
Availability: All requesters
Suggested Grade: 6-Adult
Order Number: not applicable
Format: Online Spanish lessons
Source: Spanish Learning Resources
World Wide Web URL: http://www.studyspanish.com/

Let's Go Shopping
Involves observation, role playing, and more as students observe people at a shopping mall.
Availability: All requesters
Suggested Grade: 7-9
Order Number: not applicable
Format: Online Lesson Plan
Source: Gary Miller
World Wide Web URL:
http://youth.net/cec/ceclang/ceclang.02.txt

Like the Back of My Hand
Introduces students to writing for fun.
Availability: All requesters
Suggested Grade: 9-12
Order Number: not applicable
Format: Online Lesson Plan
Source: Barbara Howard
World Wide Web URL:
http://youth.net/cec/ceclang/ceclang.10.txt

Literature Review
Designed to help students review a literary work or unit before an exam.
Availability: All requesters
Suggested Grade: 10-12
Order Number: not applicable
Format: Online Lesson Plan
Source: Linda Burton
World Wide Web URL:
http://youth.net/cec/ceclang/ceclang.23.txt

Magic Tales of Mexico
A collection of folklore from the Texas-Mexican border featuring both English and Mexican translations of several tales passed down orally by family storytellers.
Availability: All requesters
Suggested Grade: All ages
Order Number: not applicable
Format: Downloadable Stories

Source: Gabriel A. Cordova, Jr.
World Wide Web URL:
http://www.g-world.org/magictales/magictales.shtml

Make Me!!!
You are expected to read several important persuasive documents that tie into the class work that you are currently doing in your Social Studies course and come up with a persuasive product that reflects a point of interest that will be presented to your class in a format that you think would be most effective.
Availability: All requesters
Suggested Grade: 9-12
Order Number: not applicable
Format: WebQuest
Source: Dale Griepenstroh
World Wide Web URL:
http://projects.edtech.sandi.net/miramesa/persuade/

Modern Haiku
Submit your own haikus or read those others have composed.
Availability: All requesters
Suggested Grade: 6-Adult
Order Number: not applicable
Format: Web Site
Source: Modern Haiku
World Wide Web URL: http://www.modernhaiku.org/

Moonlit Road, The
With new stories every month, in text, audio, and Mp3 versions, this web site presents classic ghost stories.
Availability: All requesters
Suggested Grade: 2-12
Order Number: not applicable
Format: Web Site
Source: Moonlit Road, The
World Wide Web URL: http://www.themoonlitroad.com/

Noun Classification in Swahili
This is a report on research in progress on the semantics and syntax of noun classes in Swahili.
Availability: All requesters
Suggested Grade: 9-Adult
Order Number: not applicable
Format: Online Article
Source: Ellen Contini-Morava
World Wide Web URL:
http://www3.iath.virginia.edu/swahili/swahili.html

Number Bingo
A game to be used as a review exercise for identifying, writing, and pronouncing numbers in French.
Availability: All requesters
Suggested Grade: 7-10
Order Number: not applicable
Format: Online Lesson Plan
Source: Fabienne Governale
World Wide Web URL:
http://www.eduref.org/Virtual/Lessons/Foreign_Language/French/FRN0202.html

Photograph Lesson
Students will write poems to accompany photographs.
Availability: All requesters
Suggested Grade: 6-12
Order Number: not applicable
Format: Online Lesson Plan
Source: Marcia LaViolette
World Wide Web URL:
http://youth.net/cec/ceclang/ceclang.06.txt

Punctuation: Less Is More?
Explores the evolution of using punctuation and discusses the degree to which it is used today.
Availability: All requesters
Suggested Grade: Teacher Reference
Order Number: not applicable
Production Date: 1992
Format: Online Article
Source: John Dawkins
World Wide Web URL:
http://www.indiana.edu/~reading/ieo/digests/d75.html

Real Chinese
Learn some basic Chinese.
Availability: All requesters
Suggested Grade: 7-12
Order Number: not applicable
Format: Online Course
Source: BBC Learning
World Wide Web URL:
http://www.bbc.co.uk/languages/chinese/real_chinese/

Sample from the Hawk Davidson: Extreme Athlete Series
A sample book from this series is available.
Availability: One copy to professional staff of schools, libraries, and homeschoolers in the United States. Make request on official stationery.
Suggested Grade: 5-Adult
Order Number: order by title
Format: Book
Special Notes: Second grade readability
Source: High Noon Books
Attn: Customer Services
20 Commercial Boulevard
Novato, CA 94949-6191
Phone: 1-800-422-7249
Fax: 1-888-287-9975
World Wide Web URL: http://www.highnoonbooks.com
Email Address: mailatp@aol.com

Semiotics and the English Language Arts
Discusses this issue.

Availability: All requesters
Suggested Grade: Teacher Reference
Order Number: not applicable
Production Date: 1991
Format: Online Article
Source: Charles Suhor
World Wide Web URL:
http://www.ericdigests.org/pre-9219/english.htm

Shiritori
Presents the rules for a game that will teach students to spell foreign words correctly.
Availability: All requesters
Suggested Grade: All ages
Order Number: not applicable
Format: Online Article
Source: Thad Schmenk
World Wide Web URL:
http://teachers.net/lessons/posts/1273.html

Spanish Steps
Kick-start your Spanish with this short course for beginners.
Availability: All requesters
Suggested Grade: 3-12
Order Number: not applicable
Format: Online Course
Source: BBC Learning
World Wide Web URL:
http://www.bbc.co.uk/languages/spanish/lj/

Story Pyramid
A strategy to help students with reading comprehension.
Availability: All requesters
Suggested Grade: All ages
Order Number: not applicable
Format: Online Lesson Plan
Source: Donna Calder
World Wide Web URL:
http://youth.net/cec/ceclang/ceclang.40.txt

Talk French
A language course for absolute beginners.
Availability: All requesters
Suggested Grade: 3-12
Order Number: not applicable
Format: Online Course
Source: BBC Learning
World Wide Web URL:
http://www.bbc.co.uk/education/languages/french/talk/index.shtml

Talk Italian
The ideal introduction to Italian.
Availability: All requesters
Suggested Grade: 3-12
Order Number: not applicable
Format: Online Course
Source: BBC Learning
World Wide Web URL:
http://www.bbc.co.uk/education/languages/italian/talk/

Talk Spanish
A language course for absolute beginners.
Availability: All requesters
Suggested Grade: 3-12
Order Number: not applicable
Format: Online Course
Source: BBC Learning
World Wide Web URL:
http://www.bbc.co.uk/education/languages/spanish/talk/index.shtml

Teacher CyberGuide--The Glass Menagerie
Help students get more out of this Tennessee Williams production.
Availability: All requesters
Suggested Grade: 11-12
Order Number: not applicable
Format: Downloadable Teacher's Guides
Source: Carolyn A. Curtice
World Wide Web URL:
http://www.sdcoe.k12.ca.us/score/Glass/glasstg.html

Tell a Story! A Guide to Storytelling
Follows these steps to help you write a story.
Availability: All requesters
Suggested Grade: K-12
Order Number: not applicable
Format: Online Article
Source: Aaron Shepard
World Wide Web URL:
http://www.aaronshep.com/storytelling/Tips.html

Test Your French
Find out how much French you know.
Availability: All requesters
Suggested Grade: 7-12
Order Number: not applicable
Format: Online Course
Source: BBC Learning
World Wide Web URL:
http://www.bbc.co.uk/languages/french/gauge/index.shtml

Test Your German
Find your level in German.
Availability: All requesters
Suggested Grade: 7-12
Order Number: not applicable
Format: Online Course
Source: BBC Learning
World Wide Web URL:
http://www.bbc.co.uk/languages/german/gauge/index.shtml

Test Your Spanish
Test your knowledge of Spanish.

Availability: All requesters
Suggested Grade: 7-12
Order Number: not applicable
Format: Online Course

Source: BBC Learning
World Wide Web URL:
http://www.bbc.co.uk/languages/spanish/gauge/

Think Different--Learn Dutch
Lessons for learning Dutch--either in crash course form or more complete.

Availability: All requesters
Suggested Grade: 4-12
Order Number: not applicable
Format: Web Site

Source: Gudmundur Helgason
World Wide Web URL: http://www.learndutch.org/

Twists, Slugs and Roscoes: A Glossary of Hardboiled Slang
Love a mystery story, but can't translate what the detective is saying? This glossary is the answer.

Availability: All requesters
Suggested Grade: 6-Adult
Order Number: not applicable
Format: Online Glossary

Source: William Denton
World Wide Web URL:
http://www.miskatonic.org/slang.html

Wagiman Online Dictionary
A complete dictionary of Aboriginal Australian.

Availability: All requesters
Suggested Grade: 6-Adult
Order Number: not applicable
Format: Online Glossary

Source: Stephen Wilson
World Wide Web URL:
http://sydney.edu.au/arts/linguistics/research/wagiman/

Wired for Books
Here you will find audio as well as video presentations of book and poetry readings. Includes children's stories and interviews with authors.

Availability: All requesters
Suggested Grade: All ages
Languages: English; Spanish
Order Number: not applicable
Format: Web Site

Source: Ohio University Telecommunications Center
World Wide Web URL: http://wiredforbooks.org/

Word Play Fun.Not Your Ordinary Literary Masterpiece
Students interactively explore the mystery genre in order to become more familiar with various forms of word play (similes, metaphors, puns, hyperbole, personification, and alliteration.)

Availability: All requesters
Suggested Grade: 4-9
Order Number: not applicable
Format: Online Lesson Plan

Source: Mary Mills
World Wide Web URL: http://www.lessonplanspage.com/LAScienceArtWordPlayDeviceAndMysteryFunUnit49.htm

Works of Robert Louis Stevenson
Here are the works of this American poet, to be read online, printed, or downloaded for further study.

Availability: All requesters
Suggested Grade: 6-12
Order Number: not applicable
Format: Online Books

Source: SunSITE
World Wide Web URL:
http://sunsite.berkeley.edu/Literature/

Worthless Word for the Day
These might be some useful words in a word game, but they probably won't come up in conversation very often.

Availability: All requesters
Suggested Grade: All ages
Order Number: not applicable
Format: Web Site

Source: Michael A. Fischer
World Wide Web URL: http://home.comcast.net/~wwftd/

Yanyula
Presents the conventions of this Australian language.

Availability: All requesters
Suggested Grade: 6-Adult
Order Number: not applicable
Format: Web Site

Source: Naomi Keith, Peter Yuen, and Mary Laughren
World Wide Web URL:
http://www.emsah.uq.edu.au/linguistics/austlang/Yanyula/yframe.html

Yiddish Dictionary Online
Type in a word and get the Yiddish translation, type a Yiddish word and find the English definition, or click on a letter and find common Yiddish words.

Availability: All requesters
Suggested Grade: 6-Adult
Order Number: not applicable
Format: Online Glossary

Source: Yiddishdictionaryonline.com
World Wide Web URL:
http://www.yiddishdictionaryonline.com/

A+ Math
Users can view flashcards for basic mathematical functions as well as more advanced ones. Math games are also available.
Availability: All requesters
Suggested Grade: All ages
Order Number: not applicable
Format: Web Site
Source: A+ Math
World Wide Web URL: http://www.aplusmath.com

Are You Ready for Business Calculus?
Identifies a student's weak areas and helps them to review materials to ensure they are ready for this college course.
Availability: All requesters
Suggested Grade: 11-Adult
Platform: Windows
Order Number: not applicable
Format: Downloadable FULL PROGRAM
Special Notes: May be copied.
Source: University of Arizona
World Wide Web URL:
http://www.math.arizona.edu/software/azmath.html

Calculators On-Line Center
Links to over 7,860 calculators that reside online.
Availability: All requesters
Suggested Grade: All ages
Order Number: not applicable
Format: Web Site
Source: Martindale's
World Wide Web URL:
http://www.martindalecenter.com/Calculators.html

Chickscope
A collection of web modules covering different topics in mathematics related to eggs.
Availability: All requesters
Suggested Grade: K-12
Order Number: not applicable
Format: Online Lesson Plans
Source: Beckman Institute
World Wide Web URL:
http://chickscope.beckman.uiuc.edu/explore/eggmath/

College Simulation
Students will learn how they should manage their money if they were in college.
Availability: All requesters
Suggested Grade: 9-Adult
Order Number: not applicable
Format: Online Lesson Plan
Source: Ky Willson
World Wide Web URL:
http://teachertech.rice.edu/Participants/kwillson/lessons/budget/part1.html

Computation, Complexity and Coding in Native American Knowledge Systems
Provides a detailed discussion of the history of mathematic computation as practiced by Native Americans.
Availability: All requesters
Suggested Grade: Adult
Order Number: not applicable
Format: Online Article
Source: Dr. Ron Eglash
World Wide Web URL:
http://www.rpi.edu/~eglash/eglash.dir/nacyb.dir/nacomplx.htm

Concepts and Applications of Inferential Statistics
An online textbook on statistics.
Availability: All requesters
Suggested Grade: 9-Adult
Order Number: not applicable
Format: Online Textbook
Source: Richard Lowry
World Wide Web URL:
http://faculty.vassar.edu/~lowry/webtext.html

Conversion Buddy 4.1.3
A metric unit conversion program.
Availability: All requesters
Suggested Grade: All ages
Platform: Windows
Order Number: not applicable
Format: Downloadable FULL PROGRAM
Source: Jim Presley
World Wide Web URL:
http://metrologyforum.tm.agilent.com/download4.shtml

Cube Coloring Problem
Investigate what happens when different sized cubes are constructed from unit cubes with some surface areas painted.
Availability: All requesters
Suggested Grade: 5-12
Order Number: not applicable
Format: Online Lesson Plan
Source: Linda Dickerson
World Wide Web URL:
http://youth.net/cec/cecmath/cecmath.36.txt

Curious Math
Math facts and tricks.
Availability: All requesters
Suggested Grade: 9-Adult
Order Number: not applicable
Format: Web Site
Special Notes: You must register, but registration is free.
Source: Clay Ford
World Wide Web URL: http://www.curiousmath.com/

Dictionary of Units
Provides a summary of most of the units of measurement

found in use around the world today together with the appropriate conversion factors needed to change them into a "standard" unit of the SI.

Availability: All requesters
Suggested Grade: 6-Adult
Order Number: not applicable
Format: Online Glossary

Source: Frank Tapson
World Wide Web URL:
http://www.cleavebooks.co.uk/dictunit/index.htm

Doing Mathematics With Your Child

Presents resources for parents to help their children with this important skill.

Availability: All requesters
Suggested Grade: Parents
Order Number: not applicable
Production Date: 1994
Format: Online Article

Source: Martin D. Hartog and Patricia A. Brosnan
World Wide Web URL:
http://www.math.com/parents/articles/domath.html

DoMath...And You Can Do Anything!

Find a lot of grade specific mathematical activities.

Availability: All requesters
Suggested Grade: All ages
Order Number: not applicable
Format: Web Site

Source: National Council of Teachers of Mathematics
World Wide Web URL: http://domath.nctm.org/

Fish in Your Backyard

Your mission, if you so choose, is to create an ecologically balanced pond for your yardscape or home using geometry skills and botany.

Availability: All requesters
Suggested Grade: 9-12
Order Number: not applicable
Format: WebQuest

Source: Bob Williams
World Wide Web URL:
http://www.yorkville.k12.il.us/webquests/webqbwilliams/webqswilliams.html

Great Pyramid, The

Students will learn more about geometry as they research the history of the great pyramids.

Availability: All requesters
Suggested Grade: 9-12
Order Number: not applicable
Format: WebQuest

Source: Connie Shatto
World Wide Web URL:
http://www.personal.psu.edu/faculty/j/x/jxz8/Student_Webquests/Shatto/PYRAMID1.HTM

Helping Your Child Learn Math

Tips to help parents help students.

Availability: All requesters
Suggested Grade: Parents
Order Number: not applicable
Production Date: 1998
Format: Online Article

Source: David L. Haury and Linda A. Milbourne
World Wide Web URL:
http://www.ericdigests.org/2000-2/math.htm

Interactive Mathematics Miscellany and Puzzles

Created to help users get over math anxiety, this site uses puzzles, games, and brain teasers to interest its audience in mathematics.

Availability: All requesters
Suggested Grade: All ages
Platform: Windows
Order Number: not applicable
Format: Web Site
Special Notes: A subscription may be purchased on CD-ROM--free only through the World Wide Web.

Source: CTK Software, Inc.
World Wide Web URL:
http://www.cut-the-knot.com/content.shtml

Linear Algebra Toolkit

Here is a place to practice basic linear algebra procedures.

Availability: All requesters
Suggested Grade: 9-12
Order Number: not applicable
Format: Web Site

Source: Old Dominion University and Przemyslaw Bogacki
World Wide Web URL:
http://www.math.odu.edu/~bogacki/lat/

MathDEN

Presents challenging math problems.

Availability: All requesters
Suggested Grade: All ages
Order Number: not applicable
Format: Online Course

Source: Act360 Media Ltd.
World Wide Web URL: http://www.actden.com/

MathMol Hypermedia Textbook

An introductory starting point for those interested in the field of molecular modeling.

Availability: All requesters
Suggested Grade: K-12
Order Number: not applicable
Format: Web Site

Source: New York University Scientific Visualization Laboratory
World Wide Web URL:
http://www.nyu.edu/pages/mathmol/textbook/

Maths Dictionary for Kids, A

For all ages, this site defines and gives examples of more than 300 math terms.

Availability: All requesters
Suggested Grade: All ages
Order Number: not applicable
Format: Web Site

Source: Jenny Eather
World Wide Web URL:
http://www.amathsdictionaryforkids.com/

MathWorld

Resources and examples of math concepts.

Availability: All requesters
Suggested Grade: 6-Adult
Order Number: not applicable
Format: Web Site

Source: Eric Weisstein
World Wide Web URL: http://mathworld.wolfram.com/

Metric Equivalents

Students will use a shortcut method to change one metric unit to another using a diagram students can relate to and remember.

Availability: All requesters
Suggested Grade: 9-12
Order Number: not applicable
Format: Online Lesson Plan

Source: Rebecca Tresino
World Wide Web URL:
http://youth.net/cec/cecmath/cecmath.38.txt

Min-Max Temperatures

A lesson dealing with minimum and maximum temperatures at certain cities to be applied to math classes.

Availability: All requesters
Suggested Grade: 6-12
Order Number: not applicable
Format: Online Lesson Plan

Source: John Meseke
World Wide Web URL:
http://www.mste.uiuc.edu/meseke/minmax.html

Mixed-Up Math

A mathematical puzzle game where you must find the correct equations to solve the puzzle.

Availability: All requesters
Suggested Grade: All ages
Order Number: not applicable
Format: Downloadable FULL PROGRAM

Source: Knowledge Probe Inc.
World Wide Web URL:
http://www.kprobe.com/kprobe/mu.htm

National Library of Virtual Manipulatives

A huge collection of interactive, web-based virtual manipulatives and concept tutorials for mathematics instruction.

Availability: All requesters
Suggested Grade: All ages
Order Number: not applicable
Format: Web Site

Source: Utah State University
World Wide Web URL:
http://nlvm.usu.edu/en/nav/vlibrary.html

NCTM Illuminations

Provides lesson plans, video vignettes, and more for mathematics teachers. Written to help teachers "translate NCTM principles and standards for school mathematics into classroom practice."

Availability: All requesters
Suggested Grade: All ages
Order Number: not applicable
Format: Web Site

Source: National Council of Teachers of Mathematics
World Wide Web URL: http://illuminations.nctm.org/

"New" Ways of Working with Triangles

Explores how to work with flexible triangles.

Availability: All requesters
Suggested Grade: 9-12
Order Number: not applicable
Format: Online Tutorial

Source: Hans-Georg Weigand and James P. Dildine
World Wide Web URL:
http://www.mste.uiuc.edu/weigand/triangle/

Numbers from 1 to 10 in Over 4500 Languages

Includes old world as well as new world languages.

Availability: All requesters
Suggested Grade: All ages
Order Number: not applicable
Format: Web Site

Source: Mark Rosenfelder
World Wide Web URL:
http://www.zompist.com/numbers.shtml

Platonic Realms

Delivers fresh math humor, quotes, historical notes, and mathematical challenges.

Availability: All requesters
Suggested Grade: 12-Adult
Order Number: not applicable
Format: Web Site

Source: Platonic Realms
World Wide Web URL:
http://www.mathacademy.com/pr/about.asp

Probability Tutorials

A number of tutorials for probability and statistics.

Availability: All requesters
Suggested Grade: 9-Adult
Order Number: not applicable
Format: Downloadable Tutorials

Source: Noel Vaillant
World Wide Web URL: http://www.probability.net/

Professor Freedman's Math Help
Provides information about basic math and algebra.
Availability: All requesters
Suggested Grade: 12-Adult
Order Number: not applicable
Format: Web Site
Source: Ellen Freedman
World Wide Web URL: http://www.mathpower.com

Quarks to Quasars, Powers of Ten
"A study of the effect of adding another zero."
Availability: All requesters
Suggested Grade: 6-12
Order Number: not applicable
Format: Web Site
Source: Bruce Bryson
World Wide Web URL:
http://www.wordwizz.com/pwrsof10.htm

Sample Size Calculator
An online calculator to help determine how many people you need to interview in order the get the results that reflect the target population as precisely as needed.
Availability: All requesters
Suggested Grade: 9-Adult
Order Number: not applicable
Format: Online Calculator
Source: Creative Research Systems
World Wide Web URL:
http://www.surveysystem.com/sscalc.htm

Shopping Spree
Takes students on a pretend shopping spree so they figure out discounts and sales tax to sharpen their math skills.
Availability: All requesters
Suggested Grade: 6-12
Order Number: not applicable
Format: Online Lesson Plan
Source: Julie Graves
World Wide Web URL:
http://www.educationworld.com/a_tsl /archives/02-1/lesson044.shtml

Sports and Geometry
Understand why geometry is important by seeing the connections between sports and geometry.
Availability: All requesters
Suggested Grade: 6-12
Order Number: not applicable
Production Date: 2007
Format: Online Lesson Plan
Source: Debbie Miskiel
World Wide Web URL: http://www.education-world.com/a_tsl/archives/07-1/lesson018.shtml

Water to the Max
Find the optimum angle to achieve the greatest distance when spraying water.
Availability: All requesters
Suggested Grade: 9-12
Order Number: not applicable
Format: Online Lesson Plan
Source: R. Vance Wood
World Wide Web URL:
http://youth.net/cec/cecmath/cecmath.28.txt

WebMath
A homework help site that generates answers to specific math problems that students input. Also provides the steps for solving the problems so that students learn how the answer was achieved--not just what the answer is.
Availability: All requesters
Suggested Grade: All ages
Order Number: not applicable
Format: Web Site
Source: Webmath.com
World Wide Web URL: http://www.webmath.com/

Winstats
Provides access to scatter plots and more.
Availability: All requesters
Suggested Grade: 9-Adult
Platform: Windows
Order Number: not applicable
Format: Downloadable FULL PROGRAM
Source: Peanut Software
World Wide Web URL:
http://math.exeter.edu/rparris/default.html

Adolescent & School Health
Visitors to this site will find the latest research on student health as well as information on school health strategies. Designed to improve the physical fitness of young people.
Availability: All requesters
Suggested Grade: All ages
Order Number: not applicable
Format: Web Site
Source: Adolescent and School Health
World Wide Web URL:
http://www.cdc.gov/nccdphp/dash/index.htm

Be Groovy, Stay Fit!!!
Presents information on how to stay in shape including a chart of exercises you can follow.
Availability: All requesters
Suggested Grade: All ages
Order Number: not applicable
Format: Web Site
Special Notes: This URL will lead you to a subject page. Then click on the appropriate subject heading.
Source: ThinkQuest
World Wide Web URL:
http://www.thinkquest.org/pls/html/think.library

Do You Know the Health Risks of Being Overweight?
A guide to help you lose weight which also explains why, perhaps, you should.
Availability: All requesters
Suggested Grade: 4-Adult
Order Number: not applicable
Format: Online Article; 10 pages
Special Notes: Use the on-site search engine to easily find this title. You may request a printed copy mailed to you for a fee.
Source: Federal Citizen Information Center
World Wide Web URL: http://www.pueblo.gsa.gov/

Fitness Jumpsite
Lots of information about physical fitness.
Availability: All requesters
Suggested Grade: 6-12
Order Number: not applicable
Format: Web Site
Source: Vicki Pierson and Renee Cloe
World Wide Web URL:
http://primusweb.com/fitnesspartner

GoGirlGo Secondary
This unique education program utilizes four characters to educate high school girls about health risk behaviors and life lessons such as body image, bullying, diversity, smoking, drugs, and stress. Designed for girls' sports and physical
Availability: Schools and libraries in the United States.
Suggested Grade: 9-12
Order Number: order by title
Production Date: 2004
Format: Curriculum
Special Notes: May also be downloaded from the web site.
Source: Women's Sports Foundation
Phone: 1-800-227-3988
World Wide Web URL: http://www.gogirlgo.com/

Health & Sports Inside Stuff
Rules and regulations of basketball, football, hockey, and baseball and the importance of staying healthy.
Availability: All requesters
Suggested Grade: 4-12
Order Number: not applicable
Format: Web Site
Special Notes: This URL will lead you to a subject page. Then click on the appropriate subject heading.
Source: ThinkQuest
World Wide Web URL:
http://www.thinkquest.org/pls/html/think.library

Kids Quiz
A daily quiz designed for kids between the ages of 8 and 18 about nutrition, health, physical activity, and much more.
Availability: All requesters
Suggested Grade: 3-12
Order Number: not applicable
Format: Online Quiz
Special Notes: Schools must register, but registration is free.
Source: PE Central
World Wide Web URL:
http://www.peclogit.org/kidsquiz.asp

Log It
An online program that allows 4th grade aged students and higher (as well as individuals) to record their physical activity steps and miles to encourage more activity.
Availability: All requesters
Suggested Grade: 4-Adult
Order Number: not applicable
Format: Web Site
Special Notes: Schools must register, but registration is free.
Source: PE Central and New Lifestyles
World Wide Web URL: http://www.peclogit.org/logit.asp

99 Tips for Family Fitness Fun
Fitness can be fun as well as beneficial--find out how.
Availability: All requesters
Suggested Grade: All ages
Order Number: not applicable
Format: Downloadable Brochure
Source: National Association for Sports and Physical Education and Shape Up America
World Wide Web URL:
http://www.shapeup.org/publications/99.tips.for.family.fitness.fun/

Runner's Oasis
Complete virtual run with hints and tips to properly train for that 10K run.

Availability: All requesters
Suggested Grade: 9-Adult
Order Number: not applicable
Format: Web Site
Special Notes: This URL will lead you to a subject page. Then click on the appropriate subject heading.

Source: ThinkQuest
World Wide Web URL:
http://www.thinkquest.org/pls/html/think.library

Running

Covers training, nutrition, injury prevention, and racing for high-school runners.

Availability: All requesters
Suggested Grade: 9-12
Order Number: not applicable
Format: Web Site
Special Notes: This URL will lead you to a subject page. Then click on the appropriate subject heading.

Source: ThinkQuest
World Wide Web URL:
http://www.thinkquest.org/pls/html/think.library

RunStat 3

Enter the distance and time for your run and this program calculates your pace for your run.

Availability: All requesters
Suggested Grade: 6-12
Platform: Windows
Order Number: not applicable
Format: Downloadable FULL PROGRAM
Special Notes: It is preferred that you download this program from the Web; if this does not work for you then you can send $5.00 to receive the program on disk.

Source: Scott Diamond & Cats
World Wide Web URL:
http://ibiblio.org/drears/running/products/software/runstat.html

Specific Sports Exercises

A number of exercises specific to certain sports.

Availability: All requesters
Suggested Grade: All ages
Order Number: not applicable
Format: Web Site

Source: International Fitness Association
World Wide Web URL: http://www.ifafitness.com/sports/

Sport of Bicycling, The

Road biking, mountain biking, safety and nutrition, and list of bike trails focusing on Utah, Arizona, and Colorado.

Availability: All requesters
Suggested Grade: All ages
Order Number: not applicable
Format: Web Site
Special Notes: This URL will lead you to a subject page. Then click on the appropriate subject heading.

Source: ThinkQuest
World Wide Web URL:
http://www.thinkquest.org/pls/html/think.library

Swimming with Belinda and Whitney

Swimming for fun, fitness, and exercise.

Availability: All requesters
Suggested Grade: All ages
Order Number: not applicable
Format: Web Site
Special Notes: This URL will lead you to a subject page. Then click on the appropriate subject heading.

Source: ThinkQuest
World Wide Web URL:
http://www.thinkquest.org/pls/html/think.library

Why Assess in Physical Education?

Answers this question.

Availability: All requesters
Suggested Grade: Teacher Reference
Order Number: not applicable
Format: Online Article

Source: Stephen Jefferies, Toni Jefferies, and Wendy Mustain
World Wide Web URL:
http://www.pecentral.org/assessment/assessmentresearch.html

Apollo 11 at Twenty-Five Electronic Picture Book

An electronic picture book.

Availability: All requesters
Suggested Grade: All ages
Platform: Macintosh; Windows
Order Number: not applicable
Format: Downloadable Electronic Book
Special Notes: Macintosh requires HyperCard Player 2.1; Windows requires WinPlus Runtime.

Source: Exploration in Education
World Wide Web URL: http://www.stsci.edu/exined/

Birthday Moons: It's Just a Phase You're Going Through

Learn the phases of the moon by taking a virtual trip to the Moon for your birthday!

Availability: All requesters
Suggested Grade: 4-12
Order Number: not applicable
Format: Online Lesson Plan

Source: Walter Sanford
World Wide Web URL:
http://www.wsanford.com/~wsanford/exo/b-day_moons.html

Classifying Galaxies

An interactive lesson on the Hubble System of classifying galaxies.

Availability: All requesters
Suggested Grade: 5-9
Order Number: not applicable
Format: Online Lesson Plan

Source: George and Jane Hastings
World Wide Web URL:
http://cse.ssl.berkeley.edu/segwayEd/lessons/classifying_galaxies/galaxy.htm

Commercial-Aviation

History of commercial flying.

Availability: All requesters
Suggested Grade: All ages
Languages: English; German
Order Number: not applicable
Format: Web Site
Special Notes: This URL will lead you to a subject page. Then click on the appropriate subject heading.

Source: ThinkQuest
World Wide Web URL:
http://www.thinkquest.org/pls/html/think.library

Exploring Meteorite Mysteries

This teacher's guide includes activities for earth and space sciences.

Availability: All requesters
Suggested Grade: 5-12
Order Number: not applicable
Format: Downloadable Teacher's Guide

Source: NASA Spacelink
World Wide Web URL:
http://curator.jsc.nasa.gov/outreach/expmetmys/index.cfm

Exploring the Moon

This teacher's guide includes activities for earth and space sciences.

Availability: All requesters
Suggested Grade: 4-12
Order Number: not applicable
Format: Downloadable Teacher's Guide

Source: NASA Spacelink
World Wide Web URL:
http://www.nasa.gov/audience/foreducators/topnav/materials/listbytype/Exploring.the.Moon.html

Flight Through the Past, A: Aviation in the 20th Century

Interactive learning and resource center focusing on the influence of aviation on this past century.

Availability: All requesters
Suggested Grade: 6-12
Order Number: not applicable
Format: Web Site
Special Notes: This URL will lead you to a subject page. Then click on the appropriate subject heading.

Source: ThinkQuest
World Wide Web URL:
http://www.thinkquest.org/pls/html/think.library

Galileo's Dialogue

Students will understand Galileo's the life and times that Galileo lived in and discover the controversy surround his discoveries.

Availability: All requesters
Suggested Grade: 9-12
Order Number: not applicable
Format: Online Lesson Plan

Source: Lara Maupin
World Wide Web URL:
http://www.discoveryeducation.com/teachers/free-lesson-plans/galileos-dialogue.cfm

History of Space Exploration

Includes resources for teachers on both robotic and shuttle spacecraft as well as presenting a history of space exploration.

Availability: All requesters
Suggested Grade: 6-12
Order Number: not applicable
Format: Web Site

Source: Calvin J. Hamilton
World Wide Web URL:
http://www.solarviews.com/eng/history.htm

Journey Through the Galaxy

Information and resources for teaching and learning about the solar system.

Availability: All requesters
Suggested Grade: 6-12
Order Number: not applicable
Format: Web Site
Source: Stuart Robbins and David McDonald
World Wide Web URL:
http://filer.case.edu/~sjr16/advanced/index.html

Making a Comet in the Classroom
A dramatic and effective way to begin a unit on comets is to make your own comet right in front of the class. Here's how.
Availability: All requesters
Suggested Grade: All ages
Order Number: not applicable
Format: Web Site
Source: Dennis Schatz
World Wide Web URL:
http://www.noao.edu/education/crecipe.html

Meteors and Meteor Showers
Explains what a meteor shower is and provides pictures.
Availability: All requesters
Suggested Grade: 6-12
Order Number: not applicable
Format: Web Site
Source: University of Tennessee Department of Physics & Astronomy
World Wide Web URL:
http://csep10.phys.utk.edu/astr161/lect/meteors/showers.html

NASA's Great Observatories Kit
Includes the Hubble Space Telescope, the Chandra X-Ray Observatory, and the Compton Gamma Ray Observatory.
Availability: All requesters
Suggested Grade: 5-12
Order Number: not applicable
Format: Downloadable Models
Source: NASA Spacelink
World Wide Web URL:
http://www.nasa.gov/audience/forstudents/postsecondary/features/F_NASA_Great_Observatories_PS.html

Nine Planets, The: A Multimedia Tour of the Solar System
Here is an overview of the history, mythology, and current scientific knowledge of each of the planets and moons in our solar system.
Availability: All requesters
Suggested Grade: All ages
Order Number: not applicable
Format: Online Tutorial
Source: Bill Arnett
World Wide Web URL: http://www.nineplanets.org/

Planetary Geology
A teacher's guide with activities in physical and earth sciences.
Availability: All requesters
Suggested Grade: 5-College
Order Number: not applicable
Format: Downloadable Teacher's Guide
Source: NASA Spacelink
World Wide Web URL:
http://www.nasa.gov/audience/foreducators/topnav/materials/listbysubject/Planetary_Geology_landingpage.html

Planets, The
Generates a list of what constellation each planet is in for every month of a specific year--just input the year you are looking for.
Availability: All requesters
Suggested Grade: 4-12
Order Number: not applicable
Format: Web Site
Source: Dolan
World Wide Web URL:
http://www.astro.wisc.edu/~dolan/Planets/

Que Tal in the Current Skies
Useful information about observing the visible planets, our moon, and other moons, the sun, and other "things" celestial.
Availability: All requesters
Suggested Grade: All ages
Order Number: not applicable
Format: Online Newsletter
Source: Bob Riddle
World Wide Web URL: http://currentsky.com/

Rockets
Activities are included that cover science, mathematics, and technology that teach about rockets.
Availability: All requesters
Suggested Grade: 5-College
Order Number: not applicable
Format: Downloadable Teacher's Guide
Source: NASA Spacelink
World Wide Web URL:
http://www.nasa.gov/audience/foreducators/topnav/materials/listbytype/Rockets.html

SkyDEN
Offers a visually stunning introduction to astronomy.
Availability: All requesters
Suggested Grade: All ages
Order Number: not applicable
Format: Online Course
Source: Act360 Media Ltd.
World Wide Web URL: http://www.actden.com/

Solar System Puzzle Kit
An activity for earth and space science.
Availability: All requesters
Suggested Grade: 5-12
Order Number: not applicable

Format: Downloadable Activity

Source: NASA Spacelink
World Wide Web URL:
http://www.nasa.gov/audience/foreducators/topnav/materials/listbytype/Solar_System_Puzzle_Kit.html

Space Primer

An introduction to astronautics with clear explanations of basic concepts and terms; illustrated.

Availability: Limit of 30 copies to schools, libraries, and homeschoolers world-wide. Please do not allow each individual student to write.
Suggested Grade: 5-12
Order Number: order by title
Format: Brochure
Special Notes: May also be downloaded from the web site.

Source: Aerospace Corporation, The
World Wide Web URL: http://www.aero.org
Email Address: corpcom@aero.org

Space Shuttle Glider

Build a 1:300 centimeters scale model of the U. S. Space shuttle orbiter.

Availability: All requesters
Suggested Grade: 5-12
Order Number: not applicable
Format: Downloadable Model

Source: NASA Spacelink
World Wide Web URL:
http://www.nasa.gov/audience/foreducators/topnav/materials/listbytype/Space.Shuttle.Glider.html

Suited for Spacewalking

Lots of activities for teaching about how spacesuits operate to keep spacewalkers healthy and safe.

Availability: All requesters
Suggested Grade: 5-12
Order Number: not applicable
Format: Downloadable Teacher's Guide

Source: NASA Spacelink
World Wide Web URL:
http://www.nasa.gov/audience/foreducators/topnav/materials/listbytype/Suited_for_Spacewalking_Educator_Guide.html

Toilet Paper Solar System

This activity will help students to describe the relative distances of planets from our sun.

Availability: All requesters
Suggested Grade: All ages
Order Number: not applicable
Format: Online Lesson Plan

Source: Elizabeth Roettger
World Wide Web URL:
http://www.nthelp.com/eer/HOAtpss.html

Universe in the Classroom, The

An electronic newsletter for teachers, youth group leaders, librarians, and anybody else who wants to help children of all ages learn more about the wonders of the universe.

Availability: All requesters
Suggested Grade: All ages
Order Number: not applicable
Format: Online Newsletter

Source: Astronomical Society of the Pacific
World Wide Web URL:
http://www.astrosociety.org/education/publications/tnl/tnl.html

Ask a Biologist
Read the answers to other questions posted or ask a biologist your own question.
Availability: All requesters
Suggested Grade: All ages
Order Number: not applicable
Format: Web Site
Source: Arizona State University, School of Life Sciences
World Wide Web URL: http://askabiologist.asu.edu/

Behavior of Ants, The
Students will use the steps of the Scientific Method to independently develop and test their own ideas through experimentation with ants.
Availability: All requesters
Suggested Grade: 5-8
Order Number: not applicable
Format: Online Lesson Plan
Source: David Shindelman
World Wide Web URL:
http://biology.arizona.edu/sciconn/lessons2/shindelman/Objectives.htm

Biology Data Tip Archives
Great data activities for studying biology.
Availability: All requesters
Suggested Grade: 6-12
Order Number: not applicable
Format: Online Lesson Plans
Source: Bridge
World Wide Web URL:
http://www.vims.edu/bridge/bioarchives.html

Bone Curriculum
Educational resources on skeletal structures and tissues.
Availability: All requesters
Suggested Grade: 9-Adult
Order Number: not applicable
Format: Web Site
Source: American Society for Bone and Mineral Research
World Wide Web URL:
http://depts.washington.edu/bonebio/ASBMRed/ASBMRed.html

Botany Online
An online book covering plant anatomy, genetics, organic chemistry and much more.
Availability: All requesters
Suggested Grade: 9-Adult
Languages: English; German
Order Number: not applicable
Format: Online Book
Source: Peter V. Sengbusch
World Wide Web URL:
http://www.biologie.uni-hamburg.de/b-online/e00/contents.htm

Diffusion, Osmosis and Cell Membranes
Students will explore some of the properties and processes of the cell membrane including permeability, passive transport, equilibrium, and more.
Availability: All requesters
Suggested Grade: 5-12
Order Number: not applicable
Format: Online Lesson Plan
Source: John R. McCandless, Jr.
World Wide Web URL:
http://biology.arizona.edu/sciconn/lessons2/McCandless/page1.htm

Future Is Wild, The
Based on the book of the same name, this project asks students to predict how a species population might evolve due to the Earth's changing climate.
Availability: All requesters
Suggested Grade: 10
Order Number: not applicable
Format: Online Lesson Plan
Source: Debbie Whittington
World Wide Web URL:
http://www.eduref.org/Virtual/Lessons/Science/Animals/ANM0211.html

Human Body, The: A Life-Size Model on Paper
Students learn about parts of the body as they create a life-size paper model of the human body's parts.
Availability: All requesters
Suggested Grade: All ages
Order Number: not applicable
Format: Online Lesson Plan
Source: Gary Hopkins
World Wide Web URL:
http://www.educationworld.com/a_lesson/00-2/lp2190.shtml

I Can Do That!
Learn about DNA, RNA, cells, protein, and cloning.
Availability: All requesters
Suggested Grade: 6-12
Order Number: not applicable
Format: Web Site
Source: Eureka!Science
World Wide Web URL:
http://www.eurekascience.com/ICanDoThat/

It's All in the Blood
In this lesson, students explore the way metaphors can be used to help explain complex body systems; they then use metaphors to create drawings or skits showing the varied functions of blood in the body.
Availability: All requesters
Suggested Grade: 6-12
Order Number: not applicable
Production Date: 2008
Format: Online Lesson Plan

Source: Catherine Hutchings
World Wide Web URL:
http://learning.blogs.nytimes.com/2008/10/28/its-all-in-the-blood/?scp=1&sq=all%20in%20the%20blood&st=cse

Online Biology Dictionary
A dictionary of almost 2,000 terms relating to the biological sciences.
Availability: All requesters
Suggested Grade: 9-12
Order Number: not applicable
Format: Online Glossary
Source: Biology-Online.org
World Wide Web URL:
http://www.biology-online.org/dictionary.asp

Plant Biology for Non-Science Majors
Lecture notes for this three-credit course taught at the University of Maryland.
Availability: All requesters
Suggested Grade: 12-Adult
Order Number: not applicable
Format: Online Lecture Notes
Source: David Straney and Edgar Moctezuma
World Wide Web URL:
http://www.life.umd.edu/classroom/bsci124/main.html

Real Bionic Man, The
Explores the work being done by scientists to create sophisticated artificial human parts and how each device functions in place of an actual biological structure.
Availability: All requesters
Suggested Grade: 9-12
Order Number: not applicable
Format: Online Lesson Plan
Source: Mary Ann Herbst
World Wide Web URL:
http://school.discovery.com/lessonplans/programs/therealbionicman/

Real Eve, The
A lesson plan for use about evolution.
Availability: all requesters
Suggested Grade: 6-12
Order Number: not applicable
Format: Online Lesson Plan
Source: Joy Brewster
World Wide Web URL:
http://www.discoveryeducation.com/teachers/free-lesson-plans/the-real-eve.cfm

Rx for Survival
Anchored by a six-hour PBS television series, this site offers all sorts of games, experiments, resources, and more to supplement health, biology, and general science classes.
Availability: All requesters
Suggested Grade: 7-Adult
Order Number: not applicable
Format: Web Site
Source: WGBH Educational Foundation and Vulcan Productions, Inc.
World Wide Web URL:
http://www.pbs.org/wgbh/rxforsurvival/

Spiders: An Organism for Teaching Biology
In this unit, students explore basic ecology concepts and scientific processes using spiders as model organisms.
Availability: All requesters
Suggested Grade: 5-12
Order Number: not applicable
Format: Online Lesson Plan
Source: Debra Scheidemantel
World Wide Web URL:
http://biology.arizona.edu/sciconn/lessons2/scheidemantel/overview.html

2Can Support Portal--Bioinformatics
Provides short and concise introductions to basic concepts in molecular and cell biology and bioinformatics.
Availability: All requesters
Suggested Grade: 9-Adult
Order Number: not applicable
Format: Web Site
Source: European Bioinformatics Institute
World Wide Web URL:
http://www.ebi.ac.uk/2can/home.html

What's Wrong with the Plants?
Students will sharpen their investigative skills as they attempt to determine what is wrong with some unhealthy plants.
Availability: All requesters
Suggested Grade: 9-12
Order Number: not applicable
Format: Online Lesson Plan
Source: Dee Dee Loredo
World Wide Web URL:
http://biology.arizona.edu/sciconn/lessons2/Loredo/Overview.htm

Your DNA: What Can You Afford (Not) to Know?
In this lesson, students understand and evaluate the implications of low-price DNA sequencing from multiple points of view.
Availability: All requesters
Suggested Grade: 6-12
Order Number: not applicable
Production Date: 2008
Format: Online Lesson Plan
Source: Catherine Hutchings
World Wide Web URL:
http://learning.blogs.nytimes.com/2008/10/07/your-dna-what-can-you-afford-not-to-know/?scp=6&sq=Your%20DNA&st=cse

Acid Rain and Our Nation's Capital
Focuses on acid rain and the deterioration it is causing on our Nation's capital.
Availability: All requesters
Suggested Grade: 4-12
Order Number: not applicable
Format: Online Booklet; 34 pages
Source: USGS Information Services
World Wide Web URL: http://pubs.usgs.gov/gip/acidrain/

Ask Professor Questor!
An "advice" column on energy and energy savings. Send your energy questions to the professor, and she will answer them.
Availability: All requesters
Suggested Grade: All ages
Order Number: not applicable
Format: Online Article
Source: California Energy Commission
World Wide Web URL: http://www.energyquest.ca.gov/

California Water Facts
Presents information about this natural resource as it relates to California.
Availability: Limit of 10 copies to schools, libraries, and homeschoolers world-wide.
Suggested Grade: 6-12
Languages: English; Spanish
Order Number: order by title
Format: Booklet
Source: Water Education Foundation
Education Director
717 K Street, Suite 317
Sacramento, CA 95814
Phone: 1-916-444-6240
Fax: 1-916-448-7699
World Wide Web URL: http://www.watereducation.org
Email Address: dfarmer@watereducation.org

CGS Notes
Information about many of the minerals founds in the state of California.
Availability: All requesters
Suggested Grade: 6-12
Order Number: not applicable
Format: Online Articles
Source: California Geological Survey
World Wide Web URL:
http://www.consrv.ca.gov/cgs/information/publications/cgs_notes/Pages/index.aspx

Ecosystem Services
Defines ecosystems, the services or resources they produce, and the threats to these resources.
Availability: All requesters
Suggested Grade: 6-Adult
Order Number: not applicable
Format: Online Fact Sheet
Source: Ecological Society of America, The
World Wide Web URL:
http://www.esa.org/education_diversity/factsheets.php

Environmental Justice
Defines environmental justice and addresses the causes, effects, history, and role of ecology in environmental justice.
Availability: All requesters
Suggested Grade: 6-Adult
Order Number: not applicable
Format: Online Fact Sheet
Source: Ecological Society of America, The
World Wide Web URL:
http://www.esa.org/education_diversity/factsheets.php

Everyday Uses of Minerals--Teacher Packet 3
Lots of information about mines and mineral resources.
Availability: One copy to schools and libraries in the United States and Canada--to school addresses only.
Suggested Grade: K-12
Order Number: order by title
Format: Teacher's Packet
Special Notes: Extra copies are $8.00 each.
Source: Mineral Information Institute
12999 E. Adam Aircraft Circle
Englewood, CO 80112
Phone: 1-303-948-4236
Fax: 1-303-948-4265
World Wide Web URL: http://www.mii.org
Email Address: mii@mii.org

GeoMan's Glossary of Earth Science Terms
A searchable dictionary of earth science definitions,.
Availability: All requesters
Suggested Grade: 6-Adult
Order Number: not applicable
Format: Online Dictionary
Source: Mike Strickler
World Wide Web URL:
http://jersey.uoregon.edu/~mstrick/geology/geo_glossary_page.html

Hantavirus
A case study of Hantavirus which shows how ecology and ecologists have had a direct impact on human health, the economy, or quality of life.
Availability: All requesters
Suggested Grade: 6-Adult
Order Number: not applicable
Format: Online Fact Sheet
Source: Ecological Society of America, The
World Wide Web URL:
http://www.esa.org/education_diversity/factsheets.php

Lyme Disease
A case study of Lyme Disease which shows how ecology

and ecologists have had a direct impact on human health, the economy, or quality of life.

Availability: All requesters
Suggested Grade: 6-Adult
Order Number: not applicable
Format: Online Fact Sheet

Source: Ecological Society of America, The
World Wide Web URL:
http://www.esa.org/education_diversity/factsheets.php

Minerals by Name

Just click on the name of a mineral and you will learn more about that mineral.

Availability: All requesters
Suggested Grade: 7-Adult
Order Number: not applicable
Format: Web Site

Source: Amethyst Galleries, Inc.
World Wide Web URL:
http://www.galleries.com/minerals/byname.htm

NeMO

Studies the dynamic interactions between submarine volcanic activity and seafloor hotsprings at an observatory, Axial seamount.

Availability: All requesters
Suggested Grade: 3-12
Order Number: not applicable
Format: Web Site

Source: Pacific Marine Environmental Laboratory
World Wide Web URL:
http://www.pmel.noaa.gov/vents/nemo/index.html

Pointless Pollution Kit

A collection of interactive lessons, hands-on activities, and information about nonpoint source pollution, the number one cause of water pollution.

Availability: Single copies to schools, libraries, and homeschoolers world-wide.
Suggested Grade: 3-12
Order Number: order by title
Format: Booklet
Special Notes: May also be downloaded from the web site.

Source: Clean Ocean Action
18 Hartshorne Drive, Suite 2
Sandy Hook, NJ 07732
Phone: 1-732-872-0111
Fax: 1-732-872-8041
World Wide Web URL: http://www.cleanoceanaction.org
Email Address: education@cleanoceanaction.org

Promoting a Concern for the Environment

Discusses this issue.

Availability: All requesters
Suggested Grade: Teacher Reference
Order Number: not applicable
Production Date: 1992
Format: Online Article

Source: Joe E. Heimlich
World Wide Web URL:
http://www.ericdigests.org/1992-1/concern.htm

Save the Rainforest

Provides a virtual tour of the rainforest and lots of information about why we need them and why they are becoming endangered ecosystems.

Availability: All requesters
Suggested Grade: All ages
Order Number: not applicable
Format: Web Site

Source: Save the Rainforest.org
World Wide Web URL: http://www.savetherainforest.org/

Smart Energy Choices Bookmark

Lists smart energy choices to follow at home, on the road, and at the store.

Availability: Limit of 25copies to schools and libraries world-wide.
Suggested Grade: All ages
Order Number: order by title
Format: Bookmark

Source: Society of Petroleum Engineers
222 Palisades Creek Drive
Richardson, TX 75080-2040
Phone: 1-972-952-9393, ext. 1125
Fax: 1-866-719-8241
Email Address: EnergyEd@Energy4me.org

Soil Assessment

Tells how to assess the soil in your area.

Availability: Limit of 1copy to schools, libraries, and homeschoolers in the United States and Canada.
Suggested Grade: 4-12
Order Number: order by title
Format: Instructions for teachers

Source: Kenilworth Park and Aquatic Gardens
Education Coordinator
1900 Anacostia Drive, SE
Washington, DC 20020
Phone: 1-202-426-6905
Fax: 1-202-426-5991
World Wide Web URL: http://www.nps.gov/keaq
Email Address: Kate-Bucco@nps.gov

Solar Today

Timely information on sustainable, environmentally sound buildings, power generation, community development, industry, and business.

Availability: One copy to schools, libraries, and homeschoolers in the United States.
Suggested Grade: 9-Adult
Order Number: order by title
Format: Magazine; published bimonthly

Source: American Solar Energy Society
Attn: Dona McClain
4760 Walnut Street, Suite 106
Boulder, CO 80301
Phone: 1-303-443-3130, ext 106
World Wide Web URL: http://www.ases.org
Email Address: ases@ases.org

10 Tips for Kids

Provides ten ways kids can be a part of the solution to preventing pollution.

Availability: Single copies to schools, libraries, and homeschoolers world-wide.
Suggested Grade: 3-12
Order Number: order by title
Format: Card

Source: Clean Ocean Action
18 Hartshorne Drive, Suite 2
Sandy Hook, NJ 07732
Phone: 1-732-872-0111
Fax: 1-732-872-8041
World Wide Web URL: http://www.cleanoceanaction.org
Email Address: education@cleanoceanaction.org

ThinkGreen.com

Environmental themed resources explaining how landfills are built, how landfill gas is used to create energy, and much more about how waste is a resource to be used.

Availability: All requesters
Suggested Grade: 3-12
Order Number: not applicable
Format: Web Site

Source: Waste Management
World Wide Web URL: http://www.thinkgreen.com/

Top Water Smart Tips

Top conservation tips for the bathroom, kitchen, and outdoors.

Availability: All requesters
Suggested Grade: 6-Adult
Languages: English; Spanish
Order Number: not applicable
Format: Downloadable Brochure

Source: Texas Water Development Board
World Wide Web URL:
http://www.twdb.state.tx.us/assistance/conservation/pubs.asp

Trail Guide to Boardwalk and River Trail

Explains the wetlands area found in this national park and how it has changed over the years.

Availability: Limit of 1 copy to schools, libraries, and homeschoolers in the United States and Canada.
Suggested Grade: 4-12
Order Number: order by title
Format: Article

Source: Kenilworth Park and Aquatic Gardens
Education Coordinator
1900 Anacostia Drive, SE
Washington, DC 20020
Phone: 1-202-426-6905
Fax: 1-202-426-5991
World Wide Web URL: http://www.nps.gov/keaq
Email Address: Kate-Bucco@nps.gov

Trees for America Brochure

Contains illustrated tree-planting instructions, information about Arbor Day, a graphic example of the importance of trees to our world, and more.

Availability: One copy to schools, libraries, and homeschoolers in the United States.
Suggested Grade: 2-12
Order Number: order by title
Format: Brochure
Special Notes: May also be downloaded from the web site.

Source: National Arbor Day Foundation
211 North 12th Street
Lincoln, NE 68508
World Wide Web URL:
www.arborday.orghttp://www.arborday.org
Email Address: education@arborday.org

UN Atlas of the Oceans

Lots of information pertaining to the sustainable development of the oceans. Images, statistics, articles, and more are presented.

Availability: All requesters
Suggested Grade: 9-Adult
Order Number: not applicable
Format: Web Site

Source: United Nations, et al
World Wide Web URL:
http://www.oceansatlas.com/index.jsp

Watershed Workbook for Teachers

A teacher's guide for helping students learn more about watersheds.

Availability: All requesters
Suggested Grade: 5-12
Order Number: not applicable
Format: Online Teacher's Guide

Source: Kenilworth Park and Aquatic Gardens
World Wide Web URL:
http://www.nps.gov/keaq/forteachers

ABC's of Nuclear Science, The
Provides a brief introduction to nuclear science.
Availability: All requesters
Suggested Grade: 10-Adult
Order Number: not applicable
Format: Web Site
Source: Nuclear Science Division Lawrence Berkeley National Laboratory
World Wide Web URL: http://www.lbl.gov/abc/

Acid Deposition
Defines acid deposition and discusses risk factors, ecological effects and impacts, and what scientists are doing to better understand the problem.
Availability: All requesters
Suggested Grade: 6-Adult
Order Number: not applicable
Format: Online Fact Sheet
Special Notes: PDF file
Source: Ecological Society of America, The
World Wide Web URL:
http://www.esa.org/education_diversity/pdfDocs/aciddeposition.pdf

Acid Rain Revisited
Addresses what has happened since the 1990 Clean Air Act Amendments.
Availability: All requesters
Suggested Grade: 6-Adult
Order Number: not applicable
Format: Online Fact Sheet
Special Notes: PDF file
Source: Ecological Society of America, The
World Wide Web URL:
http://www.esa.org/education_diversity/pdfDocs/acidrainrevisited.pdf

Ask a Scientist
Through this service, you can email your question to volunteer scientists located throughout the world and receive an answer.
Availability: All requesters
Suggested Grade: All ages
Order Number: not applicable
Format: Web Site
Source: Newton BBS
World Wide Web URL:
http://www.newton.dep.anl.gov/AAS

Ask Dr. Universe
Not only will you find answers to many science questions that have already been asked, but you can ask Dr. Universe your own questions, too.
Availability: All requesters
Suggested Grade: All ages
Order Number: not applicable
Format: Web Site
Source: Washington State University
World Wide Web URL: http://www.wsu.edu/DrUniverse/

Basic Volcanic Terms and Volcanology
Defines the scientific terms relating to volcanic activity. Also provides a thorough explanation of how and why a volcano erupts.
Availability: All requesters
Suggested Grade: 4-12
Order Number: not applicable
Format: Downloadable Article
Source: Lassen Volcanic National Park
World Wide Web URL:
http://www.nps.gov/lavo/forteachers/otherresources.htm

Beakman's Electric Motor
Directions for making a working electric motor.
Availability: All requesters
Suggested Grade: 7-12
Order Number: not applicable
Format: Online Article
Source: Chris Palmer
World Wide Web URL:
http://fly.hiwaay.net/~palmer/motor.html
Email Address: cmpalmer@ingr.com

Biocomplexity
Defines biocomplexity, characteristics, types of studies, case studies, and future research.
Availability: All requesters
Suggested Grade: 6-Adult
Order Number: not applicable
Format: Online Fact Sheet
Source: Ecological Society of America, The
World Wide Web URL:
http://www.esa.org/education_diversity/factsheets.php

Biodiversity
Defines biodiversity and explains what threatens it, why it is important, and what ecologists are doing to better understand it.
Availability: All requesters
Suggested Grade: 6-Adult
Order Number: not applicable
Format: Online Fact Sheet
Source: Ecological Society of America, The
World Wide Web URL:
http://www.esa.org/education_diversity/factsheets.php

Biology Project, The
Presents tutorials, problem sets, activities, and other resources for learners in biochemistry, cell biology, developmental biology, and more.
Availability: All requesters
Suggested Grade: 9-Adult
Languages: English; Spanish
Order Number: not applicable
Format: Web Site

Source: University of Arizona
World Wide Web URL: http://www.biology.arizona.edu/

Biology Tutorials
A number of biology tutorials.
Availability: All requesters
Suggested Grade: 9-12
Order Number: not applicable
Format: Online Tutorials
Source: Biology-Online.org
World Wide Web URL:
http://www.biology-online.org/tutorials/home.htm

Biomass Energy
Discusses this form of energy.
Availability: All requesters
Suggested Grade: All ages
Order Number: not applicable
Format: Online Article
Source: California Energy Commission
World Wide Web URL: http://www.energyquest.ca.gov/

Bizarre Stuff You Can Make in Your Kitchen
"...sort of a warped semi-scientific cookbook for tricks, gimmicks, and pointless experimentation, concoctions, and devices, using, for the most part, things found in the house." "If you happen to learn something in the process, consider yourself a better person for it."
Availability: All requesters
Suggested Grade: All ages
Order Number: not applicable
Format: Web Site
Source: Brian Carusella
World Wide Web URL: http://bizarrelabs.com/

Build-a-Bot Techlab
Discover the basic skills needed for building robots and get started building your own.
Availability: All requesters
Suggested Grade: 9-Adult
Order Number: not applicable
Format: Online Course
Special Notes: Site is no longer being updated, but content is valuable.
Source: BBC Learning
World Wide Web URL:
http://www.bbc.co.uk/science/robots/techlab/sub_selector.shtml

Carbon Sequestration in Soils
Defines carbon sequestration and addresses benefits and potential costs of management techniques, the role of forests, and what scientists are doing to understand soil carbon sequestration.
Availability: All requesters
Suggested Grade: 6-Adult
Order Number: not applicable
Format: Online Fact Sheet
Source: Ecological Society of America, The
World Wide Web URL:
http://www.esa.org/education_diversity/factsheets.php

Century of Earthquakes, A
On April 18, 1906 a powerful earthquake shook San Francisco leading to fires that devastated the city. That earthquake brought seismology into the forefront as a science in the U. S. This poster outlines the lessons learned from the 1906 San Francisco earthquake and discusses 100 years of large earthquakes, including the Sumatra earthquake that caused the devastating tsunami.
Availability: Limit of one copy to schools, libraries, and homeschoolers world-wide.
Suggested Grade: 5-Adult
Order Number: order by title
Format: Poster
Special Notes: Email requests only.
Source: Incorporated Research Institutions for Seismology
1200 New York Avenue, N. W., Suite 800
Washington, DC 20005
World Wide Web URL: http://www.iris.edu
Email Address: EandOproduct@iris.edu

Chalkbored
Resources for high school chemistry: worksheets, labs, handouts, and PowerPoint lessons.
Availability: All requesters
Suggested Grade: 9-12
Order Number: not applicable
Format: Web Site
Source: Jeremy Schneider
World Wide Web URL:
http://www.chalkbored.com/lessons/chemistry-12.htm

Chemical Reactions
Students will learn about atoms, matter, and chemical reactions.
Availability: All requesters
Suggested Grade: 6-12
Order Number: not applicable
Format: WebQuest
Source: Lisa Kendra
World Wide Web URL:
http://www.can-do.com/uci/ssi2002/chemicalreactions.html

COAST
Many resources for studying about oceans.
Availability: All requesters
Suggested Grade: 4-12
Order Number: not applicable
Format: Web Site
Source: Consortium for Oceanographic Activities for Students and Teachers
World Wide Web URL: http://www.coast-nopp.org/

Coral Reefs
Addresses what coral reefs are, their ecological role, and

major threats to their sustainability.
Availability: All requesters
Suggested Grade: 6-Adult
Order Number: not applicable
Format: Online Fact Sheet

Source: Ecological Society of America, The
World Wide Web URL:
http://www.esa.org/education_diversity/factsheets.php

Dan's Wild, Wild Weather Page
Information and activities for studying the weather.
Availability: All requesters
Suggested Grade: All ages
Order Number: not applicable
Format: Web Site

Source: Dan Satterfield
World Wide Web URL: http://www.wildwildweather.com/

Devoured by the Dark
A bi-weekly, on-line "horror" story about three young people who try to save their town from the Dark.
Availability: All requesters
Suggested Grade: 6-12
Order Number: not applicable
Format: Online Story

Source: California Energy Commission
World Wide Web URL: http://www.energyquest.ca.gov/

Dinosaurs: Facts and Fiction
Answers a series of basic questions on dinosaurs.
Availability: All requesters
Suggested Grade: 4-12
Order Number: not applicable
Format: Online Leaflet; 10 pages

Source: USGS Information Services
World Wide Web URL: http://pubs.usgs.gov/gip/dinosaurs/

Don't Burn, Build!
You are part of an elite engineering team, personally invited by the Indian government, to participate in a major competition to design a new bridge for the city of Calcutta, or Kolkata.
Availability: All requesters
Suggested Grade: 9-12
Order Number: not applicable
Format: WebQuest

Source: Kate Kairys, Katie O'Gorman, and Alice Chen
World Wide Web URL:
http://chalk.richmond.edu/education/projects/webquests/bridge/

Earth Science Explorer
An earth science museum on the Web, devoted to teaching about dinosaurs. Includes a student area as well as an area for teachers.
Availability: All requesters
Suggested Grade: All ages
Order Number: not applicable
Format: Web Site

Source: Wheeling Jesuit University
World Wide Web URL:
http://www.cotf.edu/ete/modules/msese/explorer.html

EdHeads: Activate Your Mind
A site about simple machines, the weather and even a virtual knee replacement surgery--all examples of how machines work.
Availability: All requesters
Suggested Grade: 2-12
Order Number: not applicable
Format: Web Site

Source: Edheads.org
World Wide Web URL:
www.edheads.orghttp://www.edheads.org

Energy4me Kit
Classroom presentation kit on all forms of energy with questions, grade-level activities, a brochure, bookmark, and poster.
Availability: Single copies to schools and libraries world-wide.
Suggested Grade: K-12
Order Number: order by title
Format: Packet of materials

Source: Society of Petroleum Engineers
222 Palisades Creek Drive
Richardson, TX 75080-2040
Phone: 1-972-952-9393, ext. 1125
Fax: 1-866-719-8241
Email Address: EnergyEd@Energy4me.org

Energy Science Projects
Energy based science projects.
Availability: All requesters
Suggested Grade: All ages
Order Number: not applicable
Format: Web Site

Source: California Energy Commission
World Wide Web URL:
http://www.energyquest.ca.gov/projects/index.html

Energy Story, The
Tells the story of what energy is, where it comes from, how it is used, and how to save it.
Availability: All requesters
Suggested Grade: All ages
Order Number: not applicable
Format: Online Article

Source: California Energy Commission
World Wide Web URL: http://www.energyquest.ca.gov/

Exploring the Earth Using Seismology
Explains how analyzing seismic waves create by earthquakes allows scientists to explore the Earth's deep interior.

Availability: Limit of one copy to schools, libraries, and homeschoolers world-wide.
Suggested Grade: 5-Adult
Order Number: order by title
Format: Handout
Special Notes: Email requests only. This publication can also be downloaded from the web site.

Source: Incorporated Research Institutions for Seismology
1200 New York Avenue, N. W., Suite 800
Washington, DC 20005
World Wide Web URL: http://www.iris.edu
Email Address: EandOproduct@iris.edu

Exploring the Earth Using Seismology

The paths of some of the seismic waves created by earthquakes and the ground motion that they caused are shown in this poster.

Availability: Limit of one copy to schools, libraries, and homeschoolers world-wide.
Suggested Grade: 5-Adult
Languages: English; Spanish
Order Number: order by title
Format: Poster
Special Notes: Email requests only.

Source: Incorporated Research Institutions for Seismology
1200 New York Avenue, N. W., Suite 800
Washington, DC 20005
World Wide Web URL: http://www.iris.edu
Email Address: EandOproduct@iris.edu

Farm to Fork Pasta Sample

A small bag showing separate sections of durum wheat, semolina and pasta with an information card.

Availability: Single copies to schools, libraries, and homeschoolers in the United States.
Suggested Grade: K-12
Order Number: order by title
Format: Sample of wheat

Source: North Dakota Wheat Commission
2401 46th Avenue SE, Suite 104
Mandan, ND 58554-4829
Phone: 1-701-328-5111
Fax: 1-701-663-5787
World Wide Web URL: http://www.ndwheat.com
Email Address: ndwheat@ndwheat.com

Finding Funding for Environmental Education Efforts

Presents steps in identifying potential sources for funding and how to apply for those funds.

Availability: All requesters
Suggested Grade: Teacher Reference
Order Number: not applicable
Production Date: 1993
Format: Online Article

Source: Joe E. Heimlich and Dawn D. Puglisi
World Wide Web URL:
http://www.ericdigests.org/1993/funding.htm

Floods

Outlines the basics of floods, how they are measured, their benefits, flood control, and land management.

Availability: All requesters
Suggested Grade: 6-Adult
Order Number: not applicable
Format: Online Fact Sheet

Source: Ecological Society of America, The
World Wide Web URL:
http://www.esa.org/education_diversity/factsheets.php

Fossil Fuels

Explains what fossil fuels are.

Availability: All requesters
Suggested Grade: 4-12
Order Number: not applicable
Format: Online Article

Source: California Energy Commission
World Wide Web URL: http://www.energyquest.ca.gov/

Galloping Gertie

In this unit students explore bridges and the various forces that affect their stability.

Availability: All requesters
Suggested Grade: 5-12
Order Number: not applicable
Format: Online Lesson Plan

Source: Shirley Willingham
World Wide Web URL:
http://teachertech.rice.edu/Participants/swilling/lessons2/bridges/kidpages/index.html

Geothermal Energy

Explains this form of energy.

Availability: All requesters
Suggested Grade: 4-12
Order Number: not applicable
Format: Online Article

Source: California Energy Commission
World Wide Web URL: http://www.energyquest.ca.gov/

Glossary of Environment and Microbiology Terms

Don't be embarrassed when someone starts discussing F/M ratios and MCRTs--find out what they are in this glossary.

Availability: All requesters
Suggested Grade: 6-Adult
Order Number: not applicable
Format: Online Glossary

Source: Alken-Murray Corp.
World Wide Web URL:
http://www.alken-murray.com/glossarybug.html

Growing Cane Sugar Crystals on a Small Scale

Two methods of growing crystals of "sucrose" in the classroom are detailed in this kit.

Availability: One kit to schools and homeschoolers WEST OF THE MISSISSIPPI ONLY. May be copied. Send a self-addressed business-size envelope. Make request on official stationery.
Suggested Grade: 4-12
Order Number: order by title
Format: Teacher's Kit

Source: C & H Sugar Co., Inc.
Connie C. Hunter
Consumer Affairs Administrator
830 Loring Avenue
Crockett, CA 94525
Fax: 1-510-787-4245
Email Address: conniehunter@chsugar.com

Here Comes the Sun

A self-guided tutorial on the sun and its effects on the earth.
Availability: All requesters
Suggested Grade: 4-12
Order Number: not applicable
Format: Online Tutorial

Source: Plymouth State College Meteorology Program
World Wide Web URL:
http://vortex.plymouth.edu/sun.html

History of Seismology, The

Depicting original sketches, photographs and colorful new imagery, this poster captures the major milestones of the development in the field of seismology.
Availability: Limit of one copy to schools, libraries, and homeschoolers world-wide.
Suggested Grade: 5-Adult
Order Number: order by title
Format: Poster
Special Notes: Email requests only.

Source: Incorporated Research Institutions for Seismology
1200 New York Avenue, N. W., Suite 800
Washington, DC 20005
World Wide Web URL: http://www.iris.edu
Email Address: EandOproduct@iris.edu

How Are Earthquakes Located?

Explains how earthquakes are located using seismology.
Availability: Limit of one copy to schools, libraries, and homeschoolers world-wide.
Suggested Grade: 5-Adult
Order Number: order by title
Format: Handout
Special Notes: Email requests only. This publication can also be downloaded from the web site.

Source: Incorporated Research Institutions for Seismology
1200 New York Avenue, N. W., Suite 800
Washington, DC 20005
World Wide Web URL: http://www.iris.edu
Email Address: EandOproduct@iris.edu

How Does a Seismometer Work?

Clearly answers this question.
Availability: Limit of one copy to schools, libraries, and homeschoolers world-wide.
Suggested Grade: 5-Adult
Order Number: order by title
Format: Handout
Special Notes: Email requests only. This publication can also be downloaded from the web site.

Source: Incorporated Research Institutions for Seismology
1200 New York Avenue, N. W., Suite 800
Washington, DC 20005
World Wide Web URL: http://www.iris.edu
Email Address: EandOproduct@iris.edu

How Often Do Earthquakes Occur?

Explains that earthquakes are always happening somewhere.
Availability: Limit of one copy to schools, libraries, and homeschoolers world-wide.
Suggested Grade: 5-Adult
Order Number: order by title
Format: One page handout
Special Notes: Email requests only. This publication can also be downloaded from the web site.

Source: Incorporated Research Institutions for Seismology
1200 New York Avenue, N. W., Suite 800
Washington, DC 20005
World Wide Web URL: http://www.iris.edu
Email Address: EandOproduct@iris.edu

Hydro-Electric Energy

Defines and discusses hydro power.
Availability: All requesters
Suggested Grade: 4-12
Order Number: not applicable
Format: Online Article

Source: California Energy Commission
World Wide Web URL: http://www.energyquest.ca.gov/

Hydrosphere Ecolinks

Provides links to classroom activities, web sites, lessons, and more on this subject.
Availability: All requesters
Suggested Grade: 4-12
Order Number: not applicable
Format: Web Site

Source: Miami Museum of Science/Science Learning Network
World Wide Web URL: http://www.miamisci.org/ecolinks/

Hypoxia

Defines hypoxia and discusses its causes, effects, how it develops, and how to protect waters from it.
Availability: All requesters
Suggested Grade: 6-Adult
Order Number: not applicable
Format: Online Fact Sheet

Source: Ecological Society of America, The
World Wide Web URL:
http://www.esa.org/education_diversity/factsheets.php

Invasion
Presents information on the increase of invasions by nonnative species, the threats they impose, and what can be done.
Availability: All requesters
Suggested Grade: 6-Adult
Order Number: not applicable
Format: Online Fact Sheet
Source: Ecological Society of America, The
World Wide Web URL:
http://www.esa.org/education_diversity/factsheets.php

Light
Explains how all of the colors of the spectrum are made up of different lights.
Availability: All requesters
Suggested Grade: 6-12
Order Number: not applicable
Format: Online Lesson Plan
Source: Consuela Llamas
World Wide Web URL:
http://teachertech.rice.edu/Participants/cllamas/lessons/science/light/studentlight.htm

Living Oceans
A very complete online tutorial that teaches about our oceans.
Availability: All requesters
Suggested Grade: 6-12
Order Number: not applicable
Format: Online Tutorial
Source: SeaWIFS Project
World Wide Web URL:
http://oceancolor.gsfc.nasa.gov/SeaWiFS/LIVING_OCEAN/

MicrobeWorld
Provides educational activities and multimedia resources for studying microbiology.
Availability: All requesters
Suggested Grade: 6-12
Order Number: not applicable
Format: Web Site
Source: American Society for Microbiology
World Wide Web URL: http://www.microbeworld.org/

Motion Mountain: The Physics Textbook
Over 1200 pages; here is a complete physics textbook.
Availability: All requesters
Suggested Grade: 6-12
Order Number: not applicable
Format: Downloadable Book
Source: Christoph Schiller
World Wide Web URL: http://www.motionmountain.net/

Nuclear Energy
Explains nuclear energy.
Availability: All requesters
Suggested Grade: 4-12
Order Number: not applicable
Format: Online Article
Source: California Energy Commission
World Wide Web URL: http://www.energyquest.ca.gov/

Ocean in Motion
Facts, information and quizzes about the ocean.
Availability: All requesters
Suggested Grade: 4-12
Order Number: not applicable
Format: Online Articles
Source: Office of Naval Research
World Wide Web URL:
http://www.onr.navy.mil/focus/ocean/motion/default.htm

Ocean Water
Information about this resource.
Availability: All requesters
Suggested Grade: 4-12
Order Number: not applicable
Format: Online Articles
Source: Office of Naval Research
World Wide Web URL:
http://www.onr.navy.mil/focus/ocean/water/default.htm

Periodic Table Adventure
Includes lessons on the history of the periodic table, a WebQuest, and more lessons to make learning about the periodic table fun.
Availability: All requesters
Suggested Grade: 6-12
Order Number: not applicable
Format: Web Site
Source: D. Gibson
World Wide Web URL:
http://web.buddyproject.org/web017/web017/

Physical Science Activity Manual
This book contains 34 hands-on activities to bring excitement to your classroom.
Availability: All requesters
Suggested Grade: Teacher Reference
Order Number: not applicable
Format: Downloadable Book
Source: Center of Excellence for Science and Mathematics Education, The
World Wide Web URL:
http://www.utm.edu/departments/cece/cesme/psam/psam.shtml

Physics Classroom, The
An online physics tutorial for high school physics students.
Availability: All requesters
Suggested Grade: 9-12
Order Number: not applicable
Format: Online Tutorial
Source: Tom Henderson
World Wide Web URL: http://www.physicsclassroom.com/

Plant Health Instructor, The
Offers online laboratories and demonstrations that teach basic principles of plant health science.
Availability: All requesters
Suggested Grade: All ages
Order Number: not applicable
Format: Web Site
Source: American Phytopathological Society, The
World Wide Web URL:
http://www.apsnet.org/edcenter/Pages/phi.aspx

Red Gold: The Epic Story of Blood
Includes lesson plans, a teacher's guide, and lots of information about blood. Discusses facts and myths about blood as well.
Availability: All requesters
Suggested Grade: 6-12
Order Number: not applicable
Format: Web Site
Source: Thirteen Online
World Wide Web URL: http://www.pbs.org/wnet/redgold/

Research Vessels
Information about these vessels which give us so much information.
Availability: All requesters
Suggested Grade: 4-12
Order Number: not applicable
Format: Online Articles
Source: Office of Naval Research
World Wide Web URL:
http://www.onr.navy.mil/focus/ocean/vessels/default.htm

Sciencebase.com
Numerous science articles on all sorts of topics in the field.
Availability: All requesters
Suggested Grade: 9-Adult
Order Number: not applicable
Format: Online Articles
Source: David Bradley
World Wide Web URL: http://sciencebase.com/

Science Fair Primer
Presents ideas developed over twenty years of teaching science that are designed to help students develop successful science fair projects.
Availability: All requesters
Suggested Grade: All ages
Order Number: not applicable
Format: Online Primer
Source: Ted Rowan
World Wide Web URL:
http://users.rcn.com/tedrowan/primer.html

Science is Fun
This chemistry professional shares the fun of science through home science activities, demonstration shows, and more.
Availability: All requesters
Suggested Grade: All ages
Order Number: not applicable
Format: Web Site
Source: Bassam Z. Shakhashiri
World Wide Web URL: http://scifun.chem.wisc.edu/

ScienceMaster
News, homework help, links, articles, and more in all major areas of science.
Availability: All requesters
Suggested Grade: 6-12
Order Number: not applicable
Format: Web Site
Source: KGM Group, Inc., The
World Wide Web URL: http://www.ScienceMaster.com/

Seeing, Hearing, and Smelling the World
Explains all about the five senses.
Availability: All requesters
Suggested Grade: All ages
Languages: English; Spanish
Order Number: not applicable
Format: Web Site or Downloadable Book
Source: Howard Hughes Medical Institute
World Wide Web URL: http://www.hhmi.org/senses/

Short Dictionary of Scientific Quotations, A
Attributes, and explains, quotes from famous men of science, as well as men not of the science world. Example: the founder of IBM was known to have said "I think there's a world market for about five computers."
Availability: All requesters
Suggested Grade: 6-12
Order Number: not applicable
Format: Online Glossary
Source: naturalSCIENCE Journals
World Wide Web URL:
http://naturalscience.com/dsqhome.html

Student's Guide to Alternative Fuel Vehicles, A
Here's information about the type of vehicles we will probably be driving in the future.
Availability: All requesters
Suggested Grade: 6-12
Order Number: not applicable
Format: Online Article
Source: California Energy Commission
World Wide Web URL:
http://www.energyquest.ca.gov/transportation/index.html

Sumatra-Andaman Island Earthquake
This assembly of seismograms displays the vertical movement of the Earth's surface due to seismic waves generated by the earthquake.
Availability: Limit of one copy to schools, libraries, and homeschoolers world-wide.

Suggested Grade: 5-Adult
Order Number: order by title
Format: Poster
Special Notes: Email requests only.

Source: Incorporated Research Institutions for Seismology
1200 New York Avenue, N. W., Suite 800
Washington, DC 20005
World Wide Web URL: http://www.iris.edu
Email Address: EandOproduct@iris.edu

Taconite Pellet Kit

Samples of rock, concentrate, and iron pellets used to make steel.

Availability: Available while supplies last to schools, libraries, and homeschoolers in the United States and Canada.
Suggested Grade: All ages
Order Number: order by title
Format: Samples

Source: Iron Mining Association of Minnesota
324 West Superior Street, Suite 502
Duluth, MN 55802
World Wide Web URL:
www.taconite.orghttp://www.taconite.org

Teachers' Domain

Focuses on life sciences and provides a free multimedia digital library of resources for teachers and students alike.

Availability: All requesters
Suggested Grade: All ages
Order Number: not applicable
Format: Web Site

Source: WGBH Educational Foundation
World Wide Web URL: http://www.teachersdomain.org/

Try Science

Find interactive adventures, experiments, fields trips, and more to learn about science and technology.

Availability: All requesters
Suggested Grade: All ages
Order Number: not applicable
Format: Web Site

Source: TryScience.org
World Wide Web URL: http://www.tryscience.com/

T.W.I.N.K.I.E.S. Project, The

The above acronym stands for Tests With Inorganic Noxious Kakes in Extreme Situations. It is the result of a series of experiments conducted during finals week by some college students to determine the properties of that incredible food, the Twinkie.

Availability: All requesters
Suggested Grade: 6-12
Order Number: not applicable
Format: Web Site

Source: Chris Gouge and Todd Stadler
World Wide Web URL: http://www.twinkiesproject.com/

Ultimate Science Fair Project Resource, The

All the information you need for conducting or participating in a science fair.

Availability: All requesters
Suggested Grade: All ages
Order Number: not applicable
Format: Web Site

Source: Dr. Shawn & Dr. Michelle
World Wide Web URL: http://science-project.com/

Using the Child's Environment to Teach at Home and School

Presents ideas, and the rationale behind them, for teaching environmental education to students using the concept of "home."

Availability: All requesters
Suggested Grade: Teacher Reference
Order Number: not applicable
Production Date: 1994
Format: Online Article

Source: Joe E. Heimlich
World Wide Web URL:
http://www.ericdigests.org/1995-1/teach.htm

Watch Earthquakes as They Occur

Explains how the seismic monitor, located at this web site, works to show live earthquakes.

Availability: Limit of one copy to schools, libraries, and homeschoolers world-wide.
Suggested Grade: 5-Adult
Order Number: order by title
Format: One page handout
Special Notes: Email requests only. This publication can also be downloaded from the web site.

Source: Incorporated Research Institutions for Seismology
1200 New York Avenue, N. W., Suite 800
Washington, DC 20005
World Wide Web URL: http://www.iris.edu
Email Address: EandOproduct@iris.edu

What Does Ecology Have to Do with Me?

Presents an introduction to the science of ecology and its role in human society.

Availability: One copy to schools, libraries, and homeschoolers world-wide.
Suggested Grade: 6-Adult
Order Number: not applicable
Format: Online Fact Sheet
Special Notes: Single print copies may be mailed to requester.

Source: Ecological Society of America, The
World Wide Web URL:
http://www.esa.org/education_diversity/webDocs/ecologyANDme.php

Willo: The Dinosaur With a Heart

Learn what scientists have discovered from their study of Willow--a 66-million-year-old Thescelosaurus.

Availability: All requesters
Suggested Grade: All ages
Order Number: not applicable
Format: Web Site

Source: North Carolina Museum of Natural Sciences and North Carolina State University
World Wide Web URL: http://www.dinoheart.org

Wind Energy

Explains how we can get energy from the wind.

Availability: All requesters
Suggested Grade: 4-12
Order Number: not applicable
Format: Online Article

Source: California Energy Commission
World Wide Web URL: http://www.energyquest.ca.gov/

Wonders of the Seas

Provides information about different animals that live in the oceans, with text and images.

Availability: All requesters
Suggested Grade: All ages
Order Number: not applicable
Format: Web Site

Source: Oceanic Research Group, The
World Wide Web URL:
http://www.oceanicresearch.org/education/wonders/lesson.html

YES Mag Projects

Projects designed for students to do at home.

Availability: All requesters
Suggested Grade: All ages
Order Number: not applicable
Format: Web Site

Source: YES Mag
World Wide Web URL:
http://www.yesmag.bc.ca/projects/projects.html

Africanized Honey Bees on the Move Lesson Plans
A number of lesson plans, for all ages, about the move of Africanized honey bees into the Southwest.
Availability: All requesters
Suggested Grade: K-12
Order Number: not applicable
Format: Online Lesson Plans
Special Notes: May also be purchased for $17.00.
Source: University of Arizona Africanized Honey Bee Education Project, The
World Wide Web URL:
http://ag.arizona.edu/pubs/insects/ahb/ahbhome.html

Alaska Wildlife Notebook Series
Includes descriptions of more than 100 of Alaska's wild fish and game animals.
Availability: All requesters
Suggested Grade: All ages
Order Number: not applicable
Format: Downloadable Fact Sheets
Special Notes: May be purchased, in print form, for $12.50.
Source: Alaska Department of Fish & Game
World Wide Web URL: http://www.adfg.alaska.gov/index.cfm?adfg=educators.notebookseries

Amphibian Embryology Tutorial
An online tutorial for learning more about amphibians.
Availability: All requesters
Suggested Grade: 10-Adult
Order Number: not applicable
Format: Online Tutorial
Source: Jeff Hardin
World Wide Web URL:
http://worms.zoology.wisc.edu/frogs/welcome.html

Animal Bytes
Brief information about amphibians, birds, fish, insects, invertebrates, mammals, and reptiles.
Availability: All requesters
Suggested Grade: All ages
Order Number: not applicable
Format: Web Site
Source: Sea World/Busch Gardens
World Wide Web URL: http://www.seaworld.org/animal-info/animal-bytes/index.htm

Animal Diversity Web
An online database of animal natural history, distribution, classification, and conservation biology.
Availability: All requesters
Suggested Grade: 6-12
Order Number: not applicable
Format: Online Database
Source: University of Michigan Museum of Zoology
World Wide Web URL:
http://animaldiversity.ummz.umich.edu/site/index.html

Animals A-Z
Find out about birds, mammals, reptiles, and more.
Availability: All requesters
Suggested Grade: All ages
Order Number: not applicable
Format: Web Site
Source: Oakland Zoo
World Wide Web URL:
http://www.oaklandzoo.org/atoz/atoz.html

ButterflySite.com
Explore 12 butterfly topics with pages packed full of butterfly information.
Availability: All requesters
Suggested Grade: All ages
Order Number: not applicable
Format: Web Site
Source: Randi Jones
World Wide Web URL: http://www.thebutterflysite.com/

Carter House Natural Science Museum
Take a virtual nature walk and then a virtual tour of the museum.
Availability: All requesters
Suggested Grade: All ages
Order Number: not applicable
Format: Web Site
Special Notes: This URL will lead you to a subject page. Then click on the appropriate subject heading.
Source: ThinkQuest
World Wide Web URL:
http://www.thinkquest.org/pls/html/think.library

Cetacean Fact Packs
Facts sheets about whales and dolphins.
Availability: All requesters
Suggested Grade: All ages
Order Number: not applicable
Format: Downloadable Fact Sheets
Source: American Cetacean Society
World Wide Web URL:
http://www.acsonline.org/factpack/index.html

Checklist of Kansas Dragonflies
Illustrates the many types of dragonflies found in Kansas and tells about their habits and habitat.
Availability: One copy to schools, libraries, and homeschoolers world-wide. May be copied.
Suggested Grade: 5-Adult
Order Number: Vol. 43, No. 2
Production Date: 1996
Format: Booklet
Special Notes: May also be downloaded from the web site.
Source: Kansas School Naturalist, The
Department of Biology, Box 4050
Emporia State University
Emporia, KS 66801-5087
Phone: 1-620-341-5614

Fax: 1-620-341-5607
World Wide Web URL:
www.emporia.edu/ksn/http://www.emporia.edu/ksn/
Email Address: ksnaturl@emporia.edu

Checklist of Kansas Jumping Spiders
Life cycle and habitat information about this fascinating, colorful hunting spider.
Availability: One copy to schools, libraries, and homeschoolers world-wide. May be copied.
Suggested Grade: 5-Adult
Order Number: Vol. 47, No. 1
Production Date: 2001
Format: Booklet
Special Notes: May also be downloaded from the web site.
Source: Kansas School Naturalist, The
Department of Biology, Box 4050
Emporia State University
Emporia, KS 66801-5087
Phone: 1-620-341-5614
Fax: 1-620-341-5607
World Wide Web URL:
www.emporia.edu/ksn/http://www.emporia.edu/ksn/
Email Address: ksnaturl@emporia.edu

Checklist of Kansas Orbweaving Spiders
Worldwide, there are 3,846 describes species of orbweaving spiders--currently 63 different orbweavers are known to exist in Kansas. Here is more information about this spider.
Availability: One copy to schools, libraries, and homeschoolers world-wide. May be copied.
Suggested Grade: 5-Adult
Order Number: Vol. 52, No. 2
Production Date: 2005
Format: Booklet
Special Notes: May also be downloaded from the web site.
Source: Kansas School Naturalist, The
Department of Biology, Box 4050
Emporia State University
Emporia, KS 66801-5087
Phone: 1-620-341-5614
Fax: 1-620-341-5607
World Wide Web URL:
www.emporia.edu/ksn/http://www.emporia.edu/ksn/
Email Address: ksnaturl@emporia.edu

Collection and Maintenance of Ants and Studying Ants
Shows how to collect and maintain ants with the minimum amount of work and expense.
Availability: One copy to schools, libraries, and homeschoolers world-wide. May be copied.
Suggested Grade: 5-Adult
Order Number: Volume 41, No. 1
Production Date: 1994
Format: Booklet
Special Notes: May also be downloaded from the web site.
Source: Kansas School Naturalist, The
Department of Biology, Box 4050
Emporia State University
Emporia, KS 66801-5087
Phone: 1-620-341-5614
Fax: 1-620-341-5607
World Wide Web URL:
www.emporia.edu/ksn/http://www.emporia.edu/ksn/
Email Address: ksnaturl@emporia.edu

Elephant Information Repository
An in-depth resource for elephant related news, events, and a "trunk" full of elephant related information.
Availability: All requesters
Suggested Grade: 6-12
Order Number: not applicable
Format: Web Site
Source: Paul MacKenzie
World Wide Web URL: http://elephant.elehost.com/

eNature.com
An enormous collection of field guides to plant and animal species, habitat guides, and much more.
Availability: All requesters
Suggested Grade: K-12
Order Number: not applicable
Format: Web Site
Source: enature.com
World Wide Web URL: http://www.enature.com/

Feral Pigeons
Information about the life and habitat of these birds.
Availability: One copy to schools, libraries, and homeschoolers world-wide. May be copied.
Suggested Grade: 5-Adult
Order Number: Volume 45, No. 2
Production Date: 1998
Format: Booklet
Special Notes: May also be downloaded from the web site.
Source: Kansas School Naturalist, The
Department of Biology, Box 4050
Emporia State University
Emporia, KS 66801-5087
Phone: 1-620-341-5614
Fax: 1-620-341-5607
World Wide Web URL:
www.emporia.edu/ksn/http://www.emporia.edu/ksn/
Email Address: ksnaturl@emporia.edu

Field Trip Earth
Take your students on a world tour as they learn about Appalachian black bears, red wolves of Alligator River, the elephants of Cameroon and many more species without ever leaving the classroom.
Availability: All requesters
Suggested Grade: All ages
Order Number: not applicable
Format: Web Site

Source: North Carolina Zoological Society
World Wide Web URL: http://www.fieldtripearth.org/

Florida Panther Net
A complete web site devoted to teaching students about the state animal of Florida. Includes games, activities, lesson plans, and more.
Availability: All requesters
Suggested Grade: All ages
Order Number: not applicable
Format: Web Site
Source: Florida Panther Net
World Wide Web URL: http://www.floridapanthernet.org/

For the Birds
How to attract different species of birds, feed them, and select suitable homes.
Availability: All requesters
Suggested Grade: All ages
Order Number: not applicable
Production Date: 1997
Format: Online Book; 50 pages
Special Notes: Use the on-site search engine to easily find this title. You may request a printed copy mailed to you for a fee.
Source: Federal Citizen Information Center
World Wide Web URL: http://www.pueblo.gsa.gov/

Froggy Page, The
Information about frogs from literature to science.
Availability: All requesters
Suggested Grade: All ages
Order Number: not applicable
Format: Web Site
Source: Sandra Loosemore
World Wide Web URL: http://www.frogsonice.com/froggy/

Fruit Bats, Cats, and Naked Mole Rats: Lifelong Learning at the Zoo
Focuses on how learners process information and how professional staff and visitors can promote learning at the zoo.
Availability: All requesters
Suggested Grade: Teacher Reference
Order Number: not applicable
Production Date: 1994
Format: Online Article
Source: Barbara S. Thomson and Jason J. Diem
World Wide Web URL:
http://www.ericdigests.org/1995-1/bats.htm

Greater Prairie Chicken
Information about the life and habitat of this animal.
Availability: One copy to schools, libraries, and homeschoolers world-wide. May be copied.
Suggested Grade: 5-Adult
Order Number: Volume 45, No. 1
Production Date: 1998
Format: Booklet
Special Notes: May also be downloaded from the web site.
Source: Kansas School Naturalist, The
Department of Biology, Box 4050
Emporia State University
Emporia, KS 66801-5087
Phone: 1-620-341-5614
Fax: 1-620-341-5607
World Wide Web URL:
www.emporia.edu/ksn/http://www.emporia.edu/ksn/
Email Address: ksnaturl@emporia.edu

Hawaiian Plant Detectives
Facts, photos, and more about native Hawaiian plants.
Availability: All requesters
Suggested Grade: 4-12
Order Number: not applicable
Format: Web Site
Source: Kapunahala, Puuhale, and Wheeler Elementary Schools
World Wide Web URL:
http://www.k12.hi.us/~kapunaha/student_projects/hawn_plants/HawaiianPlant.htm

Insects in the Classroom Lesson Plans
All sorts of lesson plans for students from age 3 on up.
Availability: All requesters
Suggested Grade: preK-12
Order Number: not applicable
Format: Online Lesson Plans
Source: Texas A & M University, Department of Entomology
World Wide Web URL:
http://iitc.tamu.edu/1998and2000/lesson_plans.html

Kentucky Bug Connection Teaching Resources
Entomology resources for parents and educators.
Availability: All requesters
Suggested Grade: 6-12
Order Number: not applicable
Format: Online Lesson Plans and Curriculum Guides
Source: University of Kentucky Entomology
World Wide Web URL:
http://www.uky.edu/Agriculture/CritterFiles/casefile/bugconnection/teaching/teaching.htm

Mammals, Amphibians, and Reptiles
Lists the species found in Acadia National Park.
Availability: Limit of 5 copies to schools, libraries, and homeschoolers world-wide.
Suggested Grade: 6-Adult
Order Number: order by title
Production Date: 2006
Format: Brochure
Source: Acadia National Park Information
P. O. Box 177
Bar Harbor, ME 04609
Phone: 1-207-288-3338

Fax: 1-207-288-8813
World Wide Web URL: http://www.nps.gov/acad
Email Address: acadia_information@nps.gov

Mammals at the National Zoo
From acouchi to zebra, here are the animals that live at the National Zoo with links to fact sheets and articles about them.
Availability: All requesters
Suggested Grade: All ages
Order Number: not applicable
Format: Downloadable Fact Sheets
Source: Smithsonian National Zoological Park
World Wide Web URL:
http://nationalzoo.si.edu/Animals/AnimalIndex/mammalsalpha.cfm

Manatees: An Educator's Guide
Tells about the endangered manatee and its environment.
Availability: Single copies to schools, libraries, and homeschoolers world-wide. Make request on official stationery. Send a 9 x 12 inch envelope with $2.07 postage affixed for US requests; 2.85 for Canada.
Suggested Grade: K-12
Order Number: order by title
Format: Teacher's Guide
Special Notes: Includes a poster.
Source: Save the Manatee Club
500 N. Maitland Ave.
Maitland, FL 32751
Phone: 1-800-432-5646
Fax: 1-407-539-0871
World Wide Web URL: http://www.savethemanatee.org
Email Address: education@savethemanatee.org

Melissa Kaplan's Herp Care Information Collection
Everything you want to know about raising reptiles as pets--includes a section on convincing parents you can take care of one and that they are really cool pets.
Availability: All requesters
Suggested Grade: All ages
Order Number: not applicable
Format: Web Site
Source: Melissa Kaplan
World Wide Web URL: http://www.anapsid.org/

MendelWeb
Information on the genetics of plants.
Availability: All requesters
Suggested Grade: 9-12
Order Number: not applicable
Format: Web Site
Source: Roger B. Blumberg
World Wide Web URL: http://www.mendelweb.org/

New Zealand Brown Teal Online
Provides information about this critically endangered duck and the efforts to help conserve and manage them.
Availability: All requesters
Suggested Grade: All ages
Order Number: not applicable
Format: Web Site
Source: brownteal.com
World Wide Web URL: http://www.brownteal.com/

Now You See Them, Now You Don't: Vanishing Vernal Pools
Learn about species and landscape common to these special wetlands appearing in late winter and spring, then vanishing during summer.
Availability: All requesters
Suggested Grade: 4-12
Order Number: not applicable
Format: Web Site
Special Notes: This URL will lead you to a subject page. Then click on the appropriate subject heading.
Source: ThinkQuest
World Wide Web URL:
http://www.thinkquest.org/pls/html/think.library

Official Seed Starting Home Page, The
A site started simply for the love of gardening. Information about how to grow flowers, vegetables, and herbs is found here.
Availability: All requesters
Suggested Grade: All ages
Order Number: not applicable
Format: Web Site
Source: Weekend Gardener, The
World Wide Web URL: http://www.chestnut-sw.com/seedhp.htm

POP Goes Antarctica?
Follow this teacher as she joins a team of scientists to research the effects of persistent organic pollutants on the food web of Antarctica.
Availability: All requesters
Suggested Grade: 6-12
Order Number: not applicable
Format: Web Site
Source: Susan Cowles
World Wide Web URL:
http://literacynet.org/polar/pop/html/project.html

Prairie Fires
Discusses the history of prairie fires in Kansas and explains why they benefit wildlife.
Availability: Classroom quantities to schools, libraries, and homeschoolers world-wide. May be copied.
Suggested Grade: 5-Adult
Order Number: Vol. 39, No. 2
Production Date: 1993
Format: Article
Special Notes: May also be downloaded from the web site.

Source: Kansas School Naturalist, The
Department of Biology, Box 4050
Emporia State University
Emporia, KS 66801-5087
Phone: 1-620-341-5614
Fax: 1-620-341-5607
World Wide Web URL:
www.emporia.edu/ksn/http://www.emporia.edu/ksn/
Email Address: ksnaturl@emporia.edu

Reptiles & Amphibians
A list of all the reptiles and amphibians at the National Zoo with links to more information about each.

Availability: All requesters
Suggested Grade: All ages
Order Number: not applicable
Format: Downloadable Fact Sheets

Source: Smithsonian National Zoological Park
World Wide Web URL:
http://nationalzoo.si.edu/Animals/ReptilesAmphibians/Index/default.cfm

Salmon Homing Instincts
Follows the interesting lifestyle of the salmon and how they find their way back to the stream in which they were hatched.

Availability: All requesters
Suggested Grade: 3-9
Order Number: not applicable
Format: Online Lesson Plan

Source: Deborah A. Werner
World Wide Web URL:
http://www.eduref.org/Virtual/Lessons/Science/Animals/ANM0049.html

Snakes of Massachusetts
Lots of information on snakes.

Availability: All requesters
Suggested Grade: All ages
Order Number: not applicable
Format: Web Site

Source: University of Massachusetts Extension
World Wide Web URL: http://www.masnakes.org/

Teacher's Guides
Here are a number of teacher's guides (all downloadable) for teaching students about how people interact with the environment and how we can best care for Earth's resources.

Availability: All requesters
Suggested Grade: All ages
Order Number: not applicable
Format: Downloadable Teacher's Guides

Source: Sea World/Busch Gardens
World Wide Web URL: http://www.seaworld.org/just-for-teachers/guides/index.htm

Toads and Frogs of West Virginia
Find out more about the species of toads and frogs who reside in this state.

Availability: Classroom quantities to schools, libraries, and homeschoolers in the United States.
Suggested Grade: 3-12
Order Number: order by title
Format: Brochure

Source: West Virginia Wildlife Resources Section
West Virginia Division of Natural Resources
324 Fourth Avenue
South Charleston, WV 25303
Phone: 1-304-558-2771
Fax: 1-304-558-3147
World Wide Web URL: http://www.wvdnr.gov

Top North American Bird Fact Sheets
includes identification information, photos, audio samples of birdsong and much more for the most popular birds of North America.

Availability: All requesters
Suggested Grade: All ages
Order Number: not applicable
Format: Online Fact Sheets

Source: Birding.com
World Wide Web URL:
http://www.birding.com/topbirds.asp

Web of Life Game
Here is a game to play that illustrates the impact of zebra mussels on the native species.

Availability: All requesters
Suggested Grade: 4-12
Order Number: not applicable
Format: Online Lesson Plan

Source: Marcella Dawson
World Wide Web URL:
http://teachertech.rice.edu/Participants/dawsonm/Lessons/game.htm

WhaleNet
Not only provides information about whales, but allows students and teachers to share information as well.

Availability: All requesters
Suggested Grade: K-12
Order Number: not applicable
Format: Web Site

Source: Wheelock College
World Wide Web URL:
http://whale.wheelock.edu/Welcome.html

Winged Wisdom
A pet bird e-zine for exotic birds and pet parrots.

Availability: All requesters
Suggested Grade: All ages
Order Number: not applicable
Format: Online Magazine
Special Notes: No new editions have been published recently but informative articles are still on-line.

Source: Birds n Ways
World Wide Web URL:
http://www.birdsnways.com/wisdom/

Yucca Plant and the Yucca Moth, The
Explains the concept of "mutualism" between the yucca plant and the yucca moth and talks about the life cycle of each.

Availability: One copy to schools, libraries, and homeschoolers world-wide. May be copied.
Suggested Grade: 5-Adult
Order Number: Vol. 41, No. 2
Production Date: 1994
Format: Article
Special Notes: May also be downloaded from the web site.

Source: Kansas School Naturalist, The
Department of Biology, Box 4050
Emporia State University
Emporia, KS 66801-5087
Phone: 1-620-341-5614
Fax: 1-620-341-5607
World Wide Web URL:
www.emporia.edu/ksn/http://www.emporia.edu/ksn/
Email Address: ksnaturl@emporia.edu

About Famous People
A number of biographies can be found here.
Availability: All requesters
Suggested Grade: 4-12
Order Number: not applicable
Format: Web Site
Source: John T. Marck
World Wide Web URL:
http://www.aboutfamouspeople.com/

Anne Frank in the World Teacher Workbook
Students will learn more about Anne Frank and the discrimination that prevailed in that time.
Availability: All requesters
Suggested Grade: 3-12
Order Number: not applicable
Format: Downloadable Teacher's Guide
Source: Utah State Office of Education
World Wide Web URL:
http://www.uen.org/annefrank/information.shtml

Astronaut Biographies
Here is biographical information on the members of the space flight crews and candidates for future missions as well.
Availability: All requesters
Suggested Grade: 6-12
Order Number: not applicable
Format: Online Biographies
Source: NASA Johnson Space Center
World Wide Web URL: http://www.jsc.nasa.gov/Bios/

Baseball Hall of Fame and Museum
Learn about the greatest players of all time, test your knowledge of this sport, and more.
Availability: All requesters
Suggested Grade: 4-12
Order Number: not applicable
Format: Web Site
Source: National Baseball Hall of Fame and Museum, The
World Wide Web URL: http://www.baseballhalloffame.org/

Biographies of Famous Chemists
A large number of biographies about famous men and women in the field of chemistry.
Availability: All requesters
Suggested Grade: 6-12
Order Number: not applicable
Format: Online Biographies
Source: University of Liverpool, Department of Chemistry
World Wide Web URL:
http://www.liv.ac.uk/Chemistry/Links/refbiog.html

Biographies of Women Mathematicians
Lots of biographies that illustrate the numerous achievements of women in the field of mathematics.
Availability: All requesters
Suggested Grade: 6-12
Order Number: not applicable
Format: Online Biographies
Source: Agnes Scott College
World Wide Web URL:
http://www.agnesscott.edu/lriddle/women/women.htm

Colonial Hall
Presents over 100 biographies of people who played a major role in the founding of the United States.
Availability: All requesters
Suggested Grade: 3-12
Order Number: not applicable
Format: Web Site
Source: John Vinci
World Wide Web URL:
http://colonialhall.com/index_t1.php

Combat Credentials
Students will research and write resumes of American presidents based on their military experience and other biographical information.
Availability: All requesters
Suggested Grade: 6-12
Order Number: not applicable
Format: Online Lesson Plan
Source: Annissa Hambouz and Tanya Yasmin Chin
World Wide Web URL:
http://learning.blogs.nytimes.com/2003/09/29/combat-credentials/?scp=1&sq=combat%20credentials&st=cse

Comprehensive Index of Sitters
Matthew Brady took many pictures of famous people during the 1800s. View the pictures and read brief biographies here.
Availability: All requesters
Suggested Grade: 4-12
Order Number: not applicable
Format: Web Site
Source: Mathew Brady
World Wide Web URL:
http://www.npg.si.edu/exh/brady/gallery/bradindx.html

Cut and Paste Biographies
Students will explore the influence of Africa-American artists, writers, and musicians on American culture. After researching different figures in these areas, students create collages representing each person's life and legacy.
Availability: All requesters
Suggested Grade: 6-12
Order Number: not applicable
Format: Online Lesson Plan
Source: Rachel Klein and Javaid Khan
World Wide Web URL:
http://learning.blogs.nytimes.com/2003/09/12/cut-and-paste-biographies/?scp=1&sq=cut%20and%20paste%20biographies&st=cse

Distinguished Women of Past and Present

A web site devoted to providing links to biographies of women who contributed to American culture in many different ways. This page will allow you to find the women by subject, another page allows you to search by name.

Availability: All requesters
Suggested Grade: 2-12
Order Number: not applicable
Format: Web Site

Source: Danuta Bois
World Wide Web URL:
http://www.DistinguishedWomen.com/subject/field.html

Dr. Martin Luther King, Jr. Scavenger Hunt

Students will learn about the leader of the Civil Rights Movement by answering a series of questions. The questions can be answered by following a series of links to other sites.

Availability: All requesters
Suggested Grade: 2-12
Order Number: not applicable
Format: Web Site

Source: Teresa Strong
World Wide Web URL: http://tstrong.com/Martin.htm

Encyclopedia of Famous Puerto Ricans

Biographical information about a number of Puerto Ricans.

Availability: All requesters
Suggested Grade: 4-12
Order Number: not applicable
Format: Web Site

Source: Ramon H. Brau and Francheska Villarinni
World Wide Web URL:
http://puertorriquenosparalahistoria.exactpages.com/

Eva Duarte de Peron: Worthy to Celebrate?

For Spanish level 3 learners and above, this WebQuest will help readers decide if Eva Peron should receive the honor of a national holiday in her memory.

Availability: All requesters
Suggested Grade: 7-Adult
Order Number: not applicable
Format: WebQuest

Source: Kelly Lighthall
World Wide Web URL: http://chalk.richmond.edu/education/projects/webquests/argentina/

Female Mathematicians

From Maria Agnesi to Lai-Sang Young, here are the biographies of a number of female mathematicians.

Availability: All requesters
Suggested Grade: 6-12
Order Number: not applicable
Format: Online Biographies

Source: School of Mathematics and Statistics
World Wide Web URL:
http://www-gap.dcs.st-and.ac.uk/~history/Indexes/Women.html

4000 Years of Women in Science

Information on more than 125 women who have contributed to science.

Availability: All requesters
Suggested Grade: 4-12
Order Number: not applicable
Format: Online Articles

Source: University of Alabama
World Wide Web URL: http://www.astr.ua.edu/4000WS/

Gallery of Achievers

Presents the stories of individuals who have shaped the twentieth century by their accomplishments.

Availability: All requesters
Suggested Grade: 4-12
Order Number: not applicable
Format: Web Site

Source: Academy of Achievement
World Wide Web URL: http://www.achievement.org/

George Armstrong Custer, Lieutenant Colonel, U. S. 7th Cavalry, 1876

A biography of this military man.

Availability: Limit of 30 copies to schools, libraries, and homeschoolers in the United States and Canada.
Suggested Grade: 4-12
Order Number: order by title
Format: Sheet of Paper

Source: Little Bighorn Battlefield National Monument
Division of Interpretation
P. O. Box 39
Crow Agency, MT 59022
Phone: 1-406-638-3217
Fax: 1-406-638-2639
World Wide Web URL: http://www.nps.gov/libi
Email Address: Marvin_Dawes@nps.gov

Great Economists and Their Times

An interactive website that traces the development of the major schools of economic thought through the work of ten important economists.

Availability: All requesters
Suggested Grade: 4-12
Order Number: not applicable
Format: Web Site

Source: Federal Reserve Bank of San Francisco
World Wide Web URL:
http://www.frbsf.org/publications/education/unfrmd.great/greattimes.html

Illustrator Biographies

Biographies of artists who illustrate books.

Availability: All requesters
Suggested Grade: 4-12
Order Number: not applicable
Format: Online Biographies

Source: Bud Plant Illustrated Books
World Wide Web URL: http://www.bpib.com/illustra.htm

Indiana's Famous People
Information about a lot of people from Indiana--including Garfield the cat.
Availability: All requesters
Suggested Grade: 4-12
Order Number: not applicable
Format: Web Site
Source: Bill Holden
World Wide Web URL:
http://www.indianatraveler.com/indiana_famous_people.htm

Martin Luther King, Jr. Papers Project
Presents the published documents of this famous man and a biography as well.
Availability: All requesters
Suggested Grade: 6-12
Order Number: not applicable
Format: Web Site
Source: Stanford University
World Wide Web URL: http://mlk-kpp01.stanford.edu/

Medieval People
Biographies of medieval artists, musicians, authors, religious figures, royalty, nobility, and more.
Availability: All requesters
Suggested Grade: 4-12
Order Number: not applicable
Format: Web Site
Source: Beau A. C. Harbin
World Wide Web URL: http://www.netserf.org/People/

National Women's Hall of Fame
Read biographies of the great women who have contributed to our history.
Availability: All requesters
Suggested Grade: 6-12
Order Number: not applicable
Format: Web Site
Source: National Women's Hall of Fame
World Wide Web URL: http://www.greatwomen.org/

Presidents of the United States, The
Biographical information for all U. S. Presidents.
Availability: All requesters
Suggested Grade: All ages
Order Number: not applicable
Format: Online Articles
Source: White House
World Wide Web URL:
http://www.whitehouse.gov/history/presidents/

Rulers
Contains lists of heads of state and heads of government of all currently existing countries and territories. Birth and death years are provided as well.
Availability: All requesters
Suggested Grade: 4-12
Order Number: not applicable
Format: Web Site
Source: Rulers
World Wide Web URL: http://www.rulers.org

Simply Biographies
A number of biographies of famous inventors, history-makers, and more are found here.
Availability: All requesters
Suggested Grade: 4-12
Order Number: not applicable
Format: Web Site
Source: Anonymous
World Wide Web URL:
http://www.sacklunch.net/biography/

Strange Science: Biographies
Gives biographies of some of the people--scientists, artists and collectors--who contributed to what we know about science today.
Availability: All requesters
Suggested Grade: 4-12
Order Number: not applicable
Format: Online Biographies
Source: Michon Scott
World Wide Web URL:
http://www.strangescience.net/bios.htm

Susan B. Anthony
Presents a biography of this famous woman.
Availability: All requesters
Suggested Grade: 4-12
Order Number: not applicable
Format: Web Site
Source: Jody Litt
World Wide Web URL:
http://www.history.rochester.edu/class/sba/first.htm

Tashunka Witco, Crazy Horse
A biography of this Sioux Nation warrior.
Availability: Limit of 30 copies to schools, libraries, and homeschoolers in the United States and Canada.
Suggested Grade: 4-12
Order Number: order by title
Format: Sheet of Paper
Source: Little Bighorn Battlefield National Monument
Division of Interpretation
P. O. Box 39
Crow Agency, MT 59022
Phone: 1-406-638-3217
Fax: 1-406-638-2639
World Wide Web URL: http://www.nps.gov/libi
Email Address: Marvin_Dawes@nps.gov

Tatanka Yotanka, Sitting Bull

A biography of this Sioux Nation medicine man.

Availability: Limit of 30 copies to schools, libraries, and homeschoolers in the United States and Canada.
Suggested Grade: 4-12
Order Number: order by title
Format: Sheet of Paper

Source: Little Bighorn Battlefield National Monument
Division of Interpretation
P. O. Box 39
Crow Agency, MT 59022
Phone: 1-406-638-3217
Fax: 1-406-638-2639
World Wide Web URL: http://www.nps.gov/libi
Email Address: Marvin_Dawes@nps.gov

Theodore Roosevelt: His Life & Times on Film

Presents 104 short films (for viewing on the Internet) that reflect this man's life from the Spanish-American War in 1889 to his death in 1919.

Availability: All requesters
Suggested Grade: All ages
Order Number: not applicable
Format: Web Site

Source: Library of Congress, American Memory
World Wide Web URL:
http://memory.loc.gov/ammem/collections/troosevelt_film/

World of Scientific Biography

Presents the biographies of 222 important figures in the world of science.

Availability: All requesters
Suggested Grade: 4-12
Order Number: not applicable
Format: Web Site

Source: Eric Weisstein
World Wide Web URL:
http://scienceworld.wolfram.com/biography/

Acadia National Park History

Presents the history of this national park.

Availability: Limit of 5 copies to schools, libraries, and homeschoolers world-wide.
Suggested Grade: 6-Adult
Order Number: order by title
Production Date: 2007
Format: Brochure

Source: Acadia National Park Information
P. O. Box 177
Bar Harbor, ME 04609
Phone: 1-207-288-3338
Fax: 1-207-288-8813
World Wide Web URL: http://www.nps.gov/acad
Email Address: acadia_information@nps.gov

Apache, The

Learn the culture of the Apache people.

Availability: All requesters
Suggested Grade: All ages
Order Number: not applicable
Format: Web Site
Special Notes: This URL will lead you to a subject page. Then click on the appropriate subject heading.

Source: ThinkQuest
World Wide Web URL:
http://www.thinkquest.org/pls/html/think.library

Appomattox Court House Teacher's Packet

A teacher's packet of information for teaching about this historical park in Virginia.

Availability: All requesters
Suggested Grade: All ages
Order Number: not applicable
Format: Downloadable Packet of Materials

Source: Appomattox Court House National Historical Park
Education Coordinator
P. O. Box 218
Appomattox, VA 24522
Phone: 1-434-352-8987, ext. 31
Fax: 1-434-352-8568
World Wide Web URL:
http://www.nps.gov/apco/forteachers/index.htm
Email Address: www.nps.gov/apco

Birds of West Virginia

Lists the various birds found in West Virginia, their habitat preference, and their population status.

Availability: Classroom quantities to schools, libraries, and homeschoolers in the United States.
Suggested Grade: 3-12
Order Number: order by title
Format: Brochure

Source: West Virginia Wildlife Resources Section
West Virginia Division of Natural Resources
324 Fourth Avenue
South Charleston, WV 25303
Phone: 1-304-558-2771
Fax: 1-304-558-3147
World Wide Web URL: http://www.wvdnr.gov

Capitol of the Capital of the World

Tells about this national landmark building and explains the many sights of New York which can be seen from the observatories.

Availability: Classroom quantities to schools, libraries, and homeschoolers in the United States; limit of 5 copies world-wide.
Suggested Grade: All ages
Order Number: order by title
Format: Brochure

Source: Empire State Building Observatories
350 Fifth Avenue, 3rd Floor
New York, NY 10118
Phone: 1-212-736-3100
Fax: 1-212-947-1360
World Wide Web URL: http://www.esbnyc.com

Cherokees of California, The

Here are a number of resources on Cherokee culture, from language and recipes to music and literature.

Availability: All requesters
Suggested Grade: 6-12
Order Number: not applicable
Format: Web Site

Source: Cherokees of California, Inc.
World Wide Web URL:
http://www.powersource.com/cocinc/default.html

Chesapeake Bay Bridge-Tunnel History

Presents the history of this modern engineering wonder.

Availability: Classroom quantities to schools, libraries, and homeschoolers in the United States.
Suggested Grade: 4-12
Order Number: order by title
Format: Information Card

Source: Chesapeake Bay Bridge and Tunnel District
Attn: Patricia Sumners
P. O. Box 111
Cape Charles, VA 23310-0111
Phone: 1-757-331-2960
Fax: 1-757-331-4565
World Wide Web URL: http://www.cbbt.com

Earth Resource System

Provides demographic information for more than 2600 cities in the United States.

Availability: All requesters
Suggested Grade: 4-Adult
Order Number: not applicable
Format: Web Site

Source: ERsys.com
World Wide Web URL: http://www.ersys.com/

Eruptions of Lassen Peak, California, 1914 to 1917

Tells the history of volcanic eruptions in this National Park.

Availability: All requesters
Suggested Grade: 5-12
Order Number: not applicable
Format: Downloadable Fact Sheet

Source: Lassen Volcanic National Park
Attn: Front Desk
P. O. Box 100
Mineral, CA 96063-0100
Phone: 1-530-595-4444
Fax: 1-530-595-3262
World Wide Web URL:
Email Address: lavo_information@nps.gov

Five Themes of Geography and Current Events

Students will learn the five themes of geography.

Availability: All requesters
Suggested Grade: 4-12
Order Number: not applicable
Format: Online Lesson Plan

Source: Russ T. Hutchins
World Wide Web URL:
http://www.eduref.org/Virtual/Lessons/Social_Studies/Geography/GGR0011.html

Historical Perspectives

Tells the history of the Kenilworth Park and Aquatic Gardens wetlands.

Availability: Limit of 1 copy to schools, libraries, and homeschoolers in the United States and Canada.
Suggested Grade: 4-12
Order Number: order by title
Format: Article

Source: Kenilworth Park and Aquatic Gardens
Education Coordinator
1900 Anacostia Drive, SE
Washington, DC 20020
Phone: 1-202-426-6905
Fax: 1-202-426-5991
World Wide Web URL: http://www.nps.gov/keaq
Email Address: Kate-Bucco@nps.gov

Illinois Facts and Figures

Many articles about education, resources, manufacturing and more for the state of Illinois.

Availability: All requesters
Suggested Grade: All ages
Order Number: not applicable
Format: Online Articles

Source: Illinois Department of Commerce & Economic Opportunity
World Wide Web URL:
http://www.illinoisbiz.biz/dceo/Bureaus/Facts_Figures/Factsheets/

Lassen Volcanic National Park, The Story Behind the Landscape

Find out more about the formation of this National Park.

Availability: One copy to schools, libraries, and homeschoolers in the United States and Canada.
Suggested Grade: 4-12
Order Number: order by title
Format: DVD

Source: Lassen Volcanic National Park
Division of Interpretation & Education
P. O. Box 100
Mineral, CA 96063-0100
Phone: 1-530-595-6133
Fax: 1-530-595-6139
World Wide Web URL: http://www.nps.gov/lavo
Email Address: lavo_information@nps.gov

LearnCalifornia

Learn about the history of California.

Availability: All requesters
Suggested Grade: 4-12
Order Number: not applicable
Format: Web Site

Source: California State Archives
World Wide Web URL: http://www.learncalifornia.org/

Let's Tour the Carlsbad Caverns

A WebQuest devoted to these beautiful caverns.

Availability: All requesters
Suggested Grade: 4-12
Order Number: not applicable
Format: WebQuest

Source: Gerald Robillard
World Wide Web URL:
http://www.swlauriersb.qc.ca/english/edservices/pedresources/webquest/cave_hunt.htm

Montezuma Castle and Tuzigoot National Monuments Teacher's Guide

Brings the national Parks right into your classroom.

Availability: All requesters
Suggested Grade: 4-12
Order Number: not applicable
Format: Downloadable Teacher's Guide

Source: Montezuma Castle National Monument
World Wide Web URL: www.nps.gov/moco/forteachers/curriculummaterials.htmhttp://www.nps.gov/moco/forteachers/curriculummaterials.htm

Paths into the Past--Acadia's Historic Trails

A general history of Acadia's hiking trails.

Availability: Limit of 5 copies to schools, libraries, and homeschoolers world-wide.
Suggested Grade: All ages
Order Number: order by title
Format: Newsletter

Source: Acadia National Park
Information
P. O. Box 177
Bar Harbor, ME 04609
Phone: 1-207-288-3338

Fax: 1-207-288-8813
World Wide Web URL: http://www.nps.gov/acad
Email Address: acadia_information@nps.gov

Plants and Animals of Lassen Volcanic National Park, The

Presents information about the rich diversity of plant and animal life found in this national park.

Availability: All requesters
Suggested Grade: 4-12
Order Number: not applicable
Format: Downloadable Article

Source: Lassen Volcanic National Park
World Wide Web URL:
http://www.nps.gov/lavo/forteachers/otherresources.htm

Salt Marsh Vegetation: Examples from the Tijuana Estuary

Describes salt marsh vegetation and explains how marsh plants are able to tolerate the stresses of their variable environment.

Availability: Single copies to schools, libraries, and homeschoolers in the United States and Canada.
Suggested Grade: 7-12
Languages: English; Spanish
Order Number: order by title
Production Date: 1982
Format: Booklet

Source: California Sea Grant Program
University of California
9500 Gilman Drive
La Jolla, CA 92093-0231
Phone: 1-858-534-4440
Fax: 1-858-453-2948
World Wide Web URL:
Email Address: pubadmin@seamail.ucsd.edu

Southern Native American Pow Wows

Pow wows are famous for their pageantry of colors and dance. Join in celebration.

Availability: All requesters
Suggested Grade: All ages
Order Number: not applicable
Format: Web Site
Special Notes: This URL will lead you to a subject page. Then click on the appropriate subject heading.

Source: ThinkQuest
World Wide Web URL:
http://www.thinkquest.org/pls/html/think.library

Teaching About the Louisiana Purchase

Helpful information to teach students about the Treaty of France and the Louisiana Purchase.

Availability: All requesters
Suggested Grade: 2-12
Order Number: not applicable
Production Date: 2003
Format: Online Article

Source: John J. Patrick
World Wide Web URL:
http://www.ericdigests.org/2004-1/purchase.htm

Tour the USA

Learn about the landmarks in the United States.

Availability: All requesters
Suggested Grade: 4-9
Order Number: not applicable
Format: WebQuest

Source: Linda Starr
World Wide Web URL:
http://www.educationworld.com/a_tech/webquest_orig/webquest_orig004.shtml

Tracks: Impressions of America

A multimedia learning resource to help students explore American history and geography.

Availability: All requesters
Suggested Grade: 4-12
Order Number: not applicable
Format: Web Site

Source: Agency for Instructional Technology
World Wide Web URL: http://www.ecb.org/tracks/

WebRangers

More than 50 games and activities to help students of all ages learn about our National Parks.

Availability: All requesters
Suggested Grade: All ages
Order Number: not applicable
Format: Web Site

Source: National Park Service, U. S. Department of the Interior
World Wide Web URL:
http://www.webrangers.us/index.cfm

Written in the Rocks

Presents the geologic history of this national park.

Availability: Limit of 5 copies to schools, libraries, and homeschoolers world-wide.
Suggested Grade: 6-Adult
Order Number: order by title
Production Date: 2005
Format: Brochure

Source: Acadia National Park Information
P. O. Box 177
Bar Harbor, ME 04609
Phone: 1-207-288-3338
Fax: 1-207-288-8813
World Wide Web URL: http://www.nps.gov/acad
Email Address: acadia_information@nps.gov

About Cyprus
Presents virtually all the information you need to know when studying about Cyprus.
Availability: Limit of 5 copies to schools, libraries, and homeschoolers in the United States and Canada.
Suggested Grade: 8-12
Order Number: order by title
Format: Booklet
Source: Cyprus Press Office
13 East 40th Street
New York, NY 10016
Phone: 1-212-481-6023
Fax: 1-212-689-5716
Email Address: cyprus@un.int

Achievements and Challenges of Guatemala, The
Lots of lessons on some of the aspects of Guatemalan life and history that are of great significance to understanding the people of Guatemala and their situation.
Availability: All requesters
Suggested Grade: 6-12
Order Number: not applicable
Format: Online Lesson Plans
Source: Odyssey, The
World Wide Web URL:
http://www.worldtrek.org/odyssey/teachers/guatlessons.html

Achievements and Challenges of Peru, The
Lots of lessons on some of the aspects of Peruvian life and history that are of great significance to understanding the people of Peru today and their situation.
Availability: All requesters
Suggested Grade: 6-12
Order Number: not applicable
Format: Online Lesson Plans
Source: Odyssey, The
World Wide Web URL:
http://www.worldtrek.org/odyssey/teachers/perulessons.html

Achievements and Challenges of Zimbabwe, The
Lots of lessons on some of the aspects of Zimbabwean life and history that are of great significance to understanding the people of Zimbabwe today and their situation.
Availability: All requesters
Suggested Grade: 6-12
Order Number: not applicable
Format: Online Lesson Plans
Source: Odyssey, The
World Wide Web URL:
http://www.worldtrek.org/odyssey/teachers/zimblessons.html

Afghanistan: The Harrison Forman Collection
Presents photographs taken in 1969 of this country, before the Russian invasion. The site documents the life and culture of the area during the 1960s.
Availability: All requesters
Suggested Grade: 6-12
Order Number: not applicable
Format: Web Site
Source: Harrison Forman
World Wide Web URL:
http://www4.uwm.edu/libraries/digilib/afghan/

AfriCam
Sit at your computer and watch live pictures of Africa's greatest wilderness areas.
Availability: All requesters
Suggested Grade: All ages
Order Number: not applicable
Format: Web Site
Source: AfriCam
World Wide Web URL:
http://www.africam.com/wildlife/index.php

African Art Museum
Features over 1,200 artifacts from 100 ethnic groups in Africa. Items include wooden and bronze statues, masks, religion, objects, and much more. Information about the art, culture, and history of each group is provided. Some items featured may be purchased.
Availability: All requesters
Suggested Grade: 4-12
Order Number: not applicable
Format: Web Site
Source: Dr. Ilya Raskin and Yuri Raskin
World Wide Web URL: http://www.zyama.com/

Another Face--Masks Around the World
Emphasizes the faces of culture and the art of expression using masks from around the world.
Availability: All requesters
Suggested Grade: All ages
Order Number: not applicable
Format: Web Site
Source: Yi-Ching Chen
World Wide Web URL: http://gallery.sjsu.edu/masks/

Atlapedia Online
Information about every country, from a to z.
Availability: All requesters
Suggested Grade: All ages
Order Number: not applicable
Format: Web Site
Source: Latimer Clarke Corporation Pty Ltd.
World Wide Web URL: http://www.atlapedia.com/

Barev Says
Prepare for a trip to Armenia.
Availability: All requesters
Suggested Grade: 5-12
Order Number: not applicable
Format: WebQuest
Source: Randy Clawson
World Wide Web URL:
http://its.guilford.k12.nc.us/webquests/armenia/armenia.htm

Beautiful Islam
A multitude of articles and information relating to the Islam religion and its way of life.
Availability: All requesters
Suggested Grade: 9-Adult
Order Number: not applicable
Format: Web Site
Source: Beautifulislam.net
World Wide Web URL:
http://www.beautifulislam.net/index.shtml

Chinese Astrology
Tells all about the astrological signs and beliefs of the Chinese.
Availability: All requesters
Suggested Grade: All ages
Order Number: not applicable
Format: Web Site
Source: Sabrina Liao
World Wide Web URL: http://www.12zodiac.com

Country Information
Illustrates flags from all corners of the world.
Availability: All requesters
Suggested Grade: All ages
Order Number: not applicable
Format: Web Site
Source: CountryReports.org
World Wide Web URL: http://www.countryreports.org/

Cultures of the Andes
Provides basic lessons in quechua, literature in English and quechuan, and more to help students learn the cultures of the Andes.
Availability: All requesters
Suggested Grade: 4-Adult
Order Number: not applicable
Format: Web Site
Source: Ada and Russ Gibbons
World Wide Web URL: http://www.andes.org/

Cyber Nations
An online nation simulation game. Users create and manage their own nation.
Availability: All requesters
Suggested Grade: 6-12
Order Number: not applicable
Format: Online Game
Source: Cyber Nations
World Wide Web URL: http://www.cybernations.net/

EU Focus
An in-depth newsletter covering important European issues and the transatlantic relationship.
Availability: Limit of 50 copies to schools and homeschoolers in the United States.
Suggested Grade: 10-Adult
Order Number: order by title
Format: Newsletter
Source: Delegation of the European Commission
Press and Public Diplomacy
2300 M Street, N. W., 3rd Floor
Washington, DC 20037-1434
Fax: 1-202-429-1766
World Wide Web URL: http://www.eurunion.org
Email Address: delegration-usa-info@eeas.europa.eu

EU Insight
A timely EU issue brief with special attention to EU/US relations.
Availability: Limit of 50 copies to schools and homeschoolers in the United States.
Suggested Grade: 10-Adult
Order Number: order by title
Format: Newsletter
Source: Delegation of the European Commission
Press and Public Diplomacy
2300 M Street, N. W., 3rd Floor
Washington, DC 20037-1434
Fax: 1-202-429-1766
World Wide Web URL: http://www.eurunion.org
Email Address: delegration-usa-info@eeas.europa.eu

European Union, The: A Guide for Americans
Explains this organization.
Availability: Limit of 50 copies to schools and homeschoolers in the United States.
Suggested Grade: 7-Adult
Order Number: order by title
Production Date: 2011
Format: Booklet; 36 pages
Special Notes: Requests are taken via web site only.
Source: Delegation of the European Commission
Press and Public Diplomacy
2300 M Street, N. W., 3rd Floor
Washington, DC 20037-1434
Fax: 1-202-429-1766
World Wide Web URL: http://www.eurunion.org
Email Address: delegration-usa-info@eeas.europa.eu

Find Out About Finland
Presents information about Finland--from the time "when squirrel pelts were money" to today.
Availability: Limit of 5 copies to schools, libraries, and homeschoolers in the United States.
Suggested Grade: 3-12
Order Number: order by title
Production Date: 2010
Format: Booklet; 33 pages
Special Notes: Sending a self-addressed label will speed the response to your request.
Source: Embassy of Finland
Liisa Rutanen
Information Officer
3301 Massachusetts Avenue, N. W.
Washington, DC 20008
Phone: 1-202-298-5824

Fax: 1-202-298-0450
World Wide Web URL: http://www.finland.org
Email Address: sanomat.was@formin.fi

For Whom the Clock Strikes

Students will learn about celebrations marking the new year in various cultures and countries around the world.

Availability: All requesters
Suggested Grade: 6-12
Order Number: not applicable
Format: Online Lesson Plan

Source: Sierra Prasada Millman and Andrea Perelman
World Wide Web URL:
http://learning.blogs.nytimes.com/2004/12/31/for-whom-the-clock-strikes/?scp=1&sq=For%20whom%20the%20clock%20strikes%20lesson%20plan&st=cse

Guide to Australia

A complete reference guide to this beautiful country "down under."

Availability: All requesters
Suggested Grade: 4-12
Order Number: not applicable
Format: Web Site

Source: Charles Stuart University
World Wide Web URL: http://www.csu.edu.au/australia/

Masks from Around the World

Masks from Africa, India, Asia, Bali, and more are illustrated here.

Availability: All requesters
Suggested Grade: All ages
Order Number: not applicable
Format: Web Site

Source: Bob Ibold
World Wide Web URL: http://www.masksoftheworld.com/

National Geographic Society Xpeditions

A wonderful site for teachers and kids alike that is set up to support the U. S. National Geography Standards.

Availability: All requesters
Suggested Grade: All ages
Order Number: not applicable
Format: Web Site

Source: National Geographic Society Xpeditions
World Wide Web URL:
http://www.nationalgeographic.com/xpeditions

Nation of Nations, A

A complete listing of the American Indian & Alaska Native Tribes by name.

Availability: All requesters
Suggested Grade: 4-Adult
Order Number: not applicable
Format: Downloadable Fact Sheet
Special Notes: This is a PDF file which will open automatically on your computer.

Source: Indian Health Service
World Wide Web URL: http://info.ihs.gov/Files/AI_AN_TRIBAL_LISTING-linked.pdf

Panorama of the European Union

Introduces the European Union and its institutions and explores how the EU has changed daily life. Also contains a geographical map of Europe.

Availability: Limit of 50 copies to schools and homeschoolers in the United States.
Suggested Grade: 7-Adult
Order Number: order by title
Production Date: 2009
Format: Leaflet

Source: Delegation of the European Commission
Press and Public Diplomacy
2300 M Street, N. W., 3rd Floor
Washington, DC 20037-1434
Fax: 1-202-429-1766
World Wide Web URL: http://www.eurunion.org
Email Address: delegation-usa-info@eeas.europa.eu

Peace Gallery, The

Images at this web site are available at no charge to educators and students for noncommercial use. Provides more than 500 images from around the world for an understanding of other cultures.

Availability: All requesters
Suggested Grade: Teacher Reference
Order Number: not applicable
Format: Web Site

Source: Peace Gallery
World Wide Web URL: http://www.peacegallery.org

Picture Australia

Search this site in a number of ways to find images of everything Australian.

Availability: All requesters
Suggested Grade: K-12
Order Number: not applicable
Format: Web Site

Source: National Library of Australia
World Wide Web URL:
http://www.pictureaustralia.org/index.html

Portraying Finland: Facts and Insights

Information on the land and the people, history, economy, culture, and much more of Finland.

Availability: Limit of 5 copies to schools, libraries, and homeschoolers in the United States.
Suggested Grade: 5-12
Order Number: order by title
Production Date: 2008
Format: Book; 167 pages
Special Notes: Sending a self-addressed label will speed the response to your request.

Source: Embassy of Finland
Liisa Rutanen
Information Officer
3301 Massachusetts Avenue, N. W.
Washington, DC 20008
Phone: 1-202-298-5824
Fax: 1-202-298-0450
World Wide Web URL: http://www.finland.org
Email Address: sanomat.was@formin.fi

Skyscraper Page, The
Photographs and information about skyscrapers around the world.
Availability: All requesters
Suggested Grade: K-12
Order Number: not applicable
Format: Web Site
Source: Skyscraperpage.com
World Wide Web URL: http://www.skyscraperpage.com

Subjective Comparison of Germany and the United States, A
Compares the government, education system, health, religion, and lots more of Germany with the United States.
Availability: All requesters
Suggested Grade: 6-12
Order Number: not applicable
Format: Online Article
Source: Axel Boldt
World Wide Web URL: http://www.math.uni-paderborn.de/~axel/us-d.htmlcustoms

Teaching About Africa
Provides a lot of suggestions for teaching about this country.
Availability: All requesters
Suggested Grade: Teacher Reference
Order Number: not applicable
Format: Online Article
Source: Susan E. Hume
World Wide Web URL:
http://www.ericdigests.org/1996-4/africa.htm

Travelling in Europe
Helpful tips for traveling in Europe as well as a map.
Availability: Limit of 50 copies to schools and homeschoolers in the United States.
Suggested Grade: 6-12
Order Number: order by title
Production Date: 2011
Format: Fold-out Brochure
Source: Delegation of the European Commission
Press and Public Diplomacy
2300 M Street, N. W., 3rd Floor
Washington, DC 20037-1434
Fax: 1-202-429-1766
World Wide Web URL: http://www.eurunion.org
Email Address: delegration-usa-info@eeas.europa.eu

Vietnamese Water Puppets
Tells the history of this Vietnamese form of puppetry.
Availability: All requesters
Suggested Grade: All ages
Order Number: not applicable
Format: Web Site
Source: David Taylor
World Wide Web URL:
http://www.sagecraft.com/puppetry/traditions/Vietnamese.html

Welcome to Latvia
Information on the arts and culture, business, government, and much more of Latvia.
Availability: All requesters
Suggested Grade: 2-12
Order Number: not applicable
Format: Web Site
Source: Latnet
World Wide Web URL: http://www.lv/

Where in the World Did This Come From?
Written to develop a sense of interdependence with people who live in other countries and to appreciate that many people in far away places contribute greatly to our own well being and lifestyle in the United States.
Availability: All requesters
Suggested Grade: K-12
Order Number: not applicable
Format: Online Lesson Plan
Source: Alice Wasosky
World Wide Web URL:
http://www.eduref.org/Virtual/Lessons/Interdisciplinary/INT0092.html

Women in Society
Discusses the role of women in Islam.
Availability: All requesters
Suggested Grade: 9-12
Order Number: not applicable
Format: Web Site
Source: Hammuda Abdul-Ati, Ph.D.
World Wide Web URL:
http://www.jannah.org/sisters/womeninsoc.html

Women in the Quran and the Sunnah
Discusses the role of women in Islam and cites passages from the Quran.
Availability: All requesters
Suggested Grade: 9-12
Order Number: not applicable
Format: Web Site
Source: Dr. 'Abdur Rahman I. Doi
World Wide Web URL:
http://www.jannah.org/sisters/womqursun.html

Alaska's Gold
Designed to provide students and other learners with a unique way to understand Alaska's history and people.
Availability: All requesters
Suggested Grade: 3-12
Order Number: not applicable
Format: Web Site
Source: Alaska Department of Education
World Wide Web URL:
http://library.state.ak.us/goldrush/HOME.HTM

America's Story
Lots of history information about people, places, events, and more from America's rich history.
Availability: All requesters
Suggested Grade: All ages
Order Number: not applicable
Format: Web Site
Source: Library of Congress
World Wide Web URL:
http://www.americaslibrary.org/cgi-bin/page.cgi

Ancient Egypt
Learn all about ancient Egyptian life and view artifacts from this time period.
Availability: All requesters
Suggested Grade: 6-12
Order Number: not applicable
Format: Web Site
Source: British Museum, The
World Wide Web URL:
http://www.ancientegypt.co.uk/menu.html

Antietam National Battlefield Teacher's Packet
All sorts of information about this historic site on a CD for your own printing.
Availability: Single copies to schools, libraries, and homeschoolers in the United States and Canada. Materials may be copied.
Suggested Grade: K-12
Order Number: order by title
Format: Teacher's Packet on CD
Source: Antietam National Battlefield
c/o Christie Stanczak
P. O. Box 158
Sharpsburg, MD 21782
Fax: 1-301-432-4942
Email Address: christie_stanczak@nps.gov

Around the World in 1896
Students will plan, take, and document a trip around the world in 1896 using historic documents.
Availability: All requesters
Suggested Grade: 6-9
Order Number: not applicable
Format: Web Site and Lesson Plans
Source: Eva L. Abbamonte and Della Barr Brooks
World Wide Web URL: http://www.loc.gov/teachers/classroommaterials/lessons/world/

Atomic Bomb WebQuest
For this WebQuest, you are going to sit as a member of the World Court and pass judgment on the United States for its actions in dropping the atomic bomb.
Availability: All requesters
Suggested Grade: 6-12
Order Number: not applicable
Format: WebQuest
Source: Gary Mullennax, Maryville Poe, and Daniel Laine
World Wide Web URL:
http://imet.csus.edu/imet5/dan/products/webquest/new/atomicbombwebquest.htm

Battle of the Little Bighorn, The
A brief history of this battle.
Availability: Limit of 30 copies to schools, libraries, and homeschoolers in the United States and Canada.
Suggested Grade: 4-12
Order Number: order by title
Format: Sheet of Paper
Source: Little Bighorn Battlefield National Monument
Division of Interpretation
P. O. Box 39
Crow Agency, MT 59022
Phone: 1-406-638-3217
Fax: 1-406-638-2639
World Wide Web URL: http://www.nps.gov/libi
Email Address: Marvin_Dawes@nps.gov

Black Community/Black America
Discusses the "black community" in America and tells members how to participate in political agendas.
Availability: All requesters
Suggested Grade: Teacher Reference
Order Number: not applicable
Format: Online Article
Source: Calvin O. L. Henry
World Wide Web URL:
http://edchange.org/multicultural/papers/calvin.html

Black Experience in America, The
A very detailed piece of literature that tells the history of African Americans in America.
Availability: All requesters
Suggested Grade: 6-12
Order Number: not applicable
Format: Online Article
Source: Norman Coombs
World Wide Web URL: http://www.gutenberg.org/etext/67

"Brother, Can You Spare a Dime"
Explores the effects of the New Deal on the Great Depression.

Availability: All requesters
Suggested Grade: 10
Order Number: not applicable
Format: Web Site and Lesson Plans

Source: Marilyn Swan and Elaine Kohler
World Wide Web URL:
http://www.loc.gov/teachers/classroommaterials/lessons/dime/

Centennial Exhibition, The

Presents information and pictures of the Centennial Exhibition which was held in Philadelphia in 1876.

Availability: All requesters
Suggested Grade: 6-12
Order Number: not applicable
Format: Web Site

Source: Free Library of Philadelphia
World Wide Web URL:
http://libwww.library.phila.gov/CenCol/

Civil Rights/Casualties of Wartime

This is an attempt to balance the treatment of war with concern for the domestic consequences of nations going to war.

Availability: All requesters
Suggested Grade: 9-12
Order Number: not applicable
Format: Online Lesson Plan

Source: Linda Hugle
World Wide Web URL:
http://youth.net/cec/cecsst/cecsst.38.txt

Crow in the Battle of the Little Big Horn, The

Tells about these Native Americans as well as their role in this battle.

Availability: Limit of 30 copies to schools, libraries, and homeschoolers in the United States and Canada.
Suggested Grade: 4-12
Order Number: order by title
Format: Sheet of Paper

Source: Little Bighorn Battlefield National Monument
Division of Interpretation
P. O. Box 39
Crow Agency, MT 59022
Phone: 1-406-638-3217
Fax: 1-406-638-2639
World Wide Web URL: http://www.nps.gov/libi
Email Address: Marvin_Dawes@nps.gov

Fort McHenry Park Brochure

Tells all about this historic fort's role in the War of 1812 and the writing of "The Star-Spangled Banner."

Availability: Single copies to schools, libraries, and homeschoolers in the United States and Canada.
Suggested Grade: All ages
Order Number: order by title
Format: Brochure

Source: Fort McHenry National Monument and Historic Shrine
2400 East Fort Avenue
Baltimore, MD 21230-5393
Phone: 1-410-962-4290
Fax: 1-410-962-2500
World Wide Web URL: http://www.nps.gov/fomc

From Jim Crow to Linda Brown: A Retrospective of the African-American Experience from 1897 to 1953

Helps students understand themes of African American life in the first half of the 20th century and explore to what extent this experience was "separate but equal."

Availability: All requesters
Suggested Grade: 9-12
Order Number: not applicable
Format: Web Site and Lesson Plans

Source: Agnes Dunn and Eric Powell
World Wide Web URL:
http://lcweb2.loc.gov/ammem/ndlpedu/lessons/97/crow/crowhome.html

From Slaves to Soldiers: African Americans and the Civil War

Students should learn to master the basic facts of the Civil War of the United States.

Availability: All requesters
Suggested Grade: 6-12
Order Number: not applicable
Format: Downloadable Curriculum Unit

Source: William J. Garraty
World Wide Web URL:
http://www.yale.edu/ynhti/curriculum/units/2005/1/05.01.03.x.html

Great Pesthtigo Fire of 1871, The

On the evening of October 8, 1871 the worst recorded forest fire in North American history raged through Northeastern Wisconsin and Upper Michigan, destroying millions of dollars worth of property and timberland, and taking between 1,200 and 2,4000 lives. This site claims to be the most comprehensive source on the web for information about this fire.

Availability: All requesters
Suggested Grade: 6-Adult
Order Number: not applicable
Format: Web Site

Source: Deana C. Hipke
World Wide Web URL: http://www.peshtigofire.info/

Historical Text Archive

Presents articles and links of historical interest.

Availability: All requesters
Suggested Grade: 6-12
Order Number: not applicable
Format: Web Site

Source: Don Mabry
World Wide Web URL: http://historicaltextarchive.com

History Notes of Lassen Volcanic National Park & Surrounding Region

A chronological history of this national park.

Availability: All requesters
Suggested Grade: 4-12
Order Number: not applicable
Format: Downloadable Article

Source: Lassen Volcanic National Park
World Wide Web URL:
http://www.nps.gov/lavo/forteachers/otherresources.htm

Immigration/Migration: Today and During the Great Depression

Students will compare the immigration/migration experiences of their families to those of people living through the Great Depression.

Availability: All requesters
Suggested Grade: 11
Order Number: not applicable
Format: WebQuest

Source: Evelyn Bender and Byron Stoloff
World Wide Web URL:
http://www.loc.gov/teachers/classroommaterials/lessons/migrate/procedure.html

In Congress Assembled: Continuity & Change in the Governing of the U. S.

Four teaching units linked to American history readings. Topics include drafting the Constitution, adding the Bill of Rights, selecting holidays, and more.

Availability: All requesters
Suggested Grade: 6-12
Order Number: not applicable
Format: Web Site and Lesson Plans

Source: Kirk Ankeney and David Vigilante
World Wide Web URL:
http://www.loc.gov/teachers/classroommaterials/lessons/continuity-change/procedure.html

Iraq--The Cradle of Civilization at Risk

An interesting site due to the current state of affairs in Iraq. Explores the history and culture of this country and shows how history began here.

Availability: All requesters
Suggested Grade: 9-Adult
Order Number: not applicable
Format: Web Site

Source: H-Net, Humanities & Social Sciences OnLine
World Wide Web URL:
http://www2.h-net.msu.edu/~museum/iraq.html

Lakota and the Northern Cheyenne on the Little Bighorn, The

Provides information about this encampment on the Little Bighorn.

Availability: Limit of 30 copies to schools, libraries, and homeschoolers in the United States and Canada.
Suggested Grade: 4-12
Order Number: order by title
Format: Sheet of Paper

Source: Little Bighorn Battlefield National Monument
Division of Interpretation
P. O. Box 39
Crow Agency, MT 59022
Phone: 1-406-638-3217
Fax: 1-406-638-2639
World Wide Web URL: http://www.nps.gov/libi
Email Address: Marvin_Dawes@nps.gov

Legend of Captain Dave's Lost Treasure, The

An online treasure hunt, in which viewers follow the story and answer questions about pirates along the way. Due to the use of hyperlinks, it's also a good lesson in navigating the Internet.

Availability: All requesters
Suggested Grade: All ages
Order Number: not applicable
Format: Web Site

Source: Dauphin County Library System
World Wide Web URL: http://www.dcls.org/pirate/

Little Bighorn Battlefield Information/Visitor Pamphlet

Describes and illustrates this National Monument as well as presenting a history of the famous battle.

Availability: Limit of 30 copies to schools, libraries, and homeschoolers in the United States and Canada.
Suggested Grade: 4-12
Order Number: order by title
Format: Brochure

Source: Little Bighorn Battlefield National Monument
Division of Interpretation
P. O. Box 39
Crow Agency, MT 59022
Phone: 1-406-638-3217
Fax: 1-406-638-2639
World Wide Web URL: http://www.nps.gov/libi
Email Address: Marvin_Dawes@nps.gov

Myths of the Little Bighorn

Attempts to put many of the myths surrounding this famous battle to rest.

Availability: Limit of 30 copies to schools, libraries, and homeschoolers in the United States and Canada.
Suggested Grade: 4-12
Order Number: order by title
Format: Sheet of Paper

Source: Little Bighorn Battlefield National Monument
Division of Interpretation
P. O. Box 39
Crow Agency, MT 59022

Phone: 1-406-638-3217
Fax: 1-406-638-2639
World Wide Web URL: http://www.nps.gov/libi
Email Address: Marvin_Dawes@nps.gov

Never Again! - Again?
Explores the history of genocide and helps students explore what we can to prevent and stop mass killings in our world.
Availability: All requesters
Suggested Grade: 9-12
Order Number: not applicable
Format: WebQuest
Source: Carolyn O. Burleson
World Wide Web URL:
http://drb.lifestreamcenter.net/Lessons/genocide/

Paper Models of Civil War Soldiers
Print, cut, and assemble these model civil war soldiers--cool site!
Availability: All requesters
Suggested Grade: 2-Adult
Order Number: not applicable
Format: Downloadable Patterns
Source: Phil Heiple
World Wide Web URL:
http://www.rain.org/~philfear/civilwarsoldiers.html

Pearl Harbor Raid, 7 December 1941
Presents a detailed account of the December 7, 1941 attack on Pearl Harbor including a large selection of pictures.
Availability: All requesters
Suggested Grade: 6-12
Order Number: not applicable
Format: Web Site
Source: Department of the Navy
World Wide Web URL:
http://www.history.navy.mil/photos/events/wwii-pac/pearlhbr/pearlhbr.htm

Plains Indian Warrior, The
Provides brief descriptions of the weapons used by the Native American tribes involved in the Little Bighorn Battle.
Availability: Limit of 30 copies to schools, libraries, and homeschoolers in the United States and Canada.
Suggested Grade: 4-12
Order Number: order by title
Format: Sheet of Paper
Source: Little Bighorn Battlefield National Monument
Division of Interpretation
P. O. Box 39
Crow Agency, MT 59022
Phone: 1-406-638-3217
Fax: 1-406-638-2639
World Wide Web URL: http://www.nps.gov/libi
Email Address: Marvin_Dawes@nps.gov

Postcards of the Mexican Revolution
Much of Mexico's history for the decade of 1910-1920 was recorded by hundreds of photographers on postcards. This site reproduces those cards and explains the history they depict.
Availability: All requesters
Suggested Grade: 6-12
Order Number: not applicable
Format: Web Site
Source: John Hardman
World Wide Web URL:
http://www.netdotcom.com/revmexpc/default.htm

Protest Songs in the U. S.
It's quite astonishing (to me) that I found this webquest about human rights today--when Wisconsin (my home state) is going through protests as I write this. While the WebQuest is about a certain period in history, the premise behind it remains the same
Availability: All requesters
Suggested Grade: 6-Adult
Order Number: not applicable
Format: WebQuest
Source: Fernanda Rodrigues
World Wide Web URL:
http://essg.prof2000.pt/escola/webquest/index.html

U. S. Cavalry in the 1870's
Tells about the cavalry involved in the Battle of the Little Bighorn--who were these men, where did they come from, and what was their life really like?
Availability: Limit of 30 copies to schools, libraries, and homeschoolers in the United States and Canada.
Suggested Grade: 4-12
Order Number: order by title
Format: Sheet of Paper
Source: Little Bighorn Battlefield National Monument
Division of Interpretation
P. O. Box 39
Crow Agency, MT 59022
Phone: 1-406-638-3217
Fax: 1-406-638-2639
World Wide Web URL: http://www.nps.gov/libi
Email Address: Marvin_Dawes@nps.gov

Using Historical Statistics to Teach About World War II
Presents a rationale for using historical statistics to teach about World War II, discusses instructional methods for doing so, and recommends additional sources.
Availability: All requesters
Suggested Grade: Teacher Reference
Order Number: not applicable
Production Date: 2001
Format: Online Article

Source: Carl R. Siler
World Wide Web URL:
http://www.indiana.edu/~ssdc/statdig.htm

Voices of Japanese-American Internees
Using video histories of Japanese-American internees during World War II, this lesson engages students in understanding the discrimination that Japanese Americans faced before and after their internment.

Availability: All requesters
Suggested Grade: 9-Adult
Order Number: not applicable
Format: Online Lesson Plans

Source: Anti-Defamation League
World Wide Web URL:
http://www.adl.org/education/curriculum_connections/summer_2008/

Weapons of the Little Bighorn
Virtually every aspect of the Battle of the Little Bighorn is controversial including the weapons used by both the military and Indian participants. Here is information about the weapons used.

Availability: Limit of 30 copies to schools, libraries, and homeschoolers in the United States and Canada.
Suggested Grade: 4-12
Order Number: order by title
Format: Sheet of Paper

Source: Little Bighorn Battlefield National Monument
Division of Interpretation
P. O. Box 39
Crow Agency, MT 59022
Phone: 1-406-638-3217
Fax: 1-406-638-2639
World Wide Web URL: http://www.nps.gov/libi
Email Address: Marvin_Dawes@nps.gov

Carriage Road User's Map
Presents information on these unique roads within this national park.
Availability: Limit of 5 copies to schools, libraries, and homeschoolers world-wide.
Suggested Grade: 6-Adult
Order Number: order by title
Production Date: 2009
Format: Brochure
Source: Acadia National Park Information
P. O. Box 177
Bar Harbor, ME 04609
Phone: 1-207-288-3338
Fax: 1-207-288-8813
World Wide Web URL: http://www.nps.gov/acad
Email Address: acadia_information@nps.gov

Chesapeake Bay Bridge-Tunnel Brochure and Map
Presents a map of the East Coast.
Availability: Classroom quantities to schools, libraries, and homeschoolers in the United States.
Suggested Grade: 4-12
Order Number: order by title
Format: Map
Source: Chesapeake Bay Bridge and Tunnel District
Attn: Patricia Sumners
P. O. Box 111
Cape Charles, VA 23310-0111
Phone: 1-757-331-2960
Fax: 1-757-331-4565
World Wide Web URL: http://www.cbbt.com

Electronic Map Library, The
A number of maps--many for the west coast.
Availability: All requesters
Suggested Grade: All ages
Order Number: not applicable
Format: Online Maps
Source: William Bowen
World Wide Web URL: http://130.166.124.2/library.html

European Union Poster Map
A large map and poster of Europe with basic statistics on European countries.
Availability: Limit of 50 copies to schools and homeschoolers in the United States.
Suggested Grade: All ages
Order Number: order by title
Production Date: 2011
Format: Map; 36 inches x 24 inches
Source: Delegation of the European Commission
Press and Public Diplomacy
2300 M Street, N. W., 3rd Floor
Washington, DC 20037-1434
Fax: 1-202-429-1766
World Wide Web URL: http://www.eurunion.org
Email Address: delegation-usa-info@eeas.europa.eu

Iowa Transportation Map
A map of the highways and byways of scenic Iowa.
Availability: All requesters
Suggested Grade: 4-Adult
Order Number: order by title
Format: Map
Source: Iowa Tourism Office
200 East Grand Avenue
Des Moines, IA 50309
Phone: 1-515-242-4705
World Wide Web URL: http://www.traveliowa.com
Email Address: tourism@iowa.gov

Isle au Haut
A map of this remote Island within Acadia National Park.
Availability: Limit of 5 copies to schools, libraries, and homeschoolers world-wide.
Suggested Grade: 6-Adult
Order Number: order by title
Production Date: 2008
Format: Map
Source: Acadia National Park Information
P. O. Box 177
Bar Harbor, ME 04609
Phone: 1-207-288-3338
Fax: 1-207-288-8813
World Wide Web URL: http://www.nps.gov/acad
Email Address: acadia_information@nps.gov

Latitude--The Art and Science of Fifteenth Century Navigation
Teaches about the science of map making and map reading.
Availability: All requesters
Suggested Grade: 6-12
Order Number: not applicable
Format: Web Site
Source: Huntington Library
World Wide Web URL: http://www.ruf.rice.edu/~feegi/

MapQuest
Create maps instantly.
Availability: All requesters
Suggested Grade: All ages
Order Number: not applicable
Format: Web Site
Source: MapQuest.com
World Wide Web URL: http://www.mapquest.com/

Map Skills
Learn map skills and definitions when you visit this site.
Availability: All requesters
Suggested Grade: 4-12
Order Number: not applicable
Format: Web Site
Special Notes: This URL will lead you to a subject page. Then click on the appropriate subject heading.

Source: ThinkQuest
World Wide Web URL:
http://www.thinkquest.org/pls/html/think.library

Maryland Official Highway Map

A map of this state.

Availability: Single copies to schools, libraries, and homeschoolers world-wide.
Suggested Grade: 4-12
Order Number: order by title
Format: Map

Source: Maryland State Highway Administration
Highway Mapping Team
707 North Calvert Street, MS C-607
Baltimore, MD 21202
Phone: 1-410-545-8747
Fax: 1-410-209-5051
World Wide Web URL: http://www.marylandroads.com
Email Address: maps@sha.state.md.us

Mathematics of Cartography

A tutorial on map making.

Availability: All requesters
Suggested Grade: 4-12
Order Number: not applicable
Format: Online Tutorial

Source: Cynthia Lanius
World Wide Web URL:
http://math.rice.edu/~lanius/pres/map/

Minnesota State Highway Map

A downloadable map of this state which features a city index, regional maps, state, parks, and more.

Availability: All requesters
Suggested Grade: All ages
Order Number: not applicable
Format: Downloadable Map

Source: Minnesota Department of Transportation
World Wide Web URL:
http://www.dot.state.mn.us/statemap/

National Atlas of the United States of America, The

Create maps, in layers, showing all sorts of geographical information.

Availability: All requesters
Suggested Grade: 4-12
Order Number: not applicable
Format: Online Maps

Source: United States Department of the Interior
World Wide Web URL: http://nationalatlas.gov/mapmaker

Official Tennessee Transportation Map

A map of this beautiful state.

Availability: Limit of 5 copies to schools, libraries, and homeschoolers world-wide.
Suggested Grade: 4-12
Order Number: order by title
Format: Map

Source: Tennessee Department of Transportation
James K. Polk Building, Suite 700
Nashville, TN 37243-0349
Phone: 1-888-232-6713
Fax: 1-615-741-1791
World Wide Web URL:
http://www.tdot.state.tn.us/MapOrder/maporder.htm
Email Address: ruth.letson@state.tn.us

Official Wyoming Highway Map--2008

This is the official highway map of Wyoming.

Availability: Classroom quantities to schools, libraries, and homeschoolers world-wide.
Suggested Grade: 3-12
Order Number: order by title
Production Date: 2009
Format: Map

Source: Wyoming Department of Transportation, Public Affairs Office
5300 Bishop Boulevard
Cheyenne, WY 82009-3340
Phone: 1-307-777-4437
Fax: 1-307-777-4289
World Wide Web URL: http://dot.state.wy.us
Email Address: joyce.wagner@dot.state.wy.us

Outline Maps

Here you will find printable maps for all of the world as well as historical maps.

Availability: All requesters
Suggested Grade: All ages
Order Number: not applicable
Format: Online Maps

Source: Houghton Mifflin Company
World Wide Web URL: http://www.eduplace.com/ss/maps/

Perry-Castaneda Library Map Collection

An intensive collection of maps for viewing or printing.

Availability: All requesters
Suggested Grade: All ages
Order Number: not applicable
Format: Web Site

Source: Perry-Castaneda Library
World Wide Web URL:
http://www.lib.utexas.edu/maps/index.html

South Carolina County Maps

Select a South Carolina county and you can download a map of that location.

Availability: All requesters
Suggested Grade: All ages
Order Number: not applicable
Format: Downloadable Maps

Source: South Carolina Department of Transportation
World Wide Web URL:
http://www.dot.state.sc.us/getting/maps.shtmlmaprequest

South Dakota Official Highway Map
This is the official highway map of South Dakota.
Availability: Limit of 50 copies to schools, libraries, and homeschoolers world-wide.
Suggested Grade: 1-12
Order Number: order by title
Format: Map

Source: South Dakota Tourism
Robin Rattei
711 East Wells Avenue
Pierre, SD 57501-3369
Phone: 1-800-SDAKOTA
Fax: 1-605-773-3256
World Wide Web URL: http://www.travelsd.com
Email Address: sdinfo@state.sd.us

State Highway Maps of Mexico
A number of official Mexican government maps depicting the regions of this country.
Availability: All requesters
Suggested Grade: All ages
Order Number: not applicable
Format: Downloadable Maps

Source: Virtual Mexico
World Wide Web URL:
http://www.virtualmex.com/mexico_state_map.htm

State Transportation Map
A map of this historic state.
Availability: Single copies to schools, libraries, and homeschoolers world-wide.
Suggested Grade: 4-12
Order Number: order by title
Format: Map

Source: Virginia Department of Transportation
Map and Information Desk
1221 E. Broad Street
Richmond, VA 23219
Phone: 1-804-786-2801
Fax: 1-304-786-7196
World Wide Web URL:
http://www.virginiadot.org/travel/maps-default.asp

Suomi--Finland
A map of Finland--presented in Finnish.
Availability: Limit of 5 copies to schools, libraries, and homeschoolers in the United States.
Suggested Grade: 5-12
Order Number: order by title
Format: Map

Source: Embassy of Finland
Liisa Rutanen
Information Officer
3301 Massachusetts Avenue, N. W.
Washington, DC 20008
Phone: 1-202-298-5824
Fax: 1-202-298-0450
World Wide Web URL: http://www.finland.org
Email Address: sanomat.was@formin.fi

Tennessee Map and Insets
Downloadable maps include the official transportation map of Tennessee and each of the insets found on the printed version.
Availability: All requesters
Suggested Grade: All ages
Order Number: not applicable
Format: Downloadable Maps

Source: Tennessee Department of Transportation
World Wide Web URL:
http://www.tdot.state.tn.us/maps.htm

Undersea Landscape of the Gulf of Maine
A map/poster of the Gulf's landscapes, geology, and biology.
Availability: Classroom quantities to schools, libraries, and homeschoolers in the United States and Canada.
Suggested Grade: All ages
Order Number: order by title
Format: Map/Poster

Source: Maine Coastal Program
38 State House Station
Augusta, ME 04333
Phone: 1-207-287-1486
Fax: 1-207-287-8059
World Wide Web URL:
http://www.mainecoastalprogram.org
Email Address: lorraine.lessard@maine.gov

Utah State Highway Map
An interactive map of this state.
Availability: All requesters
Suggested Grade: All ages
Order Number: not applicable
Format: Downloadable Map

Source: Utah Department of Transportation
World Wide Web URL:
http://www.dot.state.ut.us/index.php/m+c/tid=346

Virginia State Transportation Map
Print all 10 of the 8 1/2 x 11 inch pieces you can download here and you will have a complete map of Virginia.
Availability: All requesters
Suggested Grade: All ages
Order Number: not applicable
Format: Downloadable Maps

Source: Virginia Department of Transportation
World Wide Web URL:
http://www.virginiadot.org/programs/prog-byways-map-printable.asp

Washington State Highway Map
A complete map of this state, divided into 18 sections for faster downloading.
Availability: All requesters
Suggested Grade: All ages
Order Number: not applicable

Format: Downloadable Map
Source: Washington State Department of Transportation
World Wide Web URL:
http://www.wsdot.wa.gov/publications/highwaymap/view.htm

You Can Find It!
Students will learn to find various locations on a map or globe using longitude and latitude.
Availability: All requesters
Suggested Grade: 3-12
Order Number: not applicable
Format: Online Lesson Plan
Source: Carl White
World Wide Web URL:
http://www.eduref.org/Virtual/Lessons/Social_Studies/Geography/GGR0042.html

ADHD and Children Who Are Gifted
Discusses this issue.
Availability: All requesters
Suggested Grade: Teacher Reference
Order Number: not applicable
Production Date: 1993
Format: Online Article
Source: James T. Webb and Diane Latimer
World Wide Web URL:
http://www.ericdigests.org/1993/adhd.htm

Alternatives to Behaviorism
Summarizes the research of Dr. Stanley Greenspan which demonstrates the superiority of relationship-based approaches to early intervention when working with autistic children.
Availability: All requesters
Suggested Grade: Teacher Reference
Order Number: not applicable
Format: Online Article
Source: Autism National Committee
World Wide Web URL:
http://www.autcom.org/articles%5CBehaviorism.html

Assessing LEP Migrant Students for Special Education Services
Describes the obligations of schools to provide services to migrant students and discusses approaches to doing so.
Availability: All requesters
Suggested Grade: Teacher Reference
Order Number: not applicable
Format: Online Article
Source: Jose R. Lozano-Rodriguez and Jaime A. Castellano
World Wide Web URL:
http://www.ericdigests.org/1999-3/lep.htm

Assessment of Culturally and Linguistically Diverse Students for Special Education Eligibility
Discusses this issue.
Availability: All requesters
Suggested Grade: Teacher Reference
Order Number: not applicable
Production Date: 2000
Format: Online Article
Source: Jane Burnette
World Wide Web URL:
http://www.ericdigests.org/2001-4/assessment.html

Autism Spectrum Disorders and Stuttering
Defines ASDs, discusses diagnosis and treatment, offers tips for parents and therapists, including structuring sessions.
Availability: Single copies to schools, libraries, and homeschoolers world-wide. May be copied.
Suggested Grade: 6-Adult
Order Number: order by title
Production Date: 2008
Format: Brochure
Source: Stuttering Foundation of America
P. O. Box 11749
Memphis, TN 38111-0749
Phone: 1-800-992-9392
World Wide Web URL: http://www.stutteringhelp.org
Email Address: info@stutteringhelp.org

Children with Communication Disorders: Update 2001
Discusses various types of communication disorders, their incidence, the learning difficulties associated with them, the special case of English language learners, and the educational significance of communication disorders.
Availability: All requesters
Suggested Grade: Teacher Reference
Order Number: not applicable
Production Date: 2001
Format: Online Article
Source: Alejandro Brice
World Wide Web URL:
http://www.ericdigests.org/2002-3/2001.htm

Down's Syndrome and Stuttering
Discusses the effect of Down's Syndrome on language and fluency.
Availability: Single copies to schools, libraries, and homeschoolers world-wide. May be copied.
Suggested Grade: K-12
Order Number: order by title
Production Date: 2004
Format: Brochure
Source: Stuttering Foundation of America
P. O. Box 11749
Memphis, TN 38111-0749
Phone: 1-800-992-9392
World Wide Web URL: http://www.stutteringhelp.org
Email Address: info@stutteringhelp.org

English Language Learner with Special Needs: Effective Instructional Strategies
Discusses this issue.
Availability: All requesters
Suggested Grade: Teacher Reference
Order Number: not applicable
Production Date: 2003
Format: Online Article
Source: Alba Ortiz
World Wide Web URL:
http://www.ericdigests.org/2003-3/english.htm

Exploring Autism
Presents much discussion and findings of the most recent research on this disorder.
Availability: All requesters
Suggested Grade: Adult
Order Number: not applicable
Format: Web Site
Source: National Alliance for Autism Research
World Wide Web URL: http://www.exploringautism.org/

Hard of Hearing and Deaf Students: A Resource Guide to Support Classroom Teachers
Provides lots of information to help teachers be effective educators to students who suffer hearing loss.
Availability: All requesters
Suggested Grade: Teacher Reference
Order Number: not applicable
Format: Online Article
Source: British Columbia Ministry of Education
World Wide Web URL:
http://www.bced.gov.bc.ca/specialed/hearimpair/

Helping Students with Disabilities Participate in Standards-Based Mathematics Curriculum
Examines how selected researchers are informing practice in four different areas.
Availability: All requesters
Suggested Grade: Teacher Reference
Order Number: not applicable
Production Date: 2003
Format: Online Article
Source: Cynthia Warger
World Wide Web URL:
http://www.ericdigests.org/2003-3/helping.htm

Learning Disabilities
Explains the differences between learning problems and disabilities.
Availability: All requesters
Suggested Grade: Teacher Reference
Order Number: not applicable
Format: Online Article; 40 pages
Special Notes: Use the on-site search engine to easily find this title. You may request a printed copy mailed to you for a fee.
Source: Federal Citizen Information Center
World Wide Web URL: http://www.pueblo.gsa.gov/

National Center to Improve Practice in Special Education
Includes discussions about the use of technology for students with disabilities and more.
Availability: All requesters
Suggested Grade: Teacher Reference
Order Number: not applicable
Format: Web Site
Source: National Center to Improve Practice
World Wide Web URL:
http://www2.edc.org/NCIP/library/toc.htm

Research on Full-Service Schools and Students with Disabilities
Presents the results of research on these "one-stop centers" for students with disabilities.
Availability: All requesters
Suggested Grade: Teacher Reference
Order Number: not applicable
Production Date: 2001
Format: Online Article
Source: Cynthia Warger
World Wide Web URL: http://www.cec.sped.org/AM/Template.cfm?Section=Home&TEMPLATE=/CM/ContentDisplay.cfm&CONTENTID=2296

Science Instruction for Students with Visual Impairments
Suggestions for the classroom.
Availability: All requesters
Suggested Grade: Teacher Reference
Order Number: not applicable
Production Date: 2001
Format: Online Article
Source: David D. Kumar, Rangasamy Ramasamy, and Greg Stefanich
World Wide Web URL:
http://www.ericdigests.org/2003-1/visual2.htm

Self-Therapy for the Stutterer
Guidelines for greater fluency to help stutterers speak better.
Availability: Single copies to schools, libraries, and homeschoolers world-wide. May be copied.
Suggested Grade: Adult
Order Number: order by title
Production Date: 2004
Format: Brochure
Source: Stuttering Foundation of America
P. O. Box 11749
Memphis, TN 38111-0749
Phone: 1-800-992-9392
World Wide Web URL: http://www.stutteringhelp.org
Email Address: info@stutteringhelp.org

Special Education Law and Children Who Stutter
Explains in simple language how children are identified, screened, evaluated, and determined to be eligible for therapy services in the school.
Availability: Single copies to schools, libraries, and homeschoolers world-wide. May be copied.
Suggested Grade: Adult
Order Number: order by title
Production Date: 2006
Format: Brochure
Source: Stuttering Foundation of America
P. O. Box 11749
Memphis, TN 38111-0749
Phone: 1-800-992-9392
World Wide Web URL: http://www.stutteringhelp.org
Email Address: info@stutteringhelp.org

Strategies for Teaching Students with Learning Disabilities
Information and resources for teaching students with learning disabilities.
Availability: All requesters
Suggested Grade: Teacher Reference

Order Number: not applicable
Format: Web Site

Source: Ed Keller
World Wide Web URL:
http://www.as.wvu.edu/~scidis/learning.html

Students with Visual Impairments
Tips to help you effectively teach students with sight impairments.
Availability: All requesters
Suggested Grade: Teacher Reference
Order Number: not applicable
Format: Online Article

Source: British Columbia Ministry of Education
World Wide Web URL:
http://www.bced.gov.bc.ca/specialed/visimpair/

Stuttering and the Bilingual Child
Gives guidelines to parents and professionals on how to help the bilingual child who stutters.
Availability: Single copies to schools, libraries, and homeschoolers world-wide. May be copied.
Suggested Grade: All ages
Order Number: order by title
Production Date: 2006
Format: Brochure

Source: Stuttering Foundation of America
P. O. Box 11749
Memphis, TN 38111-0749
Phone: 1-800-992-9392
World Wide Web URL: http://www.stutteringhelp.org
Email Address: info@stutteringhelp.org

Stuttering and Tourette's Syndrome
Discusses the possible link between these two afflictions.
Availability: Single copies to schools, libraries, and homeschoolers world-wide. May be copied.
Suggested Grade: 6-Adult
Order Number: order by title
Production Date: 2004
Format: Brochure

Source: Stuttering Foundation of America
P. O. Box 11749
Memphis, TN 38111-0749
Phone: 1-800-992-9392
World Wide Web URL: http://www.stutteringhelp.org
Email Address: info@stutteringhelp.org

Stuttering: Answers for Employers
Information and helpful strategies for employers of those who stutter--also helpful for taking with you to a job interview if you stutter.
Availability: Single copies to schools, libraries, and homeschoolers world-wide. May be copied.
Suggested Grade: 8-Adult
Order Number: order by title
Production Date: 2005
Format: Brochure

Source: Stuttering Foundation of America
P. O. Box 11749
Memphis, TN 38111-0749
Phone: 1-800-992-9392
World Wide Web URL: http://www.stutteringhelp.org
Email Address: info@stutteringhelp.org

Teaching Children with Tourette Syndrome
Discusses this issue.
Availability: All requesters
Suggested Grade: Teacher Reference
Order Number: not applicable
Production Date: 1998
Format: Online Article

Source: Bernadette Knoblauch
World Wide Web URL:
http://www.ericdigests.org/1999-4/tourette.htm

Teaching Decision Making to Students with Learning Disabilities by Promoting Self-Determination
Examines how instructional practices to promote self-determination can be used to help students with learning disabilities make effective choices and decisions.
Availability: All requesters
Suggested Grade: Teacher Reference
Order Number: not applicable
Production Date: 2003
Format: Online Article

Source: Alan Hoffman
World Wide Web URL:
http://www.ericdigests.org/2004-2/self.html

Teaching Every Student in the Digital Age: Universal Design for Learning
Written to help teachers discover what technologies can help their disabled students learn.
Availability: All requesters
Suggested Grade: Teacher Reference
Order Number: not applicable
Production Date: 2002
Format: Online Book
Special Notes: Print version may be purchased for $26.95.

Source: David H. Rose and Anne Meyer
World Wide Web URL:
http://www.cast.org/teachingeverystudent/ideas/tes/

Adults with Learning Disabilities
Explores how to effectively teach these adults.
Availability: All requesters
Suggested Grade: Teacher Reference
Order Number: not applicable
Production Date: 1998
Format: Online Article
Source: Sandra Kerka
World Wide Web URL:
http://www.ericdigests.org/1998-2/adults.htm

African Americans and Self-Help Education: The Missing Link in Adult Education
Discusses this issue.
Availability: All requesters
Suggested Grade: Teacher Reference
Order Number: not applicable
Production Date: 2000
Format: Online Article
Source: Michael L. Rowland
World Wide Web URL:
http://www.ericdigests.org/2001-3/african.htm

Afterschool Action Kit--Get Into Action
Explains what after-school programs can and should do for young people and how to locate or event start one.
Availability: Single copies to schools, libraries, and homeschoolers in the United States.
Suggested Grade: Adult
Order Number: ES 0156K
Production Date: 2000
Format: Kit of Materials
Source: ED Pubs
P. O. Box 1398
Jessup, MD 20794-1398
Phone: 1-877-4-ED-PUBS
Fax: 1-301-470-1244
World Wide Web URL:
http://www.edpubs.org/webstore/Content/search.asp

Alternatives to Ability Grouping: Still Unanswered Questions
Tries to answer some of the "unanswered" questions about this issue.
Availability: All requesters
Suggested Grade: Teacher Reference
Order Number: not applicable
Production Date: 1995
Format: Online Article
Source: Gary Burnett
World Wide Web URL:
http://www.ericdigests.org/1996-3/ability.htm

Alternative Teacher Compensation
Examines various alternative methods of teacher compensation currently proposed or in practice in school districts around the country.
Availability: All requesters
Suggested Grade: Teacher Reference
Order Number: not applicable
Production Date: 2000
Format: Online Article
Source: Brad Goorian
World Wide Web URL:
http://cepm.uoregon.edu/publications/digests/digest142.html

Apples to Apples: An Evaluation of Charter Schools Serving General Student Populations
A very detailed working paper about the effectiveness of charter schools.
Availability: All requesters
Suggested Grade: Teacher Reference
Order Number: not applicable
Format: Online Article
Source: Jay P. Greene, Greg Forster, and Marcus Winters
World Wide Web URL:
http://www.manhattan-institute.org/html/ewp_01.htm

Approval Barrier to Suburban Charter Schools, The
This report takes a look at states with high proportions of charter schools and states with relatively few such schools.
Availability: All requesters
Suggested Grade: Teacher Reference
Order Number: not applicable
Format: Downloadable Report
Source: Pushpam Jain
World Wide Web URL: http://www.edexcellence.net/publications-issues/publications/approvalbarrier.html

Asian-American Children: What Teachers Should Know
Explores this issue in a concise report.
Availability: All requesters
Suggested Grade: Teacher Reference
Languages: English; Chinese
Order Number: not applicable
Production Date: 1994
Format: Online Article
Source: Jianhua Feng
World Wide Web URL:
http://www.ericdigests.org/1994/teachers.htm

Assessing Bilingual Students for Placement and Instruction
Discusses how to evaluate bilingual students for proper classroom placement.
Availability: All requesters
Suggested Grade: Teacher Reference
Order Number: not applicable
Production Date: 1990
Format: Online Article
Source: Carol Ascher
World Wide Web URL:
http://www.ericdigests.org/pre-9217/placement.htm

Assessment Portfolios: Including English Language Learners in Large-Scale Assessments
Focuses on one type of assessment system, assessment portfolios, and discusses the advantages and challenges of using an assessment portfolio system.
Availability: All requesters
Suggested Grade: Teacher Reference
Order Number: not applicable
Production Date: 2000
Format: Online Article
Source: Emily Gomez
World Wide Web URL:
http://www.cal.org/resources/digest/0010assessment.html

Attending to Learning Styles in Mathematics and Science Classrooms
Discusses learning styles and how to teach science and mathematics.
Availability: All requesters
Suggested Grade: Teacher Reference
Order Number: not applicable
Production Date: 1997
Format: Online Article
Source: Barbara S. Thomson and John R. Mascazine
World Wide Web URL:
http://www.ericdigests.org/2000-1/attending.html

Beat the Clock
This activity helps limit time wasted by routine classroom transitions such as organizing students into cooperative groups and mastering cleanup.
Availability: All requesters
Suggested Grade: K-12
Order Number: not applicable
Production Date: 2007
Format: Online Lesson Plan
Source: Cheryl Rains
World Wide Web URL:
http://www.educationworld.com/a_tsl/archives/07-1/lesson006.shtml

Becoming a Technologically Savvy Administrator
Provides an overview of some issues associated with effective integration of technology in schools that are relevant to school leaders.
Availability: All requesters
Suggested Grade: Teacher Reference
Order Number: not applicable
Production Date: 2000
Format: Online Article
Source: Joseph Slowinski
World Wide Web URL:
http://www.ericdigests.org/2000-4/savvy.htm

Benefits of Information Technology, The
Summarizes the observed benefits of technology implementation in schools.
Availability: All requesters
Suggested Grade: Teacher Reference
Order Number: not applicable
Production Date: 1998
Format: Online Article
Source: John Kosakowski
World Wide Web URL:
http://chiron.valdosta.edu/whuitt/files/techbenefits.html

Beyond Blame: Reacting to the Terrorist Attack
A complete curriculum for middle and high school students designed to stimulate student reflection, discussion, and writing.
Availability: All requesters
Suggested Grade: 5-12
Languages: English; Spanish
Order Number: not applicable
Format: Downloadable Curriculum
Source: Education Development Center, Inc.
World Wide Web URL:
http://main.edc.org/newsroom/features/beyondblame.asp

Bridging Identities Among Ethnic Minority Youth in School
Discusses how schools contribute to student internalization of various identities, and how practitioners may assist youth in developing positive self-concepts.
Availability: All requesters
Suggested Grade: Teacher Reference
Order Number: not applicable
Production Date: 2002
Format: Online Article
Source: Christine J. Yeh and Christopher Drost
World Wide Web URL:
http://www.ericdigests.org/2002-4/youth.html

Bully-Free Classroom, The
Here are several effective strategies and activities to stop bullying before it starts.
Availability: All requesters
Suggested Grade: Teacher Reference
Order Number: not applicable
Format: Online Article
Source: Allan Feldman and Brenda Capobianco
World Wide Web URL:
http://teacher.scholastic.com/professional/classmgmt/bully_free.htm

Can Performance-Based Assessments Improve Urban Schooling?
Attempts to answer this question.
Availability: All requesters
Suggested Grade: Teacher Reference
Order Number: not applicable
Format: Online Article
Source: Carol Ascher
World Wide Web URL:
http://www.ericdigests.org/pre-9218/urban.htm

Challenges of Parent Involvement Research, The
Explains the unique problems that can come from instituting a parent involvement program.
Availability: All requesters
Suggested Grade: Teacher Reference
Order Number: not applicable
Production Date: 1998
Format: Online Article
Source: Amy Baker and Laura M. Soden
World Wide Web URL:
http://www.ericdigests.org/1998-3/parent.html

Changing Face of Racial Isolation and Desegregation in Urban Schools
Focuses on several issues in school desegregation that stem from recent changes in demography, policy, and research.
Availability: All requesters
Suggested Grade: Teacher Reference
Order Number: not applicable
Production Date: 1993
Format: Online Article
Source: Carol Ascher
World Wide Web URL:
http://www.ericdigests.org/1993/face.htm

Chinese Heritage Community Language Schools in the United States
Presents information about these schools.
Availability: All requesters
Suggested Grade: Teacher Reference
Order Number: not applicable
Production Date: 1997
Format: Online Article
Source: Theresa Hsu Chao
World Wide Web URL:
http://www.cal.org/resources/digest/chao0001.html

ClassRoom GradeBook
A complete program for making record keeping and grading much easier.
Availability: All requesters
Suggested Grade: Teacher Reference
Platform: Windows
Order Number: not applicable
Format: Downloadable FULL PROGRAM
Source: Classroomgradebook.com
World Wide Web URL:
http://www.classroomwindows.com/

Conducting a Functional Behavioral Assessment
First explains what misbehavior is and what functions that might serve for the misbehaving student, and then goes on to tell how to take care of these problems.
Availability: All requesters
Suggested Grade: Teacher Reference
Order Number: not applicable
Format: Online Article
Source: Joan M. Miller
World Wide Web URL:
http://www.teach-nology.com/tutorials/teaching/fba/

Conducting a Principal Search
Tips to follow to find the right principal for your school district.
Availability: All requesters
Suggested Grade: Teacher Reference
Order Number: not applicable
Production Date: 1999
Format: Online Article
Source: Elizabeth Hertling
World Wide Web URL:
http://cepm.uoregon.edu/publications/digests/digest133.html

Contextual Teaching and Learning: Teacher Education Programs
Identifies and documents the best practices in teacher education at five United States universities. Explores how contextual teaching and learning can improve student achievement.
Availability: Single copies to schools, libraries, and homeschoolers in the United States.
Suggested Grade: Teacher Reference
Order Number: order by title
Production Date: 1999
Format: Booklet; 15 pages
Source: ED Pubs
P. O. Box 1398
Jessup, MD 20794-1398
Phone: 1-877-4-ED-PUBS
Fax: 1-301-470-1244
World Wide Web URL:
http://www.edpubs.org/webstore/Content/search.asp

Cross-Age Tutoring in the Literacy Club
Discusses how you can set up a cross-age tutoring program for students.
Availability: All requesters
Suggested Grade: Teacher Reference
Order Number: not applicable
Production Date: 1995
Format: Online Article
Source: Carolyn Urzua
World Wide Web URL:
http://www.cal.org/resources/digest/urzua001.html

Curriculum Adequacy and Quality in High Schools Enrolling Fewer Than 400 Pupils
Presents evidence that many small high schools can maintain programs that are comparable in quality to curricula of larger schools.
Availability: All requesters
Suggested Grade: Teacher Reference
Order Number: not applicable
Production Date: 1996
Format: Online Article

Source: Christopher Roellke
World Wide Web URL:
http://www.ericdigests.org/1997-2/high.htm

Cyberspace Class: Rewards and Punishments
Recounts one teacher's method of conducting class via the World Wide Web.
Availability: All requesters
Suggested Grade: Teacher Reference
Order Number: not applicable
Production Date: 1996
Format: Online Article
Source: Barbara R. Shoemake
World Wide Web URL:
http://www.indiana.edu/~reading/ieo/digests/d117.html

Developing a School District Web Presence
Walks you through the organizational process of creating a district web site.
Availability: All requesters
Suggested Grade: Teacher Reference
Order Number: not applicable
Format: Online Article
Source: TeAch-nology.com
World Wide Web URL:
http://www.teach-nology.com/tutorials/district_web/

Diversity is About Change and Leadership
Discusses how to adapt to the ever increasing diversity of the United States.
Availability: All requesters
Suggested Grade: Teacher Reference
Order Number: not applicable
Format: Online Article
Special Notes: The author is Vice-President for Affirmative Action/Diversity at the Southeast Community College System in Lincoln, Nebraska.
Source: Jose Soto
World Wide Web URL:
http://www.edchange.org/multicultural/papers/diversity_soto.html

Diversity Tool Kit, The
Presents a calendar highlighting and describing ethnic and cultural events, a bibliography of suggested reading, and printable bookmarks that highlight each months events.
Availability: All requesters
Suggested Grade: Teacher Reference
Order Number: not applicable
Format: Downloadable Teaching Kit
Source: Susan Kotarba and Eveline Yang
World Wide Web URL: http://diversity.aclin.org/

Dozens of Ways to Grow
Explores professional development opportunities for teachers.
Availability: All requesters
Suggested Grade: Teacher Reference
Order Number: not applicable
Format: Online Article
Source: Carol Philips, Ed.D.
World Wide Web URL:
http://www2.scholastic.com/browse/article.jsp?id=3684

Education of Immigrant Children in New York City, The
Discusses a program already in place that might help other educators.
Availability: All requesters
Suggested Grade: Teacher Reference
Order Number: not applicable
Production Date: 1996
Format: Online Article
Source: Francisco L. Rivera-Batiz
World Wide Web URL:
http://www.ericdigests.org/1997-3/nyc.html

Effects of State Policies on Facilities Planning and Construction in Rural Districts
Identifies significant facilities policies and ways they can affect rural schools and communities.
Availability: All requesters
Suggested Grade: Teacher Reference
Order Number: not applicable
Production Date: 2001
Format: Online Article
Source: Barbara Kent Lawrence
World Wide Web URL:
http://www.ericdigests.org/2002-3/state.htm

Efficiency, Equity, and Local Control--School Finance in Texas
Presents examples designed to help others improve school financing operations.
Availability: All requesters
Suggested Grade: Teacher Reference
Order Number: not applicable
Production Date: 1993
Format: Online Article
Source: Carol Ascher
World Wide Web URL:
http://www.ericdigests.org/1993/texas.htm

Facilitating the Difficult Dialogue: Role Plays
Provides an opportunity for participants to share stories about when discussions on racism, sexism, classism, and more took a "turn for the worse" and how they handled it. Developed for multicultural education courses and workshops for pre-service and in-service teachers.
Availability: All requesters
Suggested Grade: Teacher Reference
Order Number: not applicable
Format: Downloadable Activity
Source: Paul Gorski
World Wide Web URL: http://www.edchange.org/multicultural/activities/roleplays.html

Foxfire Approach to Teaching and Learning, The
Describes the Foxfire Approach as defined by the core practices, the decision-making framework the approach provides for teachers, and the ways the framework fits with John Dewey's notion of experiential education.
Availability: All requesters
Suggested Grade: Teacher Reference
Order Number: not applicable
Production Date: 1999
Format: Online Article
Source: Bobby Ann Starnes
World Wide Web URL:
http://www.ericdigests.org/1999-3/foxfire.htm

From At-Risk to Excellence: Principles for Practice
Turn at risk students into students who excel.
Availability: All requesters
Suggested Grade: Teacher Reference
Order Number: not applicable
Production Date: 1997
Format: Online Article
Source: Center for Research on Education, Diversity & Excellence
World Wide Web URL:
http://www.cal.org/resources/digest/crede001.html

Gaining Control of Violence in the Schools
Presents proposals for getting violence out of the schools.
Availability: All requesters
Suggested Grade: Teacher Reference
Order Number: not applicable
Production Date: 1994
Format: Online Article
Source: Carol Ascher
World Wide Web URL:
http://www.ericdigests.org/1995-2/violence.htm

Gangs in the Schools
Discusses this issue.
Availability: All requesters
Suggested Grade: Teacher Reference
Order Number: not applicable
Production Date: 1994
Format: Online Article
Source: Gary Burnett and Garry Walz
World Wide Web URL:
http://www.ericdigests.org/1995-1/gangs.htm

Guide for Setting Ground Rules, A
This guide will provide you with strategies for effectively creating ground rules that maintain a sense of community and respect, laying a foundation for constructive dialogue in a multicultural education course or workshop. Developed for multicultural education courses and workshops for pre-service and in-service teachers.
Availability: All requesters
Suggested Grade: Teacher Reference
Order Number: not applicable
Format: Online Article
Source: Paul Gorski
World Wide Web URL:
http://www.edchange.org/multicultural/activities/groundrules.html

Guidelines and Considerations for Developing a Public Library Internet Use Policy
A detailed guide to developing such a policy.
Availability: All requesters
Suggested Grade: Teacher Reference
Order Number: not applicable
Format: Online Guide
Source: American Library Association
World Wide Web URL: http://www.ala.org/Template.cfm?Section=otherpolicies&Template=/ContentManagement/ContentDisplay.cfm&ContentID=78185

Guidelines for Programs to Reduce Child Victimization: A Resource for Communities When Choosing a Program to Teach Personal Safety to Children
Details the recommendations of NCMEC's Education Standards Task Force for communities when choosing programs to teach personal safety to children.
Availability: Limit of 10 copies to schools, libraries, and homeschoolers world-wide.
Suggested Grade: Teacher Reference
Order Number: 24
Production Date: 2000
Format: Booklet; 20 pages
Special Notes: Additional copies are $3.00 each.
Source: National Center for Missing & Exploited Children
Administrative Services
Charles B. Wang International Children's Building
699 Prince Street
Alexandria, VA 22314-3175
Phone: 1-703-274-3900
Fax: 1-703-274-2200
World Wide Web URL: http://www.missingkids.com

Identification and Recruitment of Migrant Students: Strategies and Resources
Provides an overview of how to develop a realistic and workable system for quickly finding and enrolling eligible students.
Availability: All requesters
Suggested Grade: Teacher Reference
Order Number: not applicable
Production Date: 2002
Format: Online Article
Source: Ray Melecio and Thomas J. Hanley
World Wide Web URL:
http://www.ericdigests.org/2003-4/migrant-students.html

Identity Development of Multiracial Youth, The
Explains how essential it is for educators and counselors to know how to serve the special developmental and

educational needs of multiracial students.
Availability: All requesters
Suggested Grade: Teacher Reference
Order Number: not applicable
Production Date: 1998
Format: Online Article

Source: Wendy Schwartz
World Wide Web URL:
http://www.ericdigests.org/1999-3/identity.htm

Impact of Work-Based Learning on Students, The

Discusses this issue.
Availability: All requesters
Suggested Grade: Teacher Reference
Order Number: not applicable
Production Date: 2002
Format: Online Article

Source: Michael E. Wonacott
World Wide Web URL:
http://www.ericdigests.org/2003-4/work-based.html

Information for Educators

Answers common questions educators have about Alateen and explains options for having meetings in schools.
Availability: Limit of 5 copies to schools, libraries, and homeschoolers in the United States and Canada. Make request on official stationery.
Suggested Grade: Adult
Order Number: order by title
Format: Brochure

Source: Al-Anon Family Group Headquarters, Inc.
Attn: Public Outreach Department
1600 Corporate Landing Parkway
Virginia Beach, VA 23454-5617
Phone: 1-888-425-2666
Fax: 1-757-563-1655
World Wide Web URL: http://www.al-anon.alateen.org
Email Address: wso@al-anon.org

Integrating Film and Television into Social Studies Instruction

Explains how to use this media in the social studies classroom.
Availability: All requesters
Suggested Grade: Teacher Reference
Order Number: not applicable
Production Date: 1997
Format: Online Article

Source: Matthew J. Paris
World Wide Web URL:
http://www.indiana.edu/%7Essdc/filmdig.htm

Internet Access in U. S. Public Schools and Classrooms: 1994-2002

Presents the findings of a survey regarding school connectivity; students and computer access; school web sites; and, technologies and procedures to prevent student access to innappropriate material.
Availability: Single copies to schools, libraries, and homeschoolers in the United States.
Suggested Grade: Teacher Reference
Order Number: ERN3663P
Production Date: 2004
Format: Booklet; 60 pages
Special Notes: May also be downloaded from the Web site.

Source: ED Pubs
P. O. Box 1398
Jessup, MD 20794-1398
Phone: 1-877-4-ED-PUBS
Fax: 1-301-470-1244
World Wide Web URL:
http://www.edpubs.org/webstore/Content/search.asp

Job Training Versus Career Development: What Is Voc Ed's Role?

Discusses this issue.
Availability: All requesters
Suggested Grade: Teacher Reference
Order Number: not applicable
Production Date: 1996
Format: Online Article

Source: Bettina A. Lankard
World Wide Web URL:
http://www.ericdigests.org/1997-1/job.html

Just in Case...You Are Dealing with Grief Following the Loss of a Child

Offers guidelines on a healthy approach to the grieving process.
Availability: Limit of 50 copies to schools, libraries, and homeschoolers world-wide.
Suggested Grade: Parents
Languages: English; Spanish
Order Number: English 10; Spanish 46
Production Date: 1987
Format: Brochure
Special Notes: Additional copies are 10 cents each.

Source: National Center for Missing & Exploited Children
Administrative Services
Charles B. Wang International Children's Building
699 Prince Street
Alexandria, VA 22314-3175
Phone: 1-703-274-3900
Fax: 1-703-274-2200
World Wide Web URL: http://www.missingkids.com

Kling Static Cling Sheets

Two static cling sheets, useful for creating overlays and other things.
Availability: One copy to schools and libraries world-wide.
Suggested Grade: Teacher Reference
Order Number: order by title
Format: Static Cling Sheets

Source: MagnaPlan Corporation
1320 Route 9, 3314
Champlain, NY 12919-5007
Phone: 1-518-298-8404

Fax: 1-518-298-2368
World Wide Web URL: http://www.visualplanning.com
Email Address: info@visualplanning.com

Mad, Mad World of Textbook Adoption, The
Statewide textbook adoption, the process by which 21 states dictate the textbooks that schools and districts can use, is fundamentally flawed. Here is information.

Availability: Single copies to schools, libraries, and homeschoolers in the United States and Canada. Additional copies are $10.00 each.
Suggested Grade: Teacher Reference
Order Number: order by title
Production Date: 2004
Format: Article
Special Notes: May also be downloaded from the web site.

Source: Thomas B. Fordham Foundation, The
c/o Dunst Fulfillment
106 Competitive Goals Drive
Eldersburg, MD 21784
Phone: 1-888-TBF-7474
World Wide Web URL: http://www.edexcellence.net
Email Address: fordham@dunst.com

Meeting the Goals of School Completion
Discusses this issue.

Availability: All requesters
Suggested Grade: Teacher Reference
Order Number: not applicable
Production Date: 1991
Format: Online Article

Source: Joseph C. Grannis
World Wide Web URL:
http://www.ericdigests.org/pre-9220/goals.htm

Middle School Education--The Critical Link in Dropout Prevention
Explores how a successful middle school career can lead to a successful high school education.

Availability: All requesters
Suggested Grade: Teacher Reference
Order Number: not applicable
Production Date: 1989
Format: Online Article

Source: Amy Stuart Wells
World Wide Web URL:
http://www.ericdigests.org/pre-9213/middle.htm

Multicultural Education and Technology: Perfect Pair or Odd Couple?
Looks at how technology can support multicultural education efforts.

Availability: All requesters
Suggested Grade: Teacher Reference
Order Number: not applicable
Production Date: 2001
Format: Online Article

Source: Patricia L. Marshall
World Wide Web URL:
http://www.ericdigests.org/2002-3/odd.htm

Multicultural Education List
Here is a mailing list that will deliver information right to your computer and allow discussion with other educators and people interested in multicultural education.

Availability: All requesters
Suggested Grade: Teacher Reference
Order Number: not applicable
Format: Electronic mailing list

Source: Shawgi Tell
World Wide Web URL:
http://www.yvwiiusdinvnohii.net/special/listsrv.htm

National Information Infrastructure, The: Keeping Rural Values and Purposes in Mind
Examines the practical significance for rural communities of the emerging national information infrastructure and highlights some related potential pitfalls.

Availability: All requesters
Suggested Grade: Teacher Reference
Order Number: not applicable
Production Date: 1997
Format: Online Article

Source: Craig Howley and Bruce Barker
World Wide Web URL:
http://www.ericdigests.org/1998-2/rural.htm

Ongoing Dilemmas of School Size: A Short Story
Discusses this issue.

Availability: All requesters
Suggested Grade: Teacher Reference
Order Number: not applicable
Production Date: 1996
Format: Online Article

Source: Craig B. Howley
World Wide Web URL:
http://www.ericdigests.org/1997-2/size.htm

Outdoor Education and Troubled Youth
Examines the parallel development of outdoor education and outdoor therapeutic programs in working with troubled and adjudicated youth.

Availability: All requesters
Suggested Grade: Teacher Reference
Order Number: not applicable
Production Date: 1995
Format: Online Article

Source: Dene S. Berman and Jennifer Davis-Berman
World Wide Web URL:
http://www.ericdigests.org/1996-1/outdoor.htm

Parent and Community Involvement in Rural Schools
Discusses how rural communities differ from urban and suburban ones in reference to parent involvement.

Availability: All requesters
Suggested Grade: Teacher Reference
Order Number: not applicable
Production Date: 1997
Format: Online Article

Source: Stan Maynard and Aimee Howley
World Wide Web URL:
http://www.ericdigests.org/1998-1/rural.htm

Peer Review of Teachers
Discusses the method of evaluating teacher performance.
Availability: All requesters
Suggested Grade: Teacher Reference
Order Number: not applicable
Production Date: 1999
Format: Online Article

Source: Elizabeth Hertling
World Wide Web URL:
http://cepm.uoregon.edu/publications/digests/digest126.html

Performance Contracts for Administrators
Discusses tying pay to performance.
Availability: All requesters
Suggested Grade: Teacher Reference
Order Number: not applicable
Production Date: 1999
Format: Online Article

Source: Elizabeth Hertling
World Wide Web URL:
http://www.ericdigests.org/2000-1/contracts.html

Perspectives on Rural Child Care
Reviews what is known about the nature of rural child care and suggests implications for practitioners and policymakers.
Availability: All requesters
Suggested Grade: Teacher Reference
Order Number: not applicable
Production Date: 1997
Format: Online Article

Source: Betty A. Beach
World Wide Web URL:
http://www.ericdigests.org/1997-3/rural.html

Population Educator, The
A newsletter with tips on how to incorporate population education activities into the classroom.
Availability: All requesters
Suggested Grade: K-12
Order Number: not applicable
Format: Downloadable Newsletter

Source: Population Connection
World Wide Web URL:
http://www.populationeducation.org

Reaching Every Child
Discusses how to make it easier for all students to do what's expected when learning new rules and procedures.
Availability: All requesters
Suggested Grade: Teacher Reference
Order Number: not applicable
Format: Online Article

Source: Sharon Maroney
World Wide Web URL:
http://teacher.scholastic.com/products/instructor/reaching.htm

Research Quick Start Guide: Ethnic Identity in the United States
In addition to providing guidelines on selecting these library resources, several sample reference works are listed.
Availability: All requesters
Suggested Grade: Teacher Reference
Order Number: not applicable
Format: Web Site

Source: Stanford University Libraries
World Wide Web URL:
http://www-sul.stanford.edu/depts/ssrg/adams/shortcu/ethi.html

Retaining Good Teachers in Urban Schools
Tells ways to keep good teachers in what can sometimes be, bad schools.
Availability: All requesters
Suggested Grade: Teacher Reference
Order Number: not applicable
Production Date: 1991
Format: Online Article

Source: Carol Ascher
World Wide Web URL:
http://www.ericdigests.org/1992-4/good.htm

Retaining Principals
Discusses this topic.
Availability: All requesters
Suggested Grade: Teacher Reference
Order Number: not applicable
Production Date: 2001
Format: Online Article

Source: Elizabeth Hertling
World Wide Web URL:
http://cepm.uoregon.edu/publications/digests/digest147.html

Retention and Social Promotion: Research and Implications for Policy
Discusses this issue.
Availability: All requesters
Suggested Grade: Teacher Reference
Order Number: not applicable
Production Date: 2000
Format: Online Article

Source: Charles L. Thompson and Elizabeth K. Cunningham
World Wide Web URL:
http://www.ericdigests.org/2001-3/policy.htm

Role of Online Communications in Schools, The: A National Study
Presents the results of a study conducted that shows the value of online access for students.
Availability: All requesters
Suggested Grade: Teacher Reference
Order Number: not applicable
Format: Online Article
Source: Center for Applied Special Technology
World Wide Web URL:
http://www.tcet.unt.edu/research/rlonline.htm

Role of Rural Schools in Rural Community Development, The
Discusses progress made in using rural schools as a community development resource.
Availability: All requesters
Suggested Grade: Teacher Reference
Order Number: not applicable
Production Date: 1995
Format: Online Article
Source: Bruce A. Miller
World Wide Web URL:
http://www.ericdigests.org/1996-1/rural.htm

School and Family Problems of Children with Kidney Failure
Describes psychosocial problems that can accompany kidney disease, including issues of fitting in at school, financial demands of treatment, and family stresses and the role of the social worker and other members of the health care team who are available to help families handle these problems.
Availability: Single copies to schools, libraries, and homeschoolers in the United States and Canada.
Suggested Grade: Adult
Order Number: KU-183
Production Date: 2003
Format: Fact Sheet
Source: National Institute of Diabetes and Digestive and Kidney Diseases
5 Information Way
Bethesda, MD 20892-3568
Phone: 1-800-891-5390
Fax: 1-703-738-4929
World Wide Web URL: http://www.niddk.nih.gov/
Email Address: nkudidc@info.niddk.nih.gov

School Associated Violent Deaths Report, The
An in-house report of this organization that describes all the school associated violent deaths from 1992 to the present. The report includes categorical totals based on gender, methods and reasons for death, and state in which death occurred.
Availability: All requesters
Suggested Grade: 9-Adult
Order Number: not applicable
Format: Online Article
Source: National School Safety Center
World Wide Web URL: http://www.schoolsafety.us/media-resources/school-associated-violent-deaths

School Programs for African American Male Students
Explains some programs that can be set up to specifically help these students.
Availability: All requesters
Suggested Grade: Teacher Reference
Order Number: not applicable
Production Date: 1991
Format: Online Article
Source: Carol Ascher
World Wide Web URL:
http://www.ericdigests.org/pre-9220/males.htm

Sexual Misconduct by School Employees
Discusses this topic seen often in today's news.
Availability: All requesters
Suggested Grade: Teacher Reference
Order Number: not applicable
Production Date: 1999
Format: Online Article
Source: Brad Goorian
World Wide Web URL:
http://cepm.uoregon.edu/publications/digests/digest134.html

Southeast Asian Adolescents: Identity and Adjustment
Provides information to help teachers work effectively with these students.
Availability: All requesters
Suggested Grade: Teacher Reference
Order Number: not applicable
Production Date: 1989
Format: Online Article
Source: Carol Ascher
World Wide Web URL:
http://www.ericdigests.org/pre-9211/southeast.htm

Stafford Loan Forgiveness Program for Teachers Brochure
Highlights the general eligibility requirements of the Stafford Loan Forgiveness Program for Teachers. The brochure also provides information on how to apply and contact information for teachers who need additional information.
Availability: Single copies to schools, libraries, and homeschoolers in the United States.
Suggested Grade: Teacher Reference
Order Number: EN0998H
Production Date: 2010
Format: Brochure
Special Notes: May also be downloaded from the web site.
Source: ED Pubs
P. O. Box 1398
Jessup, MD 20794-1398

Phone: 1-877-4-ED-PUBS
Fax: 1-301-470-1244
World Wide Web URL:
http://www.edpubs.org/webstore/Content/search.asp

Student Diversity and Learning Needs

Discusses how to reach students based on varying learning needs.

Availability: All requesters
Suggested Grade: Teacher Reference
Order Number: not applicable
Production Date: 1997
Format: Online Article

Source: Joseph Sanacore
World Wide Web URL:
http://www.indiana.edu/~reading/ieo/digests/d127.html

Student Mobility and Academic Achievement

Discusses this issue.

Availability: All requesters
Suggested Grade: Teacher Reference
Languages: English; Spanish
Order Number: not applicable
Production Date: 2002
Format: Online Article

Source: Russell W. Rumberger
World Wide Web URL:
http://www.ericdigests.org/2003-2/mobility.html

Students with Celiac Disease

Information for teachers about students with celiac disease.

Availability:
Suggested Grade: Teacher Reference
Order Number: not applicable
Production Date: 8
Format: Downloadable brochure

Source: Gluten Intolerance Group of North America
World Wide Web URL:
www.gluten.nethttp://www.gluten.net

Successful Detracking in Middle and Senior High Schools

Explores this issue.

Availability: All requesters
Suggested Grade: Teacher Reference
Order Number: not applicable
Production Date: 1992
Format: Online Article

Source: Carol Ascher
World Wide Web URL:
http://chiron.valdosta.edu/whuitt/files/tracking.html

Teacher Talk

Articles and lesson plans designed for preservice and secondary education teachers.

Availability: All requesters
Suggested Grade: Teacher Reference
Order Number: not applicable
Format: Web Site

Source: Center for Adolescent Studies
World Wide Web URL:
http://www.drugstats.org/tt/tthmpg.html

Teenage Pregnancy and Drug Abuse: Sources of Problem Behaviors

Discusses this issue.

Availability: All requesters
Suggested Grade: Teacher Reference
Order Number: not applicable
Production Date: 1989
Format: Online Article

Source: Janine Bempechat, et al
World Wide Web URL:
http://www.ericdigests.org/pre-9214/drug.htm

Tips for Helping Students Recovering from Traumatic Events

Provides practical information for parents and students who are coping with the aftermath of a natural disaster, as well as teachers, coaches, school administrators, and others who are helping those affected.

Availability: Single copies to schools, libraries, and homeschoolers in the United States.
Suggested Grade: Teacher Reference
Order Number: ED001424B
Format: Brochure
Special Notes: May also be downloaded from the web site.

Source: ED Pubs
P. O. Box 1398
Jessup, MD 20794-1398
Phone: 1-877-4-ED-PUBS
Fax: 1-301-470-1244
World Wide Web URL:
http://www.edpubs.org/webstore/Content/search.asp

Transforming Myself to Transform My School

Discusses a number of steps that multicultural educators can take to improve their teaching.

Availability: All requesters
Suggested Grade: Teacher Reference
Order Number: not applicable
Production Date: 2001
Format: Online Article

Source: Paul Gorski
World Wide Web URL:
http://www.edchange.org/multicultural/papers/edchange_10things.html

Up Against Authentic History

Tips to help teachers make the most of primary source materials found online.

Availability: All requesters
Suggested Grade: Teacher Reference
Order Number: not applicable
Format: Online Article

Source: Bill Tally
World Wide Web URL:
http://www2.scholastic.com/browse/article.jsp?id=4391

Urban School Finance: The Quest for Equal Educational Opportunity
Provides ideas to gain urban school financing so that all schools can be equal.
Availability: All requesters
Suggested Grade: Teacher Reference
Order Number: not applicable
Production Date: 1989
Format: Online Article
Source: Carol Ascher
World Wide Web URL:
http://www.ericdigests.org/pre-9213/urban.htm

Urban School Restructuring and Teacher Burnout
Explores this topic.
Availability: All requesters
Suggested Grade: Teacher Reference
Order Number: not applicable
Production Date: 1991
Format: Online Article
Source: Carol Ascher and Barry Farber
World Wide Web URL:
http://www.ericdigests.org/1992-4/urban.htm

Urban Youth in Community Service: Becoming Part of the Solution
Explains how youth involvement in community service is beneficial to the community, as well as the student.
Availability: All requesters
Suggested Grade: Teacher Reference
Order Number: not applicable
Production Date: 1992
Format: Online Article
Source: Anne Lewis
World Wide Web URL:
http://www.ericdigests.org/1992-1/urban.htm

Using Culturally and Linguistically Appropriate Assessments to Ensure that American Indian and Alaska Native Students Receive the Special Education Programs and Services They Need
Discusses this issue.
Availability: All requesters
Suggested Grade: Teacher Reference
Order Number: not applicable
Production Date: 2002
Format: Online Article
Source: John W. Tippeconnic and Susan C. Faircloth
World Wide Web URL: http://www.findarticles.com/p/articles/mi_pric/is_200212/ai_1794505459

Video Games: Research, Ratings, Recommendations
Reviews research on the demographics and effects of video game playing on students.
Availability: All requesters
Suggested Grade: 9-Adult
Languages: English; Spanish
Order Number: not applicable
Production Date: 1998
Format: Online Article
Source: Bernard Cesarone
World Wide Web URL:
http://www.ericdigests.org/1999-2/video.htm

Weaving a Secure Web Around Education: A Guide to Technology Standards and Security
Provides education agencies and organizations assistance in the development, maintenance, and standardization of effective web sites.
Availability: Single copies to schools, libraries, and homeschoolers in the United States.
Suggested Grade: Teacher Reference
Order Number: ERN3553P
Production Date: 2003
Format: Booklet; 89 pages
Special Notes: May also be downloaded from the web site.
Source: ED Pubs
P. O. Box 1398
Jessup, MD 20794-1398
Phone: 1-877-4-ED-PUBS
Fax: 1-301-470-1244
World Wide Web URL:
http://www.edpubs.org/webstore/Content/search.asp

"Who I Am" Poems
Begins an active introspective process while continuing to provide opportunities for individuals to make connections with each other.
Availability: All requesters
Suggested Grade: Teacher Reference
Order Number: not applicable
Format: Online Lesson Plan
Source: Paul Gorski
World Wide Web URL:
http://www.edchange.org/multicultural/activities/poetry.html

-A-

-B-

-C-

-D-

-E-

-F-

-I-

-J-

-K-

-L-

-M-

-N-

-T-

-U-

-V-

-W-

-X-Y-Z-

SUBJECT INDEX

SUBJECT INDEX

LESSON PLANS (continued)

LESSON PLANS (continued)

TEACHER REFERENCE (continued)

TEACHER REFERENCE (continued)

The SOURCE INDEX is an alphabetical list of the organizations from which the materials listed in the SECONDARY TEACHERS GUIDE TO FREE CURRICULUM MATERIALS may be obtained. There are 733 sources listed in this 120th Edition of the GUIDE, **690 of which are new**. The numbers following each listing are the page numbers on which the materials from each source are annotated in the body of the GUIDE.

When requesting materials via mail or fax, please use a letter of request similar to the sample shown in the front part of the GUIDE. When requesting via telephone, please have the name of the material you desire in front of you (along with the order number if necessary). Please read each listing carefully to be certain that the material you are requesting is available via the method through which you choose to order. If you are going to a web site, be careful typing in the URL of the site–one slight typing error and the site won't be found.

Bold type indicates a source that is new in the 2013-2014 edition. Complete addresses for each source are found following the description of the material in the body of the GUIDE.